Steve Elsworth is a journalist and writer who has worked as an environmental consultant to 'Weekend World', BBC 'Breakfast Time', Central TV and Granada, as well as for several publications including the *Sunday Times*, *New Statesman*, *New Scientist* and the *Observer*. He is currently the director of the Atmosphere campaign for Greenpeace UK.

STEVE ELSWORTH

A
Dictionary of the
Environment

PALADIN
GRAFTON BOOKS
A Division of the Collins Publishing Group

LONDON GLASGOW
TORONTO SYDNEY AUCKLAND

Paladin
Grafton Books
A Division of the Collins Publishing Group
8 Grafton Street, London W1X 3LA

A Paladin Paperback Original 1990
9 8 7 6 5 4 3 2

Copyright © Steve Elsworth 1990

A CIP catalogue record for this book is
available from the British Library

ISBN 0-586-08543-2

Printed and bound in Great Britain by
Collins, Glasgow

Set in Baskerville

For Danny and Joe

Contents

vi

Introduction

There are two ways to write a book such as this: assemble a team of experts, and get them to contribute articles – or write it all yourself, starting from scratch. I chose the second way, and a lot of trouble it caused too.

The book is intended to be a basic introduction to all the current environmental issues, written in accessible language. The articles are drawn mainly from the references at the end of each section: and there are addresses of interested organizations for those readers who wish to go further.

The articles are written to be self-standing, which means a small amount of repetition for those dedicated enough to work their way through the book: and a certain amount of cross-referencing is unavoidable.

The book arose from a chance conversation with a journalist, who told me he disliked nuclear power, but couldn't remember why. I felt the same way about a number of environmental issues: half-remembered facts, interesting articles I had seen somewhere but couldn't locate, TV programmes that hovered on the edge of my brain. What I needed was a book that pulled all these references together and made sense of them.

The book looked easy in 1985. I wrote to 300 environmental organizations, asking them what they were interested in, and started collating the results. As I got further into the subject, however, things became more complicated. The original publication date – 1987 – disappeared as I sank under a sea of information.

New issues kept appearing every year. The ozone hole, the greenhouse effect, the death of the seals in the North Sea, Chernobyl, Sandoz, salmonella, toxic waste. Additional stories piled on top of the existing catalogue of destruction and waste that was already mounting month by month. As the contents list filled out, I realized that this was going to be an extremely depressing book.

Depression can be positive, however, if it works as a spur towards change. Working on this book certainly changed me. The more I found out about the issues, the more I became involved, and a natural progression occurred. I finished the manuscript, joined the environment movement, and now work as an environmental campaigner.

That doesn't mean that the book represents the views of any particular organization: it doesn't. Nor does it mean that the articles here are partial: they are as objective as I could make them, bearing in mind that I have a different view of the world to, say, the head of National Power.

The analyses contained in this book are depressing: but then people need to find out the truth if there is to be change. Myself, I am an optimist: I don't believe that humanity is so stupid as to pollute itself into extinction.

On the other hand, I don't believe that purely technological fixes will get us out of our current mess. We need to change the way that we organize the world, and our basic philosophy of existence on the planet. Sooner or later, there will be meaningful debate as to how this will be achieved: and books such as this will, I hope, play a part in preparing for that debate.

Steve Elsworth
September 1989

Acknowledgements

A number of people have assisted in the writing of this book, either by giving me ideas, reading parts of the manuscript, or supplying books and references. I would like to thank Christer Agren, Tim Birch, Andy Booth, Stewart Boyle, Philip Cade, Andy Clarke, Nigel Dudley, Patrick Green, Jeremy Harmer, Tracy Heslop, Colin Hines, Andy Kerr, Tim Lang, Andrew Lees, David Lowry, Adam Markham, Don Mathew, Malcolm McGarvin, Marek Meyer, Melanie Miller, Andy Ottoway, Dougie Patel, Nigel Rogers, Chris Rose, Jim Rose, David Simpson, and Jonathan Smales: and hope that those people whose names I have forgotten to include will forgive the omission.

More particular thanks are due to Paul Milican, who commented on the entire manuscript and updated the address list; Janet Law, who edited the manuscript, and Scilla Erskine, who indexed it; my father, for valuable advice; and John Lawton, Ian Paten, John May, and Elaine Walker, without whom the book couldn't have been written.

I am grateful to the following for permission to reproduce illustrative material:

Greenpeace; British Antarctic Survey; M. Walsh; Gemini News Service; Friends of the Earth; Times Newspapers Ltd; Countryside Commission; International Institute for Environment and Development; Institute of Chemical Engineers; Her Majesty's Stationery Office; London Food Commission; Soil Association; World Priorities; Piatkus Books; *New Scientist*.

The normal disclaimer is necessary: all errors and omissions are not the responsibility of any of the people above, but entirely my own.

Acid Rain

A better name for 'acid rain' would be 'acid air'. This pollution is caused by burning enormous quantities of coal and oil, which in turn generate vast amounts of polluting gases. Airborne by-products of certain industrial processes add to the pollutant mix.

There are several different ways in which acid air pollution occurs, and diverse pathways through which it affects the environment: the resulting imbalance of nature kills human beings, animals, trees, vegetation and lakes over enormous areas. The pollution also corrodes stone and other materials.

Acid rain is international, in that all countries create it and suffer from it. It is exported and imported between countries in millions of tonnes.

THE CAUSES OF ACID RAIN

Acid rain is caused when coal or oil is burned. Both fuels contain a certain amount of sulphur, which is released on combustion and rises into the air as sulphur dioxide gas (SO_2). Nitrogen contained in the fuels is similarly released as nitrogen oxides (NO_x): the process of burning converts some nitrogen from the air into nitrogen oxides.

When this occurs in an industrial furnace or power station, the gases float up the chimney and escape.

- Up to 50 per cent of the pollutants linger in the vicinity of the furnace, as gas, or as particles in the air, which eventually drift to earth within a 30-kilometre circle of the emission source.
- Up to 30 per cent of the pollutants mix with water in the clouds and fall as localized rain, snow, sleet, or mist.
- The remainder finds a convenient wind current and hitches a lift to wherever it is going, eventually falling to earth as dust, rain, snow or

mist. Sulphur dioxide can travel for up to 100 hours, so if it finds a 40 mph wind it can travel some distance. A small part of the acid rain falling in Europe is believed to come from the USA.

The popular conception of acid rain as polluted water travelling long distances is just one part of the chain. Most of the damage which is done occurs near the pollution source.

Acid rain is not just rain: it includes rain, snow, sleet, hail, mists, fogs, gas and dry particles. The great London smogs were an example of acid rain, as is the black snow that currently falls two or three times a year on the Cairngorms. There is so much of the pollutant currently being created – about 40 million tonnes per year over Europe alone – that it returns to earth in a number of different ways.

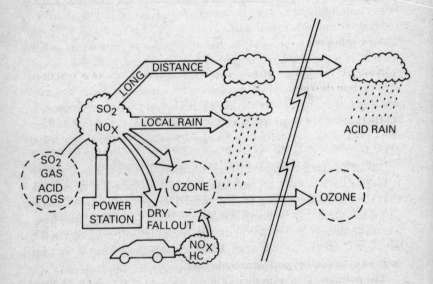

Sources of acid rain

The component of acid air pollution which is polluted rainfall is not an acid in the strict sense of the term, but it is more acid than it should be. Acidity is measured on the pH scale, which runs from pH 14 (very alkaline) through pH 7 (neutral) to pH 1 (very acid). The scale is logarithmic, so pH 3 is ten times more acid than pH 4, a hundred times more acid than pH 5, a thousand times more acid than pH 6, etc.

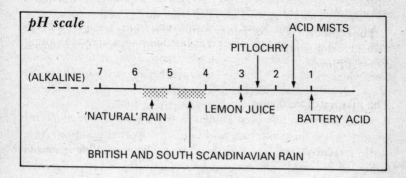

Relative acidity of rain

'Natural' rainfall is already slightly acidic, because of a reaction with carbon dioxide in the atmosphere. It is usually assumed to have an acidity range of pH 5 to pH 5.6. The rain that falls over Britain and southern Scandinavia has an average range of pH 4 to pH 4.7. The most acid rainfall recorded in the UK was at Pitlochry in 1974 – pH 2.4.

Polluted mists and fogs are frequently more acid than this: acid fogs in California have been recorded with a pH of 1.6, and it is calculated that the great London fog of 1952, which killed 4,000 people, had a pH of 1.7 (almost the strength of battery acid). The acidity arises from a transformation of the sulphur dioxide into sulphuric acid, and of the nitrogen oxides into nitric acid. This increases the acidity of the rain or mist in which the pollutant finds itself.

The pollutants occur in their original state, as SO_2 or NO_x: in their acid state, as sulphuric or nitric acid; or, in another form, when the acids break down into their component parts, as hydrogen, sulphates and nitrates. Each has a different particular effect on the environment, but all share the same consequence – that of destabilizing natural cycles.

The situation is complicated by the interaction between the sulphur and nitrogen pollutants, and also with other air pollution. Nitrogen oxides can form ozone, given the right weather conditions and the presence of hydrocarbons (see below) in the air. Ozone, which is essential for the protection of the planet when it is present in the upper atmosphere (see OZONE LAYER), is a pollutant when it is industrially created and occurs nearer the surface of the earth.

The combined effect of acid pollution and ozone is believed to be a central factor contributing to the decline and death of forests across Central Europe.

The history of acid rain

Acid air pollution has been known in the UK since the thirteenth century, when the glass-makers of London imported coal from Newcastle to replace the wood in their stoves. The resulting corrosive fumes led to complaints, commissions of inquiry, and periodic royal bans over the next seven centuries.

Acid rain in its twentieth-century manifestation – as an international import and export of airborne pollution – has its origins in the Industrial Revolution of the 1840s. The amount of coal-burning increased rapidly, and so did the pollution (see box).

The box shows some of the important dates in the acid rain story. Perhaps four incidents should be singled out.

- The first recorded fish losses occurred in 1911, in the Kvina River in southern Norway. This is an indication that the roots of the acid rain problem have been in place for some considerable time.
- The development of European industry after the Second World War led to a huge increase in coal and oil consumption: the result was a doubling of SO_2 and NO_x emissions over Europe between 1950 and 1970. The forests and soils of the area had never before experienced this pollutant load. Even the reductions currently being achieved by certain countries at the moment will not bring total European emissions down to pre-war levels.
- The London fog deaths of 1952 led to the 1956 Clean Air Act, which moved power stations outside the city limits. Recommendations to install sulphur-cleaning machinery were ignored on financial grounds. The new generation of power stations had tall chimneys, with the intent of harmlessly dispersing the pollution into the

The History of Acid Rain

1840 Industrial Revolution begins in UK.

1850 Certain Scottish lakes begin to become more acidic.

1862 Black rain observed in Scotland.

1872 'Acid rain' first used – to describe rain in Manchester.

1880 London smog kills 1,200 people.

1911 Fish loss first observed in Norwegian rivers. Fish losses spread through southern Scandinavia over following decades.

1945 Reconstruction of European industry after Second World War. Massive industrialization leads to doubling of SO_2 and NO_x emissions over 25 years.

1940s Swedes start European Air Chemistry Network to find out what is happening in the rain.

1952 Great London fog kills 4,000 people.

1956 UK Clean Air Act leads to removal of power stations from cities; rebuilt in country with tall chimneys.

1967 Thousands of Scandinavian lakes dead. Swedish scientist Svante Oden develops the concept of acid rain to describe the international import/export of pollutants.

1972 UN Conference on the Environment debates acid rain. Diplomatic pressure begins for environmental clean-up. Several large research programmes start.

1979 Thirty-three countries sign the Geneva Convention, *Long Range Transport of Air Pollutants*, deploring acid rain. No concrete measures taken yet.

1982 Survey shows 7.7 per cent of West German forests damaged. German public opinion starts to mobilize.

1983 Revised survey shows 34 per cent of West German forests damaged. German pressure begins through EC.

1984 Survey shows 50 per cent of West German forests damaged. Thirty Per Cent Club formed in March: ten nations belong, expanding to twenty by the autumn.

1986 Nordic Council scientists advocate 80 per cent reduction in European SO_2 emissions, 50 to 75 per cent reduction in NO_x.

1987	Official forestry surveys in UK show forest health to be exactly the same as in West Germany. UK forest health now classed as merely 'moderate'.
1988	UN figures indicate that Britain's trees are among the most damaged in Europe.
1989	UK Acid Waters Review Group publishes evidence of acidified lakes and streams in large areas of the UK: and comments that a 90 per cent reduction in acid deposition is necessary to return most surface waters to near pristine conditions.

atmosphere. The result of the tall chimneys was that the grim local effects of sulphur dioxide disappeared, and it was believed that the problem had been solved. Other countries followed the British, and adopted tall stacks. The massive European increase in SO_2 and NO_x production was disguised by spreading the pollution over a wider area. Emissions increased, but public perception was dulled.

• The campaign against acid rain was transformed when the European forests began to die. In early 1982 the Germans had no idea of the damage that was occurring to their trees but, two years later, they realized that half of their forests were damaged. The speed and scale of this transformation was reflected in the urgency of diplomatic negotiations. In March 1984, the Thirty Per Cent Club was formed, in which ten countries agreed to reduce their emissions of SO_2 by 30 per cent between 1980 and 1993. In the autumn, this increased to 20 countries, 21 in 1985. Some nations were committed to a greater than 30 per cent reduction, at a cost of billions of pounds.

The sources of acid rain

Sulphur pollutants (sulphur dioxide, sulphuric acid, sulphates) Caused by burning coal or oil. Main source: power stations and industry. In the UK, 73 per cent of sulphur dioxide emissions come from power stations (1987 figure).

Nitrogen pollutants (nitrogen oxides, nitric acid, nitrates) Caused by burning coal or oil, or comes from petrol-driven vehicles (see AUTOMOBILE

POLLUTION). Main source: power stations, industry, cars. In the UK, 35 per cent of NO_x comes from power stations, and 45 per cent from traffic.

Acidification of the soil is increased in some areas by the presence of ammonia from intensive livestock breeding. (Ammonia is not an acid, but becomes converted to nitric acid by bacteria in the soil.) Over-use of nitrogen-based fertilizers can also lead to excess nitrates in water bodies.

Ozone　A pollutant arising from the combination of nitrogen oxides, hydrocarbons and sunlight. Works in combination with sulphur and nitrogen pollutants, or by itself. Frequently responsible for the 'heat haze' seen on hot summer days.

As a 'secondary' pollutant (i.e., derived from another pollutant), ozone plays a complex role, and is dependent on a number of factors. It has long been acknowledged as a problem in California, but previously it was thought the northern European climate would be inhospitable to ozone formation. This analysis is now seen to be wrong.

Associated with sunlight, ozone levels hit their maximum during the summer. A certain amount of ozone exists in the air throughout the year: this 'background' level of ozone is thought to have doubled in Europe over the last century, presumably because of the increasing number of primary pollutants that are available for ozone formation.

Many plants are very susceptible to ozone. The most sensitive can be damaged by ozone concentrations of 50 parts per billion (i.e., 50 ozone molecules in a billion molecules of air) over several hours. This concentration is exceeded at every ozone monitoring site in the UK, generally for 100 to 200 hours per year.

The World Health Organization recommend that hourly ozone levels should not exceed 76–100 ppb, to protect human health. This hourly mean concentration is regularly exceeded in the air of south-east England. The highest hourly ozone concentration measured in Britain was 258 ppb during the 1976 heatwave.

The figures indicate the seriousness of the ozone problem. In the USA, the Office of Technology Assessment has estimated that ozone damage to crops costs over $3 billion a year. Research in the UK is sketchy, but developing. In 1987, a score of ozone monitoring stations were set up throughout the UK.

Hydrocarbons   In acid rain terms, 'hydrocarbon' refers to a class of pollutant that contains carbon atoms and can produce ozone in combination with NO_x in sunlight. This definition covers many hundreds of volatile compounds emitted into the atmosphere by both natural and human sources (e.g. methane, propane, toluene, ethanol).

Hydrocarbons (also called VOCs – Volatile Organic Compounds) are being given increasing attention because of their role in assisting the formation of ozone from NO_x. It has been suggested that reductions of NO_x would not necessarily reduce ozone formation because of the large amount of hydrocarbons present in the air. The process of ozone formation is very complex and not completely understood.

The response of the environmental movement has been to call for a reduction in hydrocarbon, as well as NO_x, emissions.

The UK Photochemical Oxidants Review Group (sponsored by the Department of the Environment) has published estimates of the sources of 94 per cent of the UK's volatile hydrocarbons. About 20 per cent of this figure comes from petrol exhausts, about 6 per cent from petrol evaporation and a similar amount from petroleum refining. Nearly 30 per cent comes from solvent usage, another 20 per cent from natural gas leakage (finding it and piping it to the consumer), and 6 per cent from industrial processes.

The figures give some leads for reduction of hydrocarbon emissions. Emissions from petrol engines can be largely reduced by use of catalytic converters (SEE AUTOMOBILE POLLUTION: TECHNOLOGICAL SOLUTIONS); solvent emissions can be reduced by finding substitutes for solvent-based products, e.g. by replacing solvent-based with water-based paints.

THE EFFECTS OF ACID RAIN

The process of acid rain is complex and occurs on a vast scale; the effects are similarly varied and widespread.

- Acid rain degrades lakes and streams if it falls long enough to overcome natural defence mechanisms. This has happened in Scandinavia and in certain parts of Britain. The lakes are based on rock or thin soils, and cannot buffer the acid input. They become more acidic, and all the fish die.
- The burden of circumstantial evidence is that acid air pollution kills

forests on an enormous scale. There is disagreement over the specific causes of the forest deaths, with over 180 theories as to the mechanisms involved. The most commonly accepted is the 'cup of stress' theory, in which a tree is represented as a cup full of environmental stress, composed of acid pollution, unacceptable ozone levels, nutrient deficiency caused by acid soils, weather stress, etc. Once a tree reaches this threshold level, any additional stress – a hot summer, a cold winter, an attack of beetles – will kill it. All species can be affected, although within a species some individuals will be more resistant than others.

- There is general scientific agreement as to widespread crop damage in the USA caused by ozone, and damage to test specimens in the UK. The combined effects of the various pollutants on crops are still being examined but are thought to be extremely large.
- There is agreement as to the widespread damage caused by acid pollution to materials. It corrodes sandstone, limestone, leather, paper, certain metals, historic monuments and stained glass.
- Certain birds are known to be affected by acid changes in the environment, where their food supply is disrupted. Others have suffered health damage as a result of aluminium contamination indirectly caused by acid rain. Damage to other animals, e.g. seals, through deterioration of their food supply, is suspected but difficult to prove. Changes in the flora of areas previously considered to be unaffected, such as Cornwall, have been discovered.

In a report published in November 1986, the World Wildlife Fund identified damage in the areas listed in the box on page 10.

For animals, flora, buildings, materials, damage in the rest of the world, and health effects, see References, below.

There has been some controversy as to whether British forests are suffering the same sort of decline as has occurred in Continental Europe. The UK Forestry Commission published its annual national survey results in December 1987, in which it stated:

This report, together with those from previous years (particularly that of 1986) indicates that both crown thinning and yellowing of needles (the two symptoms most frequently associated with forest decline on the Continent) are present in Britain. The extent of crown thinning and discoloration in Britain is similar to that in West Germany.

Forests

West Germany (52% of forest damaged); Switzerland (33%); Austria (16%); Netherlands (50%); Luxembourg (19%); Czechoslovakia (27%); Poland (7% to 40%); Hungary (11%); France (20% in Vosges); Belgium (18% on German border); Yugoslavia (450,000 hectares); Rumania (170,000 ha); Spain (23,000 ha); Denmark (1,000 ha).

Lakes

Norway: 35,000 square kilometres of lakeland affected, with a loss of more than half the trout populations; Sweden: 18,000 of 85,000 lakes acidified, 4,000 severely (i.e., unable to support fish life); Scotland: at least 22 major lakes acidified. Wales: most small rivers in Central and West Wales acidified, Upper Tywi and Wye strongly so; England: Duddon and Usk in Cumbria, and parts of the Lake District acidified.

Note: 'Acidified' means 'suffering an unnatural change in water acidity'. The usual result of this is that no fish can survive in the water. Times in which this occurs can vary.

As evidence to the House of Commons Select Committee on the Environment, Greenpeace produced a report that compared forest damage in the three most affected West European countries – The Netherlands, West Germany and Switzerland – with the Forestry Commission survey (see diagram). The UK forest is suffering exactly the same decline as the FRG, as can be seen by comparing the bar-charts for 1987 (for 1988 results, see FORESTRY IN THE UK).

These 1987 results were included in a survey of forest health in 22 countries published by the United Nations in late 1988. The UN's Co-operative Programme on Assessment and Monitoring of Air Pollution Effects on Forests concluded that the UK had a higher percentage of sick conifers than any other European country, and that overall its forest health was almost the worst in Europe. The report

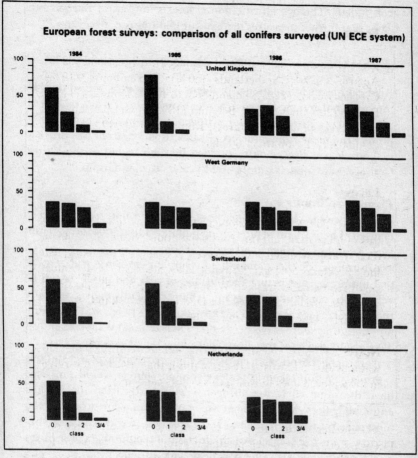

European forest surveys: comparison of all conifers surveyed (UN ECE system)

Vertical axis shows percentage of trees in each defoliation class. Data shown as columns are the percentages of trees in each damage class (Class 0 – healthy [0–10% defoliation]; Class 1 – 'warning' [11–25% loss]; Class 2 – moderate [26–60%]; Class 3 – severe [over 60%]; Class 4 – dead). The further to the right the graphs are, the more damaged the trees. The UK data show the effect of the Forestry Commission teams being over-optimistic and under-recording the actual state of the trees in 1984 and 1985. Otherwise it indicates the similarity of UK data to that from other European countries. (Species involved: in the UK – Sitka and Norway spruce, Scots pine; in Germany – Norway spruce, pine, silver fir; in Switzerland – Norway spruce, pine, silver fir, larch; in the Netherlands – Norway spruce, Corsican pine, Scots pine, douglas fir.)

Source: Greenpeace, *When the Bough Breaks*, 1988

concluded: 'The overall situation of forests in Central Europe indicates that further measures to abate air pollution are necessary.'

SOLUTIONS

Acid rain is an international problem which will be solved only by international action. The environment movement has agreed that 90 per cent cuts in sulphur and nitrogen emissions are necessary to protect the most vulnerable ecosystems. Reductions of this order of magnitude are also being mentioned by such bodies as the Nature Conservancy Council and the Acid Waters Review Group.

Primary solutions

The best way to clean up a source of pollution is not to allow it to be emitted. There are three interacting pollutants that start the acid rain cycle – sulphur, nitrogen and hydrocarbons.

Anthropogenic (i.e. human-made) sulphur emissions will be stopped mainly by preventing the burning of coal and oil. This can be achieved by conserving energy much more efficiently than is currently the practice (see ENERGY: ENERGY CONSERVATION) and by using non-polluting sources of energy (see ENERGY: RENEWABLE ENERGY). This would also have the effect of lessening the GREENHOUSE EFFECT.

Anthropogenic nitrogen emissions come partly from power stations – primary action taken to remove sulphur sources would thus also have the same effect for nitrogen – and partly from the world's automobile fleet. More efficient use of public transport would be the most effective way of reducing these emissions (see AUTOMOBILE POLLUTION: SOCIETAL SOLUTIONS). Reduction of the numbers of vehicles on the road would also alleviate the greenhouse effect.

Hydrocarbons are produced in large measure from automobiles, so reduction of the world fleet would have beneficial results here. The other main source is from solvent-based substances such as paint; substitution of solvent-based with water-based substances is in many cases possible. Emissions of hydrocarbons come, however, from other sources as well (e.g. industrial processes, petroleum refining and distribution, and natural gas leakage). The solution of this problem will need various measures.

Short-term solutions

Existing plant needs to be cleaned up in the short term to alleviate the effects of acid rain. There are a number of technologies that can achieve significant pollution reduction.

Various technological measures exist for reducing SO_2 emissions. These include:

- Flue Gas Desulphurization (FGD – a method of filtering SO_2 out of power station smoke. Used commercially on a large scale in Japan, the USA and Europe). There are various systems, with the regenerative type, such as the Wellman Lord, being preferable. Regenerative systems use relatively small quantities of cleaning agent and produce by-products that can easily be sold. Some FGD systems use large quantities of limestone to clean power station smoke, and produce vast amounts of by-product – transferring the pollution from the air to the land.
- Fluidized bed combustion (a method for more efficiently burning coal). It is favoured by the electricity industry, but is not yet commercially developed, and has not therefore been fully assessed.
- Use of low-sulphur fuel (e.g. Welsh and Scottish coal, North Sea oil). Not favoured in Britain because the more polluting substitutes are cheaper.

Technologies for reducing NO_x include:

- Special burners in power stations. These are cheap, currently being developed, but can achieve pollution reductions of only around 35 per cent.
- Flue Gas Denitrification (also known as Selective Catalytic Reduction). This is more efficient and can achieve pollution reduction of 90 per cent. It is used on a large scale in Japan and the USA, is being introduced in West Germany, but not yet elsewhere. Other new processes, including a system called NO_xOUT, are currently being tested.
- Catalytic converters on cars (see AUTOMOBILE POLLUTION: TECHNOLOGICAL SOLUTIONS). Effective speed limits for vehicles will also reduce nitrogen emissions.

Catalytic converters reduce hydrocarbon emissions.

Various palliative measures, such as liming affected lakes, will arrest the pollution temporarily. Liming is not an effective solution, however, as it is expensive, impossible on a large scale and does not restore the ecosystem that existed before the acid damage occurred. Measures will also be necessary to reduce the amount of agricultural ammonia and nitrates getting into the soil.

The politics of acid rain

Although all countries create acid rain, some create more than others. In Western Europe, the biggest polluter is Britain, pumping out about a fifth of the region's SO_2 emissions.

→ PREVAILING WINDS

WESTERN EUROPE - 30% CLUB MEMBERS

EASTERN EUROPE - 30% CLUB MEMBERS

The Thirty Per Cent Club

Pouring industrial garbage into the air is a cheap form of waste disposal, provided that it drifts into someone else's back yard. For the Western European countries, membership of the Thirty Per Cent Club is a matter of geography (see map opposite).

There are five Western European countries which have not joined the Thirty Per Cent Club. Greece has argued that its weak economy precludes any initiative. The other non-members – the UK, Eire, Spain and Portugal – are all grouped round the edge of the continent, taking advantage of clean air arriving from the Atlantic, polluting it and sending it into Europe.

The most enthusiastic members of the Thirty Per Cent Club are those countries most sensitive to environmental damage – Germany, The Netherlands, Austria, Switzerland and the Scandinavian countries. They are applying immense leverage in an attempt to get movement from the whole of Europe, especially the UK.

Emissions from Eastern Europe are almost as large as those from

---

Members of the Thirty Per Cent Club

All members pledge to reduce emissions or exports of sulphur by 30% between 1980 and 1993. Others have committed themselves further.

Austria	70% reduction by 1995	Bulgaria	30% by 1993
		Czechoslovakia	30% by 1993
Belgium	50% by 1995	GDR	30% by 1993
Canada	50% by 1994	Hungary	30% by 1993
Denmark	50% by 1995	Italy	30% by 1993
Finland	50% by 1993	Liechtenstein	30% by 1993
France	50% by 1990	USSR	30% by 1993
Luxembourg	58% by 1990	Ukraine	30% by 1993
Netherlands	50% by 1995	Byelorussia	30% by 1993
Norway	50% by 1994		
Sweden	65% by 1995		
Switzerland	57% by 1995		
FRG	65% by 1993		

Source: *Acidification and Air Pollution*, 1987

the West. (They are twice as large, if all the emissions from the Asiatic part of the USSR are taken into account.) Particular attention is being given to East Germany and Czechoslovakia which, though members of the Thirty Per Cent Club, still produce an enormous amount of sulphur dioxide; and to Romania and Poland which are unrepentant acid rain polluters.

Emissions from Eastern Europe, as well as devastating parts of East Germany, Poland and Czechoslovakia, have a significant impact on the Central European forests and Scandinavian lakes.

Some of these commitments involve enormous expense: the West Germans, for example, spending some £10 billion between 1983 and 1988 to clean up 80 per cent of their power stations. The UK has announced a programme to clean up six of its 40 fossil-fuelled stations by 2003, and is fitting low-Nox burners to ten stations. The UK has an 'aim of policy' to reduce its sulphur and nitrogen emissions by 30 per cent by the year 2000, with an intended national reduction of about 50% by 2003. This long-term programme hides the deterioration that will occur in the near future. UK sulphur dioxide emissions increased by 200,000 tonnes in 1987, and will continue to increase, if the economy expands, until 1993.

If the environment of Europe is to be protected, greater reductions than those pledged by the Thirty Per Cent Club are necessary. Looking at the problem from an environmental perspective, Scandinavian scientists have now worked out how much sulphur and acid pollution the earth can tolerate. To protect the more sensitive soils, European SO_2 reductions of 80 to 90 per cent will have to be achieved, and a reduction of at least 75 per cent in NO_x emissions. This will then reduce the deposition of these pollutants to the 'critical loads' that sensitive ecosystems appear able to tolerate.

See also AUTOMOBILE POLLUTION; ENERGY; GREENHOUSE EFFECT; WATER

REFERENCES

Department of the Environment, *Digest of Environment Protection and Water Statistics*, 1989.
Elsworth, S., *Acid Rain*, Pluto Press, 1984.

Environmental Data Services Reports, 1985–8.
Forestry Commission, *Forest Health Surveys*, Bulletin 74, 1987.

Greenpeace, *When the Bough Breaks*, Greenpeace Air Pollution Paper 1, 1988.

House of Commons Environment Committee, *Report on Acid Rain*, 1984 and 1988.

McCormick, J., *Acid Earth*, Earthscan, 1985.

National Swedish Environment Protection Board, *Acidification and Air Pollution*, 1987.

Nordic Council Working Group, *Critical Loads for Nitrogen and Sulphur*, 1986.

Park, Chris C., *Acid Rain, Rhetoric and Reality*, Methuen, 1987.

Pearce, F., *Acid Rain*, Penguin Books, 1987.

Rose, C., *Acid Rain*, World Wildlife Fund, 1986.

Swedish Ministry of Agriculture, *Acidification Today and Tomorrow*, 1982.

Swedish NGO Secretariat on Acid Rain, *Acid News*, 1983–8.

UK Acid Waters Review Group Second Report, *Acidity in United Kingdom Fresh Waters*, Department of the Environment, December 1988.

UK Photochemicals Oxidants Review Group, *Ozone in the United Kingdom*, 1988.

UN Economic Commission for Europe, *Forest Damage and Air Pollution*, 1988.

WWF International, *Acid Rain and Air Pollution*, 1989.

Savill, R., ' "Britain's trees among sickest in Europe" says UN', *Daily Telegraph*, 5 November 1988.

CONTACTS

Campaign for Lead-free Air (CLEAR)

Friends of the Earth (FoE)

Friends of the Earth (Scotland)

Greenpeace

National Society for Clean Air

Socialist Environment and Resources Association (SERA)

Swedish NGO Coalition on Acid Rain

World Wide Fund for Nature (WWF)

Young Liberals Ecology Group

Central Electricity Generating Board (CEGB)

Department of Energy (DEn)

Department of the Environment (DoE)

Department of Transport (DTp)

Animals

Animals face an increasing number of threats to their survival, as a result of direct or indirect interference by human beings. They have died as their habitats disappear (see DEFORESTATION; DESERTIFICATION; WETLANDS; COUNTRYSIDE IN THE UK; TRANSPORT POLICY IN THE UK); they have been poisoned unintentionally by the widespread distribution of harmful substances (see PCBS; PESTICIDES; MARINE POLLUTION; SEVESO; CHEMICAL WASTES); or they have been hunted, often to extinction (see SPECIES EXTINCTION; WHALES AND WHALING). Animals in the wild are dying, or dying out, in large numbers.

Closer to home, we use animals for food, for scientific research, or in zoos. A number of environmental organizations have become involved in the issue of animal rights: some are opposed to the keeping of any animals for food, experimentation or in zoos, while others have no objection to the eating of animals but strongly protest the living conditions under which millions of beasts and birds are now kept. Other organizations – the 'animal liberationists' – vociferously, sometimes physically, oppose the practice of vivisection.

The motivation of most animal pressure groups is the suffering and deprivation meted out to (literally) billions of animals and birds for purely economic reasons. These practices are the subject of the rest of this entry.

Animals as food

'Factory farming' is a relatively recent development. If animals are to be kept indoors in large numbers without widespread outbreaks of disease, artificial heat and light are necessary: so the arrival of electricity was essential before factory farms were conceived.

Once arrived, however, the industry has grown very rapidly. Maureen Duffy points out in *Men and Beasts* (1984) that every year some 33 million cattle, sheep and pigs are slaughtered in the UK –

roughly 60 a minute – in some 1,200 licensed slaughterhouses and knackers' yards. With a population of 53 to 55 million farm animals in the early 1980s, these slaughter statistics give an average life expectancy for each animal of less than two years. The figures exclude the most intensively bred species – chickens – which are slaughtered at a rate of 7 million a week. The total number of animal and bird deaths is a rough 3,000 per minute, every working day.

Treatment of animals varies according to their species.

Chickens used for battery eggs   Mark Gold's *Assault and Battery* (1983) gives an excellent description of the living conditions of battery chickens. In 1961, 19 per cent of the UK's total egg output came from battery cages: by 1984 this had risen to 96 per cent.

Battery hens are economic because they are packed into a small space. In the UK, they are usually allocated four inches of cage width per bird, four or five birds per cage. Each bird spends its life with a living area roughly the size of a page of this book. As the birds' wing span is 30 inches, being confined four to a cage 16 by 18 inches (45 by 50 cm) in dimension leaves them unable adequately to stretch or exercise their wings. Indeed, exercise is not planned as part of their lives: their role is purely to lay eggs.

Cages are usually stacked three to four tiers high in windowless buildings, with lighting up to 17 hours per day, temperature kept high, and birds fed large quantities of high-protein food. The conditions are designed to maximize egg-laying: a battery hen will lay approximately 250 eggs a year, compared to 199 from a free-range bird. Between 20,000 and 40,000 birds can be found in a battery shed, so the difference in production is important economically. Many birds become aggressive under such conditions, and debeaking is not uncommon: Gold estimates 40 per cent of birds are debeaked. This is a painful practice: the beak overlies a thin layer of soft tissue, which resembles the quick of the human fingernail.

A day after birth, chicks are separated into sexes, and the females sent off to be bred for egg-laying. They can expect to live 15 months, or in some cases two years: though they have many more years of potential egg-laying left, they cannot fill the large quotas expected of them, and are killed.

Males are genetically ill-equipped for fast fattening into chicken flesh (see below), have no economic worth and are destroyed. Some day-old chicks are 'homogenized' (crushed) by a special mill capable of mincing 500 chicks a minute: others are gassed with carbon dioxide or chloroform. There are no laws governing the killing of day-old chicks, however, and the technology for killing can be expensive: so thousands of chicks are suffocated by tying them into sacks or boxes, and waiting for them to die. The national egg-laying flock fluctuates between 40 and 60 million females. This implies that roughly the same number of male chicks is killed every year.

Eggs are inexpensive as a result of battery production, although *Assault and Battery* quotes a letter from the Ministry of Agriculture:

With regard to the vitamin content of battery eggs, a detailed study of the nutritional value of eggs conducted by this ministry found that, on average, battery hens produced eggs with 40 per cent less vitamin B12 and 30 per cent less folic acid than free-range eggs.

This kind of information does not get wide publicity, as the image of eggs is important for their marketing. Some 35 million a day are consumed in the UK, assisted by advertising campaigns targeted on our assumed link between chickens and the countryside. The connection for most eggs is non-existent.

Our other expectations are similarly manipulated: battery egg yolks tend to be an unattractive pale colour, but we associate deep yellow yolks with healthy eggs. This is therefore achieved by the (permitted) addition of colouring to the battery chicken feed. We are also encouraged to assume that brown eggs are an indication of a 'country', rather than a factory, egg: but this is not so. Shell colour depends entirely on the breed of hen.

The recent increase in sales of free-range eggs indicates that there is a market for eggs from non-factory hens. EC rules state that free-range eggs should be labelled as such, and supplied from registered packing stations. Unlabelled boxes almost always contain battery eggs.

The definition 'free range' is tightly controlled (although the Free Range Egg Association – FREGG – objects to certain loopholes in EC regulations). The birds must have continuous daytime access to open-air runs, in which the ground is mainly covered with vegetation. The amount of space in their living conditions is also controlled. There are various other classifications of egg, progressively approaching factory conditions:

- *semi-intensive*: a kind of free range, although with four times as many birds per hectare;
- *deep litter*: no specification relating to daytime runs, seven hens per square metre of floor, with at least a third of the floor area covered with straw, shavings, or turf;
- *perchery, or barn, eggs*: a high stocking intensity, similar to that for battery hens, but with perches provided for the birds.

The labelling has been criticized as misleading, 'barn' eggs in particular giving an impression that appears not to be justified by the facts. It should be noted that 'farm fresh' is meaningless, as it can be applied to battery eggs.

Intensive rearing and feeding practices, criticized because of the effects on chickens, can have side-effects on humans. The salmonella outbreak in the UK in recent years is an example of this. (See FOOD IN THE UK.)

A number of organizations publish information relating to battery hens and free-range eggs: FREGG is probably the best-known.

Chickens used for meat   Chicken meat is also big business: by 1981, according to Gold, there were 382 million chickens kept under 'broiler conditions'. Profit margins for these birds are extremely tight, so space is at a premium. Broiler breeding units usually house 8–10,000 birds (although some flocks are 25,000 strong), which are easily accommodated in the early stages: by the end of their 52-day lives, however, the flock has filled out all available space, with farmers recommended to allow a minimum of 6 by 6 inches (15 by 15 cm) per bird. Some farmers allow less space than this.

Broiler chickens are bred for docility and quick growth. Disease and injury is a constant problem, with a high rate of heart attacks, leg and back injuries caused by bone weakness, bone fractures and dislocations, and infectious illness. More than 6 per cent of all birds die before their full seven weeks' growth – which would mean some 30 million birds a year. In the USA, where some 3 billion birds are produced a year, this means 180 million premature deaths.

Turkeys   Once (like chicken) a relatively high-priced food, turkey meat is now cheaply available. Turkey production is the largest growth industry among the meat products, with the number of birds in Britain increasing from 3 million a year to more than 23 million between the 1960s and the 1980s.

Production is similar to that for broiler chickens, though not as overcrowded. In most modern units, 20,000 birds are raised in a building, in groups of 5,000. Food and water are provided in adequate proportions, and about one square metre of space is allocated per large bird. Female turkeys are killed at 13, 15 and 18 weeks, for the oven-ready market, while males are killed at 24 weeks for processed food like turkey ham or sausage.

Although in comparison with broiler chickens the turkey's life seems minimally better, there is still a 5 per cent mortality rate, with heart attacks being the main cause of death.

Cattle   Dairy herds are not intensively farmed in the UK, although in the US 50 per cent of cows are kept permanently confined in intensive units. Average herd sizes in the UK have increased, however, with herds of 100 to 200 cows being relatively common. The practice of 'zero grazing' is increasing in the UK – herds are kept in covered yards, and cut grass is brought in by tractor.

A number of practices have aroused concern. The first is that, for a cow to produce milk, she must calve once a year, but it is regarded as uneconomic for the calf to be naturally raised. The calves are taken from their mothers between three and seven days after birth, causing apparent distress to both, and then transported to market in conditions that are often unsatisfactory (see below).

Dairy cows are judged by the amount of milk they produce. At peak lactation, a cow will produce 35 to 50 litres of milk a day, and will be milked for ten months. This peak is ten times the amount that her calf would have drunk, had suckling been allowed to continue. If a new hormone (bovine growth hormone, also known as bGH or bovine somatotrophin, BST) is introduced, milk yields will increase by 25 to 40 per cent. This will produce substantial profits for the dairy industry and certain drug companies, if consumer resistance to the product is overcome. The effects on the cow can only be surmised.

Compassion in World Farming (CIWF) points out that, currently, dairy cows are slaughtered well before the end of their natural lifespan (about 20 years); 25 per cent are killed before they are three and a half years old, with only a quarter lasting beyond the age of eight. Observers have claimed that the additional stress imposed on the animals by hormone-stimulated overproduction will leave them 'burnt out' by the age of three.

Artificial insemination is now common (at least 60 per cent of conceptions), and 'embryotomy' (where a foetus of a 'high quality' cow is transferred to the womb of a lesser animal) is increasing. The latter practice, and that of mating young heifers at increasingly early ages (between 18 months and two years) can cause painful births, as the calf may be too big for the mother to deliver comfortably.

Of concern to humans is the common practice of dosing cattle with antibiotics. Richard North in *The Animals Report* (1983) comments that 17 million shots of antibiotics are given to British cattle every year. The danger here is that this over-use will encourage certain strains of bacteria to become immune to the drugs. North quotes reports in the *British Medical Journal* (1980 and 1981) that some strains of salmonella were 'multi-resistant' to the commonest antibiotics, being resistant in cattle since 1977 and in humans since 1979. Two human patients died as a result of drug-immune infection.

Growth hormones used in cattle have also had unfortunate effects on humans. The most notorious is reported in James Erlichman's *Gluttons for Punishment* (1986): DES – more commonly known as stilbenes – is a synthetic hormone originally injected into pregnant women in the UK and USA in the belief that it would avert miscarriage. As with Thalidomide, most mothers and babies escaped without damage – but at least 429 girls born to these women developed vaginal cancer in their teens or early twenties. Seventy-nine died, mostly in the USA where the drug was used more commonly, and the drug was banned from use in humans.

It was still permitted in some countries for use as a growth hormone in cows, however. Stilbenes offer unusually quick weight gain, are cheap, and can be injected easily into muscle tissue. In 1980, a number of children in Milan were reported with abnormalities: infant boys were growing breasts, and girls were developing mature sexual organs. Italian health inspectors discovered that all the children had been eating veal baby food contaminated with the female growth hormone, stilbenes. The drug was illegal in Italy and France, but was probably obtained and used illicitly. Theoretically, the meat could have come from Britain: use of stilbenes was banned here only in 1982.

Consumer protest on the continent finally forced the EC to ban all growth hormones in 1985, in the face of fierce opposition from Britain. The UK was given extended permission to use growth implants until 1989, a year after the legislation was to become effective elsewhere.

Consumer protest has also achieved another significant victory: the use of veal crates in the UK is to be discontinued. The crates achieved notoriety because of a spirited campaign by the animal rights movement: calves were imprisoned in a 2-foot-wide box (60 cm), often tethered with a short chain as well, and deprived of water, salt and solid food. A diet based on EC surplus skimmed milk was fed to the animals, who lived a cramped, deprived, often lightless life until they were killed in their fourteenth week.

These crates are banned in the UK from January 1990, and directives are being prepared at the EC: although with the crates in wide use in The Netherlands, Italy, and France, a Europe-wide ban may be difficult to achieve.

Pigs   In 1960, more than half our pig farmers had breeding stocks of less than 20 sows: by 1980, more than half of all pig herds had more than 100 sows. Pigs in the UK are kept in a variety of systems, including 'free range', but between 50 and 70 per cent are kept in close confinement. This will mean, after mating, the sow is kept for four months in a stall, recommended width (Ministry of Agriculture) of 1.97 to 2.13 feet (about 60 cm), in which the animal can stand up, lie down, eat and drink.

After giving birth, the piglets are in many cases allowed to stay with their mother for only two or three weeks, then removed (normal weaning is after two months). The sow is returned to the stall, and seven days later is again served by the boar. The reproductive cycle starts again: early weaning means that five litters can be produced every two years, instead of the traditional four. The process is carried to its logical conclusion: Richard North mentions the practice of sometimes delivering piglets by hysterectomy from five-year-old sows, who would otherwise be at risk of delivering stillborn piglets. The mothers are then immediately slaughtered.

Pigs are intelligent animals, and these conditions promote boredom, discomfort and less than perfect health. Intensive pigs display examples of apparent disturbed behaviour, including rooting the concrete floors, biting the metal bars of their cages, and inexplicable outbreaks of aggression. They are also prone to swine vesicular disease, which according to Richard North entered the scene in the early 1970s and is a typical corollary of intensive pig-keeping or poor husbandry. SVD is controlled only by compulsory slaughtering, which has cost £12 million in the UK to date.

Transport and death   The animal movement not only protests the living conditions of 'farm' animals: it also objects to the way in which they are transported to the slaughterhouses and then killed.

Cattle and pigs, but especially pigs, are so affected by the stress of the slaughterhouse that they can produce poor meat. *The Animals Report* (Richard North, 1983) describes the phenomenon:

Pre-slaughter stress makes some animals produce post-mortem acid in their muscles at accelerated and increased rates which, in combination with warmth in the slaughterhouse, produces in pigs a quality in their meat which is known as PSE (pale, soft, and exudative). This means that the meat is colourless, squidgy, and sweats. Anywhere between one in five and one in ten of pigs are affected . . .

As usual in the curiously depraved world of animal exploitation, the problem of PSE meat is seen as one for the consumer and the farmer. The unfortunate fact that animals suffer dramatic hormonological changes due to the misery and shock of their last few hours is not regarded as something which ought to worry us from their point of view.

Mark Gold comments that, for chickens, it is the total number being killed that provides the difficulties. The birds are hung upside down by their legs on a conveyor belt, dipped in a water bath charged with low-level electric current to stun them, then have their throats cut by an automatic knife. In theory, they bleed to death while still stunned, before entering the scald tank: in practice, birds can have their throats cut while still fully conscious, or even enter the scald tank while still alive. Gold notes that automatic killers are advertised as between 94 and 96 per cent efficient – but, with 450 million deaths a year, this percentage carries the implication that up to 27 million birds are not killed efficiently.

Transport of birds to the slaughterhouse is also criticized. There is no time limit to the length of journeys, or to the period in which birds can be left standing on lorries. Up to 7,000 birds can be carried in one lorry load, in crates 3 feet by 2 feet by 1 foot (90 × 60 × 30 cm). After an entire life spent in one building, with a controlled environment, this new experience will be at least disorienting, at worst terrifying. Extremes of climate can also take their toll. Almost 13 million chickens, turkeys, geese and ducks were exported in 1988 (*Agscene*, June 1989).

Similar criticisms are laid against the transport of live animals. In 1988, 249,000 calves and and 497,600 sheep and lambs were exported from the UK for further fattening and slaughter, plus thousands of horses, cows and pigs – nearly a million animals, transported long distances by road, then by sea, then by road again, in conditions which do not inspire confidence as to their wellbeing. Compassion in World Farming points out that the UK is poised to become a Euro-giant in sheep exporting. In 1986, 195,000 live animals crossed the Channel. This increased to 373,000 in 1987 and to almost half a million a year later.

Animals used in scientific research

In 1981, according to Maureen Duffy in *Men and Beasts*, 4,344,843 animals were experimented on in registered laboratories: a large number, though 250,000 smaller than in 1980 and the lowest number since 1963. By 1987, this figure was 3.6 million: again, a reduction on previous years, but still an average of around 10,000 experiments a day.

Until recently, the legislation governing animal experiments was the 1876 Cruelty to Animals Act, designed to regulate an experiment if it is considered it 'presents a risk of pain, distress, discomfort or interference with an animal's ordinary state of health or well-being'. The Act was drafted in circumstances very different to today's: the number of experiments in 1878 was 270, rising to 38,000 by 1905. By the early 1980s, 15 members of the Home Office inspectorate were supposed to monitor 527 registered laboratories, in which 12,000 active licence-holders worked.

Richard North (in *The Animals Report*) provides a partial break-down of the 4.34 million animals experiments carried out in 1981, from Home Office statistics:

- over 1.69 million experiments were carried out for 'the selection of potential medical, dental or veterinary products and appliances';
- nearly 19,000 endured 'application of substance to the eye';
- 92,300 endured 'interference with the central nervous system';

- 24,000 experiments were conducted 'to select, develop, or study the use, hazards, or safety of cosmetics and toiletries';
- 4,800 animals, half of them rats, endured 'infliction of physical trauma to simulate human injury, other than by burning or scalding'.

The moral and philosophical arguments about vivisection are complex. The Research Defence Society ('Founded in 1908 . . . to make generally known the value and the necessity of experiments on animals; the restrictions placed on them by the Act of 1876; and the great saving of human and animal lives already obtained by means of such experiments') has put forward various arguments, listed on page 28.

The *For all our sakes* leaflet makes some statements that are open to question: of the 20 per cent of animal experimentation devoted to consumer or worker protection, no mention is made of whether this research is essential, or whether it is in response to commercial pressure to produce yet another lipstick, deodorant or sun-tan oil. 'Consumer protection' sounds more principled than 'profit-motivated product development'.

The document also makes the comment that 80 per cent of experiments are on mice or rats. This carries an implicit message that these animals are somehow lesser breeds, and therefore more suited to experimentation – an arguable assumption that appears to appeal more to the emotional attraction of some species than to scientific reality. The percentages quoted for dogs and cats, incidentally, would have resulted in 11,000 experiments on dogs and 6,000 on cats in 1981.

The comment about hundreds of thousands of people dying from polio in the absence of animal experimentation is hypothetical, and can be neither proved nor disproved.

The 'human health' argument, to some extent, divides the public response to vivisection. Many animal rights organizations argue for a complete ban on all animal experiments: others argue for research essential to the protection of human health to be carried out, with a drastic reduction in total numbers of experiments.

The problem is whether the assurances of scientists as to the validity of their experiments can be accepted. Richard North

- 80 per cent of all animal experiments in Britain are for medical, dental, or veterinary advancement. The remainder are for the protection of consumers or workers in industry.
- In the past 50 years, medical research expenditure has increased, in real terms, 40-fold. In the same period the number of animal experiments has increased only 25-fold.
- There has been a steady decrease in the number of animal experiments in the last ten years.
- We eat more than 400 million animals (cattle, pigs, and poultry) each year in Britain – about seven each.
- Over 80 per cent of all experiments involve rats or mice. Dogs account for only 0.25 per cent and cats 0.14 per cent of the total. The RSPCA kills very large numbers of unwanted cats and dogs every year – many times the number used in all UK laboratories.

The Research Defence Society also ascribes specific benefits in human health to animal research:

– Children have benefited most. There has been a 90% reduction in the death rate in the 1 to 14 group in the last 40 years. More than half of this was achieved by conquering the killer diseases like pneumonia, tuberculosis, diphtheria, measles and whooping cough. Animal treatment played a necessary part in developing the necessary treatments.

– Polio vaccines, developed by animal experiment, reduced the number of cases in 1958 from 2,495 (with 150 deaths) to 4 in 1975, with no deaths (if the anti-vivisectionists had succeeded in halting animal experiments in 1950, for example, hundreds of thousands of people around the world would have died from polio since then, and many more would have been disabled).

– Please remember, animals themselves, at home or on the farm, enjoy better health and an improved survival rate due to animal-tested veterinary medicines, anaesthetics, and foods.

Source: Research Defence Society, *For all our sakes – science still needs animals*, no date

discusses evidence given by the Research Defence Society to the House of Lords Select Committee considering animal experimentation: the members of the committee were puzzled why an important new drug was tested on 698 animals – which they found acceptable – and a new food colour was tested on 1,740. Both were argued as essential research.

To the outside observer, it appears that commercial need can be presented as scientific requirement, and that animals suffer as a result. There are already 3,254 colour or flavour modifiers available for food use in the UK (see FOOD ADDITIVES); the animal lobby argues that this should be regarded as enough, and that further products, if they are to be developed, should not be tested on animals. Tobacco use, processed food and sunbathing are non-essential human activities: it seems lacking in morality to test these non-essential substances on species which will gain nothing from them.

Richard North points out that research into new drugs is not necessarily entirely altruistic, either. Licences for experimentation are increasingly being given for companies who are 'trawling' for a saleable variant of a drug that is already on the market. In the decade up to 1980, the number of licences for substances which were only variations rose from 1,800 to 6,898, while the number of new chemical entities being researched was 37 in 1971 and 23 in 1981.

Vivisection controversies The anti-vivisection movement has been successful in exposing some examples of vivisection that appear to be unnecessary and cruel. The most well-known of these are:

THE DRAIZE TEST Irritant substances are applied to the eyeballs of living animals, usually rabbits, to determine their damaging effects. A substance (such as liquid bleach, a shampoo or mascara) is placed in the rabbit's eye by holding out the lower lid and placing the liquid into the 'cup' that is formed. The eyelid is then closed, the animal restrained so it cannot scratch the eye, and then the rabbit is observed for up to three weeks to determine the extent of ulceration, discomfort, or pain. The animal is then killed.

THE LD 50 TEST This stands for Lethal Dose 50 per cent, the amount of a substance which will kill half of the animals being tested. Defenders of this test say that it is essential to find the toxicity of the substance before it is released to human beings: opponents criticize it on the grounds that different species react differently to many substances; and that often the quantity of substance administered is so large as to make the results meaningless. Campaigns by the animal movement against these tests have rendered them less popular with industry, although they are still in use.

Psychological research   Particular projects have been identified, which include: separating infant rhesus monkeys from their mothers at 30 days old, then monitoring the effects of maternal deprivation over the next 12 months; sewing up the eyelids of infant monkeys, and opening them a year later to detect how short-sighted they have become; stressing one group of rats to make them permanently 'pessimistic', and rewarding another to make them 'optimistic' then placing both groups together in a vat of water from which there is no escape, to determine whether the 'optimistic' or 'pessimistic' group drowns first. *Animal Liberation* (L. Gruen, P. Singer and D. Hine, 1987) describes a number of similar experiments.

The future for scientific research   Scientific research on animals will undoubtedly continue, although considerable pressure is being exerted for reform. The Animals (Scientific Procedures) Act was passed in the UK in 1986, to become law the following year. This extends control to large areas of experimentation missed by the 1876 Act, requires stricter licensing for competence of experimenters, and, for the first time, licensing of individual experiments, and demands that one person be named in each laboratory to supervise day-to-day care of animals, in co-operation with a named vet who will be on the staff or on call. Both will be answerable for abuses.

The new controls will be accompanied by tougher penalties – prison for up to two years and unlimited fines.

The legislation has been welcomed by some animal groups, who see it as an essential first step towards full protection of laboratory animals: other groups, however, have called it a 'vivisector's charter', pointing out that enforcement will be in the hands of only 21 inspectors, and that previously outlawed areas like microsurgery, and the use of the same animal for two experiments, will now be allowed. They point to legislation before the West German Parliament, banning specific types of experiment, and the use of animals in warfare experiments, and in tobacco, detergent and cosmetic testing.

Some companies have been set up selling products which have not been tested on animals, using natural substances and alternative systems of testing. Two of these are Beauty without Cruelty and Body

Shop. As the campaigning groups continue to publicize the more extreme practices of animal experimentation, consumer pressure will become an important factor in the debate as to how many animal experiments should be tolerated – or even if the practice should be stopped altogether.

See also CHEMICAL WASTES; COUNTRYSIDE CHANGES IN THE UK; DE-FORESTATION; DESERTIFICATION; MARINE POLLUTION; PCBS; PESTICIDES; SEVESO; SPECIES EXTINCTION; TRANSPORT POLICY IN THE UK; WETLANDS; WHALES AND WHALING

REFERENCES

Duffy, Maureen, *Men and Beasts*, Paladin, 1984.

Erlichman, James, *Gluttons For Punishment*, Penguin Books, 1986.

Gold, Mark, *Assault and Battery*, Pluto Press, 1983.

Gruen, L., P. Singer, and D. Hine, *Animal Liberation*, Camden Press, 1987.

North, Richard, *The Animals Report*, Penguin Books, 1983.

Smyth, D. H., *Alternatives to Animal Experiments*, Scolar Press/ Research Defence Society, 1978.

Statistics of Scientific Procedures on Living Animals, HMSO, 1987.

Compassion in World Farming, *Agscene*, March 1987, June 1987, June 1989.

'For all our sakes – science still needs animals', Research Defence Society leaflet, undated.

Guardian, 21 May 1986.

CONTACTS

Animal Aid
Animal Liberation Front
British Union for the Abolition of Vivisection
Campaign for the Reform of Animal Experiments
Chickens' Lib
Compassion in World Farming
Free Range Egg Association (FREGG)
Lynx
National Anti-Vivisection Society
People's Trust for Endangered Species
Research Defence Society
Royal Society for the Protection of Birds (RSPB)
Royal Society for the Prevention of Cruelty to Animals (RSPCA)
Scottish Anti-Vivisection Society
Vegan Society
Vegetarian Society

Antarctica

Antarctica is the last great wilderness in the world – an enormous land mass which, because of its inaccessibility and hostile climate, has remained virtually unchanged for millions of years.

The world's only example of a large pristine environment, this 'seventh continent' has attracted a number of territorial claims this century, with reasons varying from national pride to Antarctica's possible mineral reserves.

In the last 30 years, treaties and conventions have established a workable system which allows scientific research while limiting the types of national and international activities which may take place in the area. The central treaty is open for renegotiation in 1991, so Antarctica has become an active international issue.

On the one hand, the possibility of finding mineral reserves has galvanized an increasing amount of industrial interest in the continent; on the other hand, evidence of increasing environmental disturbance has encouraged those who wish to strengthen the conservation of Antarctica *per se*. The environmental movement has put forward a suggestion that Antarctica should become a World Park: this proposal has received sympathy from Australia, France and Belgium, but few others.

Environmental resources

'Antarctica' is not one land mass, but several, given the appearance of a single continent by the overlying ice which binds together Greater Antarctica to the smaller land bodies known collectively as Lesser Antarctica. The size of the USA and Mexico combined, 99 per cent of the continent is buried under perpetual ice up to a depth of 4.5 km thick.

Antarctica is 99 per cent covered by ice, and contains most of the planet's fresh water reserves. The volume of ice is estimated at roughly 30 million cubic km (about 7 million cubic miles), formed by the compacted accumulation of 100,000 years of snow. If this ice sheet were to melt, the levels of the world's oceans would rise as much as 65 metres (over 200 feet).

It is the coldest place in the world, with average annual temperatures of minus 49 degrees C near the South Pole; technically a desert in the central region, as only 15 centimetres of snow fall each year, equivalent to 70 mm of rain; and has an average height three times greater than that of other continents.

Colder than the Arctic because of its height, the size of the ice sheet and its southerly position which shelters it from the sun, Antarctica has a significant impact on climate in the southern hemisphere, cooling the surrounding air and ocean and thus contributing to the climatic balance maintained by the equatorial and polar regions.

There is abundant wildlife in the region, based not on the continent but in the surrounding Southern Ocean, which accounts for about 10 per cent of the world's seas. The northern boundary of this ocean sinks below the warmer surrounding oceans, with an abrupt change in temperature of 2 to 3 degrees C, resulting in conditions which encourage the formation of rich supplies of oxygen and chemical nutrients. Thus the cold Southern Ocean is able to support an abundance of plants and animals.

At the bottom of the food chain is plankton, consisting of phytoplankton (i.e. plant plankton), the food source for zooplankton (i.e. small marine animals). The most important of the zooplankton is the shrimp-like Antarctic krill, which occurs in vast quantities and is the staple food for a number of larger animals – fish, squid, seabirds, seals and whales. The fish and squid are also eaten by the larger species.

Total numbers involved in the Antarctic food chain are great, and estimates are based largely on guesswork. The largest grouping of krill to date was a 'superswarm' identified in 1981, containing an estimated 10 million tonnes and occupying several square miles of sea to a depth of 180 metres (600 feet) below the surface. Scientists estimated that this single school was equivalent to about one-seventh of the world's total fish and shellfish catch for a year.

Because Antarctica has been so untouched over the centuries, it provides an important monitoring zone to determine the spread of world air pollution and the extent of pollutants such as PCBs. It is also, for other reasons, the ideal site for measuring ozone levels in the upper air (see OZONE LAYER).

The harshness of the environment, however, means that scientific research, and any exploitation of the continent at all, could disturb the delicate ecosystems that have struggled into existence. Antarctica supports a limited variety of land species, and a wealth of marine species. Over-exploitation carries, as always, the risk of ecosystem destruction; but the possibilities of regeneration are much slimmer than in other parts of the world.

History of Antarctica

Current geological thought holds that Antarctica, South America, Africa, India and Australia were originally joined together in a super-continent called Gondwana. About 180 million years ago, the continents started to separate and move apart, a process that is still continuing.

Gondwana
        Source: British Antarctic Survey / Natural Environment Research Council,
                                                                    Antarctica, n.d.

If the Gondwana hypothesis is true – and there is virtually unanimous agreement that it is – then the geological features of the different continents would be continued in Antarctica, and mineral resources found in India, Africa and South America would also be located in Antarctica.

This has implications for nations seeking to extend their exploitation of mineral reserves. John May points out in *The Greenpeace Book of Antarctica* (1988) that substantial deposits of iron in the Prince Charles mountains, and possibly the world's largest reserves of coal in the Trans-Antarctic mountains, have been confirmed. The Dufek Massif, which covers 50,000 sq. km of Antarctica, is a geological formation known as a layered intrusion. Some of the layered intrusions found on other continents, such as the Bushveld complex in South Africa, have proved to be among the richest mineral sites in the world.

For this reason, and also from nationalistic impulses, a number of countries have tried to establish their right to parts of the continent. In the early part of this century, the UK, France, Norway, Australia, New Zealand, Argentina and Chile all made formal claims to possession of sectors of Antarctica, with the UK, Argentina and Chile claiming overlapping territories. The USA accepted none of the claims and put forward its own ideas for management of the area after the Second World War.

These suggestions were not accepted internationally, either. Progress was blocked until the 1950s, when the scientific community launched the idea of an international drive to explore the continent. International Geophysical Year, 1957–8, involved scientists from a number of disciplines and 67 countries. For the first time, national claims became subordinate to international cooperation.

The success of the scientific effort was followed by a diplomatic initiative. The Antarctic Treaty, which was signed in 1959 and came into effect in 1961, established a number of provisions:

- Antarctica is to be used only for peaceful purposes, though military personnel may be used for scientific tasks;
- nuclear explosions and disposal of radioactive waste are banned;
- there is to be freedom of scientific investigation, but with all stations and equipment open to inspection by any Treaty member;
- territorial claims are not recognized, disputed, or established by the Treaty.

Responsibility for managing Antarctica rests with the twenty nations with full decision-making status under the Treaty. Called Consultative Parties, these comprise the original seven territorial claimants plus other nations which conduct substantial scientific research in the region.

Consultative Parties

Argentina	Belgium	Poland (1977)
Australia	South Africa	West Germany (1981)
Chile	Japan	Brazil (1983)
France	USA	India (1983)
New Zealand	USSR	China (1985)
Norway		Uruguay (1985)
United Kingdom		East Germany (1987)
		Italy (1987)
		Sweden (1988)
		Spain (1988)

The Treaty is open-ended – other nations can become Consultative Parties by carrying out substantial scientific activity in the region – although many developing countries without the resources for full-scale research feel that this condition excludes most of the world's nations from Antarctica. Sixteen other countries have acceded to the Treaty without consultative status, and since 1983 have been attending Treaty meetings as observers.

The Treaty could run indefinitely, although in 1991 it is open to any Consultative Party to call for a conference of the signatory nations to review its operations. Resource scarcity, economic pressures and the results of geological surveys may well lead to calls for greater industrial exploitation of the continent.

At the moment, the 20 Consultative Parties are trying to agree a legal framework under which mineral exploitation and other development could be licensed. This appeared to be in sight in New Zealand, June 1988, when an agreement was signed which set up three bodies to oversee the mining process from exploration to exploitation. The agreement was vetoed by Australia in May 1989, to the outrage of the other nations. Diplomatic negotiations continue.

Environmental protection

Two conventions have been concluded under the Antarctic Treaty: the Convention for the Conservation of Antarctic Seals (1972) and the Convention on the Conservation of Antarctic Marine Living Resources (1980). Both are still in force.

The later convention, known as CCAMLR, holds annual sessions and is charged with considering the ecosystem as a whole, rather than just individual species. CCAMLR has been criticized by the environment movement for its slowness in moving to protect fish stocks. The Antarctic cod has been used as an illustration of the dangers of over-fishing, as stocks have been heavily depleted since 1969. The USSR took 400,000 tonnes of this fish in 1970. Catches since then have averaged only a few thousand tonnes per year, with current cod stocks reported to be only a few per cent of their former level. It has now declined to the extent of becoming a protected species.

With the demise of the Antarctic cod, fishing interests have switched to the Antarctic icefish, which accounted for 30,000 of the 58,000 tonnes of fish taken in the CCAMLR area in 1986. Recommendations have been made for the conservation of this species before it suffers a similar fate to the cod. The finfish has also shown a continuing decline in stocks since the Convention came into force.

CCAMLR's inability to protect these species has led to doubts about whether it will effectively manage the krill fishery. Half a million tonnes of krill were taken out of Antarctic waters in 1981–2, although the total catch has dropped since then. The effect of krill depletion in the Antarctic foodchain is impossible to guess: some scientists believe that the declining population of elephant seals in the Southern Ocean is linked to the industrial fishing of krill. Until the fishing nations, notably the Soviet Union, change their philosophy within CCAMLR, adequate protection of commercially-targeted marine species seems impossible.

There have also been problems on land. The USA operated a pressurized-water nuclear reactor at its McMurdo base for ten years: when it was demolished in the early 1970s, over ten thousand cubic metres of contaminated soil and rock had to be removed and shipped to the USA for dumping. It took six years for the site to be cleaned up.

John May's book describes the visit of Dr Ron Lewis to Australia's Casey station in 1986. Lewis reported that Casey's rubbish tip covered 2,000 square metres and was up to 2 metres deep. Rubbish was dumped there twice daily, with no attempt to separate combustible, toxic and hazardous materials. Two hectares (5 acres) of a nearby Site of Special Scientific Interest had been bulldozed for construction material. The lichens and mosses on the hill around Casey are the most extensive and complex examples of plant life in continental Antarctica. Casey is not the worst example of a base station polluting the environment that it is supposed to be monitoring.

The environmental movement supports the notion, first put forward at the Second Conference on National Parks in 1972, that Antarctica should become the first World Park, under the auspices of the United Nations.

The World Park concept is based on these principles:

- The wilderness values of Antarctica should be protected;
- There should be complete protection for Antarctic wildlife (though limited fishing would be permissible);
- Antarctica should remain a zone of limited scientific activity, with cooperation and coordination between scientists of all nations;
- Antarctica should remain a zone of peace, free of nuclear and other weapons.

Although initially supported by New Zealand and Chile, the idea of Antarctica as a World Park has never been discussed by the Treaty States.

See also SPECIES EXTINCTION; WHALES AND WHALING

REFERENCES

British Antarctic Survey / Natural Environment Research Council, *Antarctica*, n.d.

May, John, *The Greenpeace Book of Antarctica*, Dorling Kindersley, 1988.

World Commission on Environment and Development, *Our Common Future*, Oxford University Press, 1987.

World Resources Institute, IIED, *World Resources 1986*, Basic Books, 1986.

'Antarctic Veto', *New Scientist*, 27 May 1989.

Harland, David, 'Miners Vote to Plunder the Treasures of Antarctica', *New Scientist*, 28 January 1988.

CONTACTS

British Antarctic Survey (BAS)   Greenpeace

Asbestos

Asbestos is a material that has common applications in households, industrial premises and public buildings. Until relatively recently the substance was regarded as harmless: now, however, it is accepted that asbestos has caused thousands of deaths and will cause thousands more. Most uses of asbestos are now banned or are being phased out, although some continue. Asbestos remains an environmental threat because it can be found in many locations in houses, schools, hospitals and factories.

Types of asbestos

Asbestos is a mineral rock mined in many parts of the world, especially the Soviet Union, Canada and Southern Africa. Its attraction from the technical point of view is that it can be divided into millions of fine fibres that are often soft and silky to the touch, but are also strong and resistant to heat and chemical attack. The fibres can be woven into fabrics, used as reinforcement for cement and plastics, or sprayed on to surfaces.

The danger from asbestos is to be found in the fibres themselves, especially the very fine ones which, invisible to the naked eye, can be fatal when inhaled. For that reason, processes which produce very small airborne fibres are generally the most hazardous.

There are six types of asbestos, of which three are in common industrial use:

crocidolite – 'blue' asbestos
amosite – 'brown' asbestos
chrystolite – 'white' asbestos

The names are misleading, as the colour refers to appearance when the substances are freshly mined. Ageing and heat turn all asbestos a similar colour and only scientific tests can identify a particular type.

Nowadays, about 95 per cent of all asbestos mined is chrystolite, or white asbestos.

Asbestos has been in industrial use since the last century. It is estimated as occurring in up to 3,000 different products. The UK Department of Environment publication *Asbestos Materials in Buildings* (1986) lists 27 different areas of asbestos use, including:

lagging	partition boards	iron stands
insulating boards	flooring	boilers
ropes and yarns	putties	storage heaters
cloth	cookers	asbestos cement
paper	refrigerators	radiators

Generally, these products are considered to be safe in everyday use, provided that they are not broken open, drilled or allowed to deteriorate in such a way that fibres are released. Substitutes for asbestos have been developed for many industrial applications.

Dangers of different asbestos types

The situation concerning the relative danger of the three asbestos types is confusing. It is agreed that blue and brown asbestos should be treated as extremely dangerous substances, but the health warnings about white asbestos are not as clear as they could be.

- The importing of blue asbestos has been banned in the UK since 1970.
- The importation, supply, use in manufacture and marketing of blue or brown asbestos, or products containing them, was prohibited on 1 January 1986.
- From 20 March 1986, in response to an EC directive, products containing asbestos have to be labelled 'Warning: contains asbestos – Breathing asbestos dust can be dangerous to health – Follow safety instructions'.

This chain of events appears to carry the implication that white asbestos is safe if used carefully, or is at least a tolerable risk. *Asbestos Materials in Buildings* makes the point that asbestos–cement products, which contain only 10 per cent asbestos, will continue in use as slates, corrugated sheet and cavity-roof decking. Asbestos slates are likely to be used for a number of years, and produced under British Standard specifications. The same publication later states, however: 'as there is no known threshold level for exposure to asbestos below which there

is no risk, it is advisable to reduce exposure to the minimum that is reasonably practical.'

Asbestos Killer Dust (1979), published by the British Society for Social Responsibility in Science (BSSRS), points out that Denmark, The Netherlands, Finland and Sweden think as the UK does, that blue and brown asbestos are more dangerous than white. On the other hand, again according to BSSRS, West Germany, East Germany, Italy, France, the USA, USSR, Canada, France and Norway all believe the three types of asbestos to be equally dangerous.

It does not appear that UK authorities have acted very quickly to counter the health effects of asbestos. The first cases of asbestos-linked death were reported to the British government in 1906. Regulations concerning the 'safe' use of asbestos were introduced in 1931. The Yorkshire Television documentary about an asbestos sufferer 'Alice – A Fight for Life' was a stimulus to government decision-making when it was broadcast in July 1982. Blue and brown asbestos were formally banned in 1986.

It is not impossible that white asbestos will also eventually be banned.

Asbestos diseases

There are three main asbestos-related diseases:

- *Asbestosis*, an irreversible, often fatal scarring of the lungs, that usually occurs only after heavy exposure to asbestos.
- *Lung cancer*, which can be caused by all three types of asbestos. The

chance of contracting lung cancer is greatly increased for asbestos workers who smoke.

- *Mesothelioma*, a previously rare cancer of the inner lining of the chest or abdominal wall. Very painful and always fatal, mesothelioma is almost wholly linked to asbestos exposure: 85 per cent of all mesothelioma cases are believed to be asbestos-caused.

All three diseases take a long time to develop – usually ten to twenty years, though this may be up to 40 years in the case of cancer. This may partly explain why it took so long to ban what are particularly dangerous substances. If it had not been for the outbreak of mesothelioma – a rare disease, but of an unusual form, and therefore easy to discern and record – it is arguable that the true dangers of asbestos would not yet have been fully appreciated. As Hugh Crone says in *Chemicals and Society* (1986), the incidence of asbestosis and lung cancer alone would not have been sufficient in statistics of the general population to be remarkable.

Asbestos deaths

Health and Safety Director John Rimington was quoted in 1986 as estimating some 650 asbestos deaths to be occurring per year in the UK. Most of the victims have worked in the asbestos industry or used it in the course of their work. Some who died, however, were relatives who had been affected by fibres brought home in the clothes of parents or spouses. Children are likely to be more liable to mesothelioma than adults, given the same exposure to the fibres.

Moreover, some people appear to be more sensitive to asbestos exposures than others: *Asbestos Killer Dust* gives case histories of some victims whose exposure seems very slight.

It is for this reason that the ubiquitousness of the substance poses health risks. A survey published by the Association of Metropolitan Authorities in 1985 estimated that asbestos was present in about 80 per cent of their buildings: £2 billion was needed to remove the substance from an estimated 4 million council houses.

These people are at risk from any activity that disturbs the asbestos in their homes, whether it be putting up shelves or taking out an old cooker. If they have to deal with the asbestos because it is disintegrating, or needs to be cut or drilled, they should avoid breathing any asbestos dust, and should consult Health and Safety Guidance Notes on how to handle the substance. Waste materials are classified as controlled wastes, and must be disposed of in sealed, clearly marked plastic bags at sites licensed by a Waste Disposal Authority.

The Department of the Environment takes the view that removal is not the best option, as this can cause more pollution than leaving it in place. This was not the case for the House of Commons, however: in 1978 it was decided to remove the white asbestos used for insulating purposes in the roof, and replace it with an asbestos-free substitute. This programme was halted when blue asbestos was also found: the roof was then sealed by fully-protected workmen, and regular air monitoring carried out, pending full removal.

The dangers of leaving asbestos in place were illustrated in the case of Camelot School, London. In March 1987 an electrical contractor began to strip pipes lagged with brown asbestos in the school kitchen. Asbestos debris and fibres remained in the room, at an estimated several thousand times permitted levels, while the children's lunch was being prepared. When the danger was appreciated, all the children were sent home.

In the USA, where activities endangering health are more heavily penalized than in the UK, compensation amounting to some $2.5 billion was awarded against the US's largest asbestos manufacturer. The sum was intended for the 16,500 separate lawsuits against the company – a number which could climb to a total of 60,000 over the next 20 years, as more victims succumb.

This is not the end of the asbestos industry, however. In January 1987, worldwide production of asbestos began to climb, as manufacturers moved their output to developing countries. Growing use of asbestos – especially for construction – in the USSR, and in much of Asia, has cancelled out the drop in orders from North America and Western Europe. Overall world asbestos consumption, according to the *New Scientist* (29 January 1987) is expected to rise steadily for the foreseeable future.

REFERENCES

British Society for Social Responsibility in Science, *Asbestos Killer Dust*, 1979.

Crone, Hugh D., *Chemicals and Society*, Cambridge University Press, 1986.

Department of the Environment, *Asbestos Materials in Buildings*, HMSO, 1986.

Health and Safety at Work, August 1985 and February 1986.

Ardill, John, 'Councils' Asbestos Problem', *Guardian*, 10 September 1985.

Brummer, Alex, 'Record US Payout to Asbestos Poison Victims', *Guardian*, 5 August 1985.

Lean, Geoffrey, 'Canteen Alert Highlights Schools Asbestos Peril', *Observer*, 22 March 1987.

CONTACTS

British Society for Social Responsibility in Science (BSSRS)

Society for the Prevention of Asbestosis and Industrial Diseases (SPAID)

Automobile Pollution

In 1988, 5,041 people were killed on the roads in the UK, and 317,000 injured. In comparison to these figures, certain other environmental hazards appear minimal: it is a modern paradox that we appear to accept car crash deaths as a 'normal' fact of life, while reacting emotionally against other risks which, though less likely to kill us, appear to be more frightening.

The consequences of private transport are discussed in TRANSPORT POLICY IN THE UK. This section deals with an aspect of private motoring that is less obvious than the road fatality figures – the air pollution that occurs because of the world's increasing preference for the motor car.

- In 1950, there were fewer than 50 million cars in use around the world. In 1989, this figure had increased to almost 400 million, an eight-fold increase. Each car engine pumps out about 1,000 different chemical compounds, with results varying from the well-documented to the completely unknown. Improving technology has reduced the pollution produced by individual engines, but this has been swamped by the enormous growth in total numbers of vehicles.
- In the early 1980s, it was thought that the motor vehicle markets of North America, Western Europe and Japan were approaching stability and car sales would grow by 'only' 20 per cent over the next decade. Sales in the rest of the world would increase by 75 per cent in the same period. In the mid 1980s, the UK Department of Transport estimated that there would be about 25 per cent more cars and vans on British roads by the year 2000 than in 1985, when there were 18 million (*Transport Statistics*, 1975–85). After three years of record sales, however, this figure was exceeded in 1988 (see TRANSPORT POLICY IN THE UK). Two million new cars a year are

arriving on Britain's roads, or 5,500 per day. In August 1989, over 500,000 new cars were sold – the equivalent of a forty-mile traffic jam of new cars coming out of the factories each day in the month. As under UK legislation, each car emits about a quarter of a tonne per year of carbon monoxide, hydrocarbons and nitrogen oxides, this represents an enormous pollutant load.

REASONS FOR CONCERN

Concern over the unprecedented growth of automobile pollution has centred round two areas: health and environmental damage.

Health

Although it is acknowledged that the unknown quantities in car emissions could cause problems to health, scientists are most worried by four pollutants: lead, carbon monoxide, nitrogen oxides and hydrocarbons.

Lead Exposure to lead impairs children's development and their power to perform well at certain ability tests (see WATER: UK WATER SUPPLY). The dangers of lead in air are now internationally agreed, and action is being taken to remove lead from petrol – although 'unleaded' petrol still contains a small amount of lead. In the UK, unleaded petrol was given a 10-pence price differential to leaded in the 1989 budget: and, by European Community agreement, all new cars in the UK now have to be capable of running on unleaded fuel (from October 1989).

Carbon monoxide This reduces the oxygen-carrying capacity of the blood, sometimes imperceptibly up to quite high levels of carbon monoxide absorption. Adverse health effects can occur without warning, and at relatively low levels. Most at risk are those with cardiovascular disease and coronary artery problems.

Nitrogen oxides Formed of two pollutants, nitrogen dioxide (NO_2) and nitric oxide (NO). NO_2 has been linked with increased susceptibility to respiratory infection, and can aggravate asthma at levels which are commonly found in London streets. NO_2 levels in London 1987–8 and 1988–9 have breached EC guidelines.

WORLDWIDE TRENDS IN VEHICLES

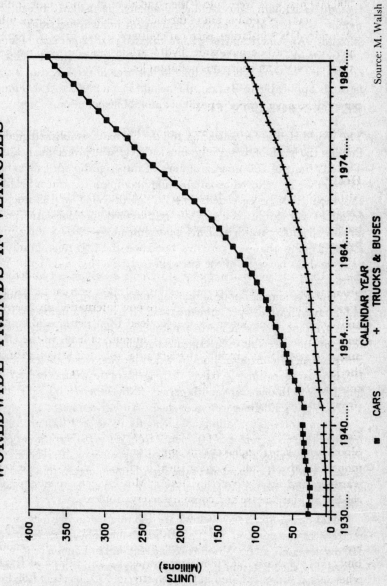

Source: M. Walsh

Hydrocarbons The polycyclic aromatic hydrocarbons (PAH) are thought to contain cancer-inducing agents, particularly benzo(a)-pyrene, which is also a carcinogenic agent in cigarette smoke (see SMOKING). An American study has estimated that 12 per cent of lung cancer deaths in the USA could be attributed to motor vehicle emissions. No work has been done in this area in the UK, but if the figure is applicable to Britain, this would mean 3,000 to 4,000 lung cancer deaths per year as a result of automobile pollution.

The World Health Organization and the EC have established guidelines for the levels of these pollutants with a view to protecting health. The EC limit of 200 microgrammes of nitrogen dioxide per cubic metre of air is regarded as an absolute maximum to protect health, and should not be exceeded. The EC 'guide value' of 135 microgrammes per cubic metre of air is designed for long-term protection of public health and the environment. A 1984–5 survey in London found that several sites breached the 200 microgramme limit, and 50 per cent of the sites exceeded the 135 microgramme limit.

WHO recommendations for carbon monoxide are for a maximum of ten microgrammes per cubic metre of air over eight hours, and 40 microgrammes per cubic metre of air over one hour. Generally, these limits are not exceeded in Britain, although in London readings by the independent organization London Scientific Services indicated carbon monoxide readings well over these levels in the winters of 1987–8 and 1988–9. In one four-month period – November 1988–February 1989 – WHO guidelines were breached twenty-five times.

Lead in air levels are falling, following the move on 1 January 1986 to lower the lead content of UK petrol from 0.4 to 0.15 grammes per litre. Whether they are falling far enough to protect health remains to be seen: the UK Department of the Environment claims that lead in air levels have been halved as a result of the switch. This fall will continue as added lead in petrol is abolished.

WHO ozone limits (see below) are 160 microgrammes per cubic metre of air as a one-hour average, although the eight-hour average is 120 mg per cubic metre. Summer ozone readings in London routinely exceed this, the highest in 1983 being 280 mg per cubic metre. Ozone has deleterious effects on the respiratory system as well as causing eye, nose and throat irritation.

The Department of Environment-sponsored body, the UK Photo-chemical Oxidants Review Group, commented in its 1987 report that ozone levels in rural England and in the city of London have exceeded the levels allowed for industrial exposure to the pollutant inside factories.

References above are to London because this is the most crowded UK city with the largest population of cars. Other large urban centres will have similar problems, though of a smaller intensity. Some local authorities are now monitoring vehicle pollutants.

Environment

Nitrogen oxides and hydrocarbons form an important part of the ACID RAIN cycle: about 30 per cent of the acidity in the rain derives from nitrogen pollution, and this has a devastating effect on lakes, rivers and streams. Hydrocarbons assist in the process of turning sulphur dioxide pollutants from industries into dilute sulphuric acid which forms the other 70 per cent of acid rainfall.

Nitrogen oxides and hydrocarbons interact in the presence of sunlight to form ozone, a pollutant which has a central role in damaging trees and crops. The amount of ozone in the air as background pollution is already sufficient to damage certain plant species (see ACID RAIN).

The precise role of these pollutants is still the subject of scientific discussion, though the general agreement is that the environment is suffering from an overload of pollutant stresses. If the forests and lakes of Europe and North America are to be protected, emissions from motor vehicles will have to be reduced at the same time as emissions from industry and from power generation. Forty per cent of the UK's nitrogen oxide emissions come from traffic (i.e. about 700,000 tonnes), 86 per cent of carbon monoxide (4.45 million tonnes) and 33 per cent of hydrocarbons (538,000 tonnes).

Globally, traffic plays an important part in the greenhouse effect:

- almost 15 per cent of the world's carbon dioxide emissions come from cars;
- large amounts of carbon monoxide are also emitted (two-thirds of the OECD's total emissions in 1980). Carbon monoxide destroys hydroxyl radicals in the atmosphere. Hydroxyl radicals are an important defence against the buildup of the greenhouse gases –

methane and tropospheric ozone: CO, therefore, is thought to play a significant role in accelerating global warming.

There are two ways of curbing pollution from traffic. One is to reduce the amounts of pollution emitted from the vehicle. The other is to reduce the number of automobiles on the road, or at least try to limit the speed of their growth. The former solution is necessary to limit immediate damage to forests, lakes and human health. The latter will become necessary, both because of the immediate effects of vehicle pollution, and the long-term consequences of the 15 per cent output of the world's anthropogenic (human-created) carbon dioxide. This percentage will increase as the world's car population grows.

SOCIETAL SOLUTIONS

Richard North's book *The Real Cost* (1986) contains a good description of the price of our devotion to private transport. In the USA, the car consumes 10 per cent of gross national product, with Americans spending 15 per cent of their personal income on automotive transport. Public transport accounts for only 3 per cent of the inter-city market, even though the railways seem purpose-built to cover the long distances in the USA at high speed. In the past ten years the American tax-payer has spent $80 billion on highways and $6 billion on railways.

Similar developments can be seen in Europe. Two-thirds of inter-city travel is by car, compared with one-third 30 years ago. In Britain, 30 per cent of all car journeys are of less than 2 km, and half are less than 8 km. Cars in Britain are used as a tax perk, with companies buying them for better-paid employees rather than giving the money direct. The tax advantages this brings have been calculated at between £1,500 to £2,000 million a year – a straight subsidy for private travel. The 1989 UK budget reduced the subsidy, but it still stands at around £1,000 million per year, more if 'hidden' subsidies like free parking are included.

North points out that only 60 per cent of British households have a car, but our transport planning seems to assume that all British citizens have one. In central London, the car accounts for only 11 per cent of journeys to work, but it takes 85 per cent of the road space; 636

cars taking up 32 km of road would carry the same amount of passengers as a 1.6 km queue of buses, or one train carrying 1,400 passengers.

Public transport

A societal solution to the problem of traffic pollution, therefore, would be to encourage the growth of public transport, so that people felt less inclined to use cars. An example of this was the cheap fares policy used by South Yorkshire, when the council decided in 1975 to peg bus fares at existing levels. By 1984 there had been a 7 per cent increase in bus travel, with young people being the quickest to learn and take advantage of the new system: young people's use of the bus service increased by 60 per cent.

The policy persuaded many people to give up their cars, even when their incomes were increasing: households with two cars would sell their second car on the strength of the bus service's cheapness and reliability. The experiment finished in 1986, when the government abolished the council, and fares were forced up by 225 per cent.

Our current policy is based upon building larger roads to accommodate the increasing amount of road traffic (see TRANSPORT POLICY IN THE UK). There is a circular logic to this. The M25 orbital motorway opened in 1986, with the south-western sector between Gatwick and Heathrow carrying 120,000 cars a day, a third more than it was designed for. Traffic projections for the 1990s were being achieved barely weeks after the motorway opened.

What the planners hadn't taken into account was the number of short-term car journeys that take place in Britain. The M25 was planned as a bypass for central London, to take traffic out of the congested city centre. However, only one journey in a thousand through London starts and finishes outside the city. The M25 is being clogged by drivers making short journeys through the outer suburbs: and the Department of Transport overlooked the possibility of these journeys when it was making its forecasting.

The transport philosophy in Britain is to isolate a traffic bottleneck and widen the road. This might work in rural areas, but not in large cities – the traffic moves a few hundred yards along and gets stuck again.

The unacknowledged limiting factor for London's traffic is the number of cars – 2.2 million registered in London, and as many again in the surrounding counties. If a through road is widened, the result is to entice people living near the road to get their cars out. Nearly one million people commute to central London every day by tube and rail, as compared to 150,000 who travel by car. Road improvement schemes will merely decant more rail travellers into their cars, increasing pollution, traffic accidents and the amount of land space that is given over to roads. Rail improvement schemes will reduce pollution, relieve traffic pressure and reduce the number of road accidents.

Other alternatives include development of cycling routes and positive encouragement of CYCLING in cities; at the moment, many cyclists are discouraged because of pollution and perceived danger on the roads. Development of cycling would reduce pollution, traffic jams and accidents, and as most UK journeys are short distance, would be ideally suited to Britain.

Car bans in cities
The consequences of over-enthusiastic devotion to the private car are already being seen in some cities. In Athens, entry to the centre of the city is currently restricted according to licence plate numbers, with plates ending in 0 to 4 being allowed in one day, and plates ending in 5 to 9 allowed in the next. This policy, severely enforced by traffic police, was introduced because of the debilitating effect of traffic fumes on people's health and on the city's historic monuments.

Rome now has the highest concentrations of carbon monoxide in Europe. Thirty-five years ago there were 30,000 locally registered vehicles, but now there are a million and a half. A local judge threatened to close the city centre to traffic unless the authorities took some action. Traffic police have started appearing on duty wearing anti-smog masks: in a 1986 health check, 30 per cent of their members were found to have chronic bronchitis. Historic monuments in the centre of the city are crumbling under the pollutant load.

In February 1987, smogs descended over Western Germany. West Berlin banned all cars from the city except those classed as low polluters – i.e. fitted with catalytic converters. Hamburg and Munich banned high polluting cars or severely restricted their entry.

All these solutions are societal – none so severe as in Singapore where drivers are fined if they have fewer than four people in a car, but all are examples of crisis management. The problems of traffic congestion and pollution are going to accelerate as the number of cars on the roads becomes ever larger.

TECHNOLOGICAL SOLUTIONS

The environment movement is questioning the role of the motor car, at a time of record car sales. While the long-term debate continues, it makes sense in the short term to clean up current car technology. Here, there are two options: the catalytic converter and the lean-burn engine.

The catalytic converter

- Cleaning up vehicle emissions in the USA was motivated by the need to protect health. People with weak hearts are placed under additional stress by excess carbon monoxide in the blood; heart disease is the most common illness in American males over the age of 40. Heart-conscious America pressurized the legislators into cleaning up the USA's traffic emissions.
- Emission standards in the USA were technology-forcing; that is, the legislators decided what emission limits they wanted, and told car manufacturers to invent systems that would satisfy the laws. These limits were established in 1970 and tightened in 1975, 1980, 1981 and 1983, and new technologies were developed accordingly.
- A catalytic converter is a kind of filter in the car exhaust system, which uses a catalyst to change or reduce the pollutants passing through it. The oxidation catalyst, introduced into the USA in 1975, slashed emissions of hydrocarbons and carbon monoxide. Catalytic converters are poisoned by the presence of lead in petrol, so the USA also brought in lead-free petrol in the mid-1970s. Lead-free petrol has thus been widely available in North America for the last fifteen years.
- Catalyst technology was improved with the invention of the three-way catalyst, which fulfilled the functions of the oxidation catalyst but in addition reduced emissions of nitrogen oxides. The three-way catalyst became essential for new cars in 1983.
- Successful use of forcing legislation in the USA has now reduced the four vehicle-based main pollutants which were giving concern on

environmental and health grounds – carbon monoxide, lead, nitrogen oxides and hydrocarbons. The car manufacturers themselves were pleased with their success. On 26 September 1986, Richard Klimisch, executive director of the Environmental Activities Staff of General Motors, told the Senate Committee on Environment and Public Works:

> General Motors is proud of the progress we have made in reducing motor vehicle emissions. The key to this progress has been the catalytic converter, which was installed in all GM cars beginning in 1975 and is installed in virtually every light-duty vehicle sold in the US today. This device has made it possible for us to achieve 96 per cent reductions in carbon monoxide and hydrocarbon emissions and a 76 per cent reduction in NO_x, as compared to uncontrolled cars. The result has been dramatic reductions in nationwide vehicle emissions over the years.

- The US success led to the adoption of American standards, or their equivalents, by other countries – Canada, Japan and Australia. Denmark, Mexico, Taiwan, South Korea and Brazil have announced their intention of following suit. By 1986, approximately 130 million cars – a third of the world's fleet – were equipped with catalytic converters.

  In 1988, catalysts had spread to Europe. They are mandatory in Sweden, Norway, Switzerland and Austria, and, because of financial incentives, were fitted to many new cars sold in West Germany and The Netherlands (10 per cent of the total in both had three-way catalysts, 50 per cent of new cars in the FRG had catalysts of some sort). Three-quarters of a million catalysts were sold to German motorists to fit in the cars that they already had.

Lean-burn engine

Catalysts were slow to arrive in Europe. The Europeans were not so concerned about the health implications of vehicle emissions, but in the early 1980s became worried by the environmental damage caused to the Central European forests.

Negotiations in the EC over traffic emission limits were subject to severe lobbying from the small-car manufacturers of Britain, France and Italy. They were frightened that legislation enforcing the use of catalysts would be a gift to Japanese car manufacturers who had been using the technology for the previous ten years.

The lobbying produced the paradoxical sight of one branch of a multinational car company saying in Washington that catalysts were wonderful, and another branch of the same company saying in Brussels that they were useless. British car manufacturers, who were exporting catalyst-fitted cars to the USA, were at the same time telling the British government that catalyst technology was unreliable and unworkable.

In 1988, Ford UK were not offering catalyst-fitted cars on the home market – but it was possible to buy almost the entire range of Fords fitted with the technology in Germany. Johnson Matthey, the Hertfordshire-based company that leads the world in catalyst expertise, has now sold 55 million catalytic converters – but not in Britain. This situation began to change in 1988, when certain manufacturers – particularly Toyota, Volkswagen and Audi – began to offer catalyst cars (*Air Pollution from Cars*, 1988). In 1989, Volvo, Saab, BMW, Vauxhall and Ford also began to offer catalysts.

Pressure against the catalyst was based on its add-on cost (between £200 and £400 per car) and on the planned development of the lean-burn engine. This engine, by increasing the amount of air in the fuel–air mix in the combustion chamber, would reduce the amount of pollution coming out of the other end. Reductions achieved to date, though large, are significantly smaller than those achieved by a three-way catalyst. The hydrocarbon emissions are still considerable, as are emissions of nitrogen oxides at high speeds. The technology was sold to the politicians, even though it was relatively undeveloped, because burning a 'lean' mix of fuel and air would mean increased miles per gallon. On the one hand there was a technology that would cost money: on the other, a technology that appeared to save it.

Different limits for different cars

Countries with strong internal environmental lobbies – West Germany, The Netherlands and Denmark – were arguing for USA emission standards to be imposed in Europe. This produced a Euro-compromise in which cars with engines over 2 litres in capacity were to have emission standards that were nearly as strict as the USA standards; cars with 1.4 to 2 litre engines would have to obey standards that were twice as lenient as USA standards; the limits for small cars would be (in Stage I of the directive) three times as permissive as the USA laws. In 1988, final limits for small cars were 'tightened' to become equivalent to those for cars with 1.4 to 2 litre engines – in Stage II of the directive, to be implemented at a later date.

The compromise proposal has produced more paradoxes. The large cars can be cleaned up only by using three-way catalysts; medium car reduction could be achieved by a combination of lean-burn engine plus an oxidation catalyst; and the small cars (Stage I) could meet the proposed limits with minor engine modifications. And if a government felt disinclined to implement the proposals, it was at liberty to do so – the directive is permissive, which means it is non-binding on EC countries. The UK has said it will comply with the EC compromise, and in 1988 published a timetable indicating compliance within five years.

The main environmental disadvantage of the compromise is that small cars are more numerous in Europe. These measures would not reduce overall emissions of nitrogen oxides by the end of the century, at a time when such a reduction is regarded as essential to protect the environment: the increasing numbers of cars on the road would swallow up the pollution improvements achieved. The Danish government initially blocked the implementation of the EC directive, on the grounds that the proposed Eurostandards would reduce nitrogen oxide emissions from its car fleet by 20 to 40 per cent, whereas the US standards would achieve reductions of 80 per cent.

In April 1989, the European Parliament shocked Europe's car makers by voting for US standards to become mandatory throughout Europe by 1993. This, mainly because of the wave of environmental concern sweeping through Europe, was accepted by the Council of Ministers in June 1989.

Conclusions

● American and Japanese car manufacturers are now in an advantageous position because they were forced to take environmentally protective measures ten years ago. In late 1986, the UK Society of Motor Manufacturers issued a list of new cars which could use unleaded petrol. Those cars capable of using leaded or unleaded petrol include all of the range provided by Volvo, Suzuki, Seat, Saab, Lada, Isuzu, Hyundai and Jensen, and large parts of the range provided by Toyota, Volkswagen, Porsche, Peugeot Talbot, Nissan, Honda and Daihatsu.

There was not a great representation here for UK car manufacturers; with the honourable exception of Jensen, the Rover 213 and 820, and the Land Rover, the British car industry seemed singularly unprepared for the introduction of lead-free petrol.

In the 1990s, all cars will have to use this fuel – and because British legislators and manufacturers have not built environmental considerations into their long-term planning, foreign manufacturers have fifteen years' start in the application of lead-free technology.

- The European discussions about the viability of lead-free petrol and catalytic converters were conducted almost in a vacuum: the negotiations seemed to ignore the fact that both systems had been implemented in the USA, with a great deal of success, since the mid-1970s. If public opinion had been better informed about overseas development, this aspect of the pollution debate would not have been glossed over for so long.

- Alternative technologies do not always solve the problem. During the 1970s it was assumed that diesel engines were less harmful to health than petrol-driven systems, so car manufacturers started switching to diesel. Worldwide diesel car production rose from 1.3 per cent of the total passenger car market to 5.4 per cent in 1983. In Western Europe, diesel car sales rose in 1985 by 21 per cent to a total of 1.67 million. In West Germany, diesel cars now account for one in every five new cars sold.

The confidence in the reduction of pollution from diesel engines, however, has recently been counterbalanced by research into the fine particulates that the engines emit. These particles are very small, about 0.2 microns in size, and hang suspended in the air before being drawn deeply into the lungs. The US Environmental Protection Agency has noted that up to 10,000 chemicals can stick to the surface of diesel particulates and be drawn deep into the lungs with them. Recent studies suggest a link between diesel emissions and lung cancer, and in 1985 one US scientist said the question now was not 'Are diesel emissions carcinogenic?' but, rather, 'Under what conditions, and how much, are they carcinogenic?'

The US was sufficiently concerned to establish particulate limits of 0.2 grammes per mile for 1987 model cars, and 0.6 grammes per mile for trucks, these improvements to be achieved by the use of engine modifications and trap-oxidisers fitted to exhausts to filter the particulates. Current EC proposals are for limits three times as lenient. They were stalled by the Danish government for the same reasons as the vehicle emissions directive (above) – the emission limits are not strict enough.

Finally, the comment should be repeated that pollution from cars will not be solved just by filtering the exhaust, although in the interim the most efficient way of accomplishing this should be found. Automobiles deplete the world's resources of fuel and land and also contribute to the GREENHOUSE EFFECT (see above). If this environmental phenomenon becomes the disastrous scenario that some observers are predicting, then all fossil-fuel combustion will have to be re-examined to see whether it is worth the environmental risk. Cars, as an important source of pollution, will not be exempt.

See also ACID RAIN; CYCLING; GREENHOUSE EFFECT; OZONE LAYER; TRANSPORT POLICY IN THE UK.

REFERENCES

GLC Scientific Services, *Nitrogen Dioxide: Environmental Health Aspects of the 1984/5 London Diffusion Tube Survey*, 1985.

Department of the Environment, *Digest of Environmental Protection and Water Statistics*, 1989.

Department of Transport, *Transport Statistics Great Britain, 1975–85*, HMSO, 1986.

Greenpeace, *Air Pollution From Cars*, 1988.

Holman, Claire, *FoE Briefing Document on Diesel Emissions*, FoE, 1986.

Holman, Claire, *Particulate Pollution from Diesel Vehicles*, FoE, 1989.

London Scientific Services, *London Air Pollution Monitoring Network*, Results, 1987.

North, Richard, *The Real Cost*, Chatto and Windus, 1986.

Proceedings of Eurasap / Transport and Road Research Laboratory Conference, October 1986.

Russell Jones, R., *Vehicle Emissions*, FoE briefing, 1986.

United Kingdom Photochemical Oxidants Review Group, *Ozone in the United Kingdom*, Department of the Environment, 1987.

Walsh, Michael P., *Car Lines*, 1986–89.

Walsh, Michael P., *Motor Vehicles and Long Range Transport of Pollutants*, Society of Automotive Engineers, 1985.

Walsh, Michael P., *Global Trends in Motor Vehicle Air Pollution Control*, Society of Automotive Engineers, 1985.

Walsh, Michael P., *Control of Diesel Particulate Emissions in Europe*, 1986.

Walsh, Michael P., *Global Trends in Motor Vehicles and their Use: Implications for Climate Modification*, World Resources Institute, 19 December 1988.

Hamer, Mick, 'Running Rings Round the Traffic Planners', *New Scientist*, 30 October 1986.

Harrison, Michael, and Levinson, Steve, 'Record August car sales increase deficit worries', *Independent*, 7 September 1988.

CONTACTS

Capital Transport
Campaign for Lead-Free Air (CLEAR)
Department of Transport
European Community (EC)
European Environmental Bureau
Ford/General Motors/Austin Rover
Friends of the Earth (FoE)
London Scientific Services
National Society for Clean Air

Road Haulage Association
Royal Society for the Prevention of Accidents (RoSPA)
Society of Motor Manufacturers and Traders (SMMT)
Town and Country Planning Association
Transport 2000
World Health Organization (WHO)

Bhopal

In the early hours of 3 December 1984, a cloud of poisonous gas was released from a pesticide plant in Bhopal, central India. It descended on huts and houses clustered round the plant, making visibility difficult and seeping into areas where the inhabitants were sleeping.

Those who were going to bed around 12.30 that night record an irritation of the eyes that quickly became unbearable; difficulty in breathing, panic, and a desperate desire to get away from the area. These witnesses are those who fled, or whose houses were well enough constructed or situated to escape the gas. Thousands of others woke from their sleep unable to breathe, coughing, spluttering and vomiting. Hundreds choked to death because of an accumulation of fluid in their lungs – in effect, drowning.

People fled their homes, either away from the city, or to the nearest hospital, or just into the street, where the gas had a similar effect as inside their houses. In the period following the accident, 50,000 patients passed through Bhopal's seven hospitals. Jayaprakash Hospital, with 125 beds, had to cope with 12,000 sick: Hamidia Medical College pitched tents to cope with the 2,500 people overflowing its 750 beds.

By dawn, the dead lay everywhere in the streets of Bhopal, their bodies bloated. These bodies were heaped into piles and cremated, according to Hindu custom or buried, according to the Muslim tradition. They were not counted. Posters containing pictures of some of the dead, each with a number, were displayed so that relatives and friends could identify them. Many remained anonymous, however, since entire families died together, with no one left to identify them.

The effect of the disaster on Bhopal's 350,000 slum-dwellers was devastating. The local authority's body count confirmed that 1,755 people died as a direct result of the gas leak, although this is the lowest figure that is quoted: the usual estimate given in press reports is 2,500.

The manager of the three local cremation grounds said that 7,000 more bodies were cremated in 1985 than in 1984, including 1,017 children in the Hindu cremation grounds (1984 figure – 249). The Bhopal Victims' Support Committee believed that the death toll could have reached 15,000. Two years after the accident, the Indian government certified that 2,352 had died from the effects of the gas. The number keeps increasing as more cases are investigated: it seems likely to be agreed finally somewhere between 3,000 and 10,000.

Approximately 200,000 people had adverse health effects resulting from the disaster, ranging from temporary blindness and burning lungs to permanent disability. Of 2,698 women who were pregnant at the time, 402 had miscarriages and 86 had stillbirths. Spontaneous abortions and stillbirths were estimated to have tripled.

A year after the leak, thousands were still being treated for the after-effects of the disaster. Ten thousand were suffering from lung problems, of which 2,500 were expected to need treatment for another four or five years. Day labourers could no longer work because their lungs were damaged; women who used to earn a living rolling cheap cigarettes found their eyes unequal to the task; 8,500 out of 85,000 patients registered with government hospitals were mentally ill. By 1987, 526,000 Bhopal citizens, more than two-thirds of the city's population, had lodged compensation claims.

Causes of the disaster

Bhopal was one of the world's worst environmental disasters. The plant responsible for the death of so many people was a pesticide facility owned by Union Carbide India Ltd – a subsidiary of Union Carbide, a transnational company based in the USA.

The Bhopal plant manufactured methyl isocyanate (MIC), which is an 'intermediate' used in pesticide production. David Weir in *The Bhopal Syndrome* (1986) describes MIC as a particularly dangerous chemical, a little lighter than water, but twice as heavy as air, meaning that when it escapes into the atmosphere it remains close to the ground. It has vigorous and heat-producing reactions with many substances, including water. In the presence of a catalyst, it can react with itself, producing a violent, runaway reaction.

Hugh Crone notes in *Chemicals and Society* (1986) that the toxic effects for MIC are very like those of phosgene, an extremely lethal gas used in the First World War. Crone estimates that low concentrations of this gas would cause lung, eye and skin irritation and some damage; and that larger doses, although not particularly large, would cause death. One tonne would contaminate 0.2 square kilometres with a vapour cloud averaging 100 metres in height. Many deaths and more casualties would be expected.

The Carbide plant had three storage tanks for MIC, each capable of holding 45 tonnes. On the day of the disaster, 120 to 240 gallons of water were introduced into one of these tanks, and a cloud of gas emerged. Its contents are still a source of disagreement, although it is assumed that a large proportion consisted of MIC. An estimated 40 tonnes of the gas escaped between 12.30 and 3.00 A.M.

Some observers have alleged that two other gases, hydrogen cyanide and phosgene, were also present in the gas cloud. *India Today* alleged that MIC is stored up to a purity of 99.5 per cent, and that 0.1 per cent of phosgene is permitted as an impurity. If 40 tonnes of MIC vaporized that night, as much as 40 kg of phosgene could have vaporized also. The presence of phosgene is denied by Union Carbide.

Union Carbide
The scale of the disaster was enormous – a city of three-quarters of a million people, with thousands dead, a quarter of the population incapacitated or injured to a lesser degree, more than half seeking compensation for physical or emotional distress.

Moving away from the personal tragedies of Bhopal, however, the general background to the case provoked concern about the behaviour of large transnational companies handling toxic substances.

A report by the International Confederation of Free Trade Unions found that there had been at least five toxic leaks from the plant in the four years leading up to the accident. Personnel cuts had been made to reduce costs, a key maintenance supervisor had been laid off a week before the tragedy, and three of the four safety systems designed to prevent a leak of MIC were out of order. The same report points out that workers had been given little or no training, that instructions were written in English rather than Hindi, and that there had been lack of proper maintenance. An inquiry by two Indian scientists, published in *Business India*, blamed the disaster on faulty design as well as operating errors by local staff.

Union Carbide classified the accident as 'unique' and said that such an incident could not occur in its sister plant in Institute, West Virginia. It subsequently admitted that small leaks of MIC had occurred 61 times from the American plant between 1980 and 1985. In the wake of the Bhopal disaster, Institute was closed for seven months for the installation of $5 million worth of safety equipment. Two months after re-opening, 500 gallons of aldicarb oxide were accidentally released from the plant, injuring 175 people in the nearby town; 20,000 people within a ten-mile radius were warned to stay indoors and keep their windows closed.

'Aldicarb' is a pesticide manufactured by Union Carbide, which in July 1985 had been used inadvertently on watermelons in California. After receiving complaints of nausea, diarrhoea, trembling and sweating from people who ate the contaminated fruit, 10 million watermelons were ordered to be destroyed – a third of California's entire crop.

In Bhopal itself, three workers were treated for exposure to chlorine gas in April 1985, after a new leak. The authorities ordered the firm to dispose of 48 tonnes of poisonous chemicals still stored in the factory, and then closed it down.

Union Carbide offered $230 million to settle all claims, later increasing this offer to $300 million. Counter-claims varied between $2 billion and $5 billion. During 1985 and 1986, the firm made two payments totalling $6 million to alleviate hardship. At the same time, an attempt to take over Union Carbide was made by the American firm GAF. Union Carbide spent $1 billion fighting off the takeover bid. The directors also settled $28 million on 42 top executives, who would be able to claim the money if the takeover was successful.

Union Carbide USA attempted to distance themselves from the actions of their subsidiary, saying that it was the responsibility of local management not the parent company. The Connecticut-based company, however, owned 50.9 per cent of the Indian unit's equity. It had power of veto over policies and practices in Bhopal.

Union Carbide's defence is that the water was introduced as an act of sabotage, although it appears that little evidence has been put forward in defence of this claim. A year after the accident, 1,400 people had been given £600 for each death in the family, with smaller grants of £90 being given to the unemployed and low paid who had to stay in hospital. In December 1985, the state government stopped giving free rations to the tens of thousands of gas victims who were unable to earn a living after the disaster.

In February 1989, the Indian Supreme Court awarded damages of $470 million against Union Carbide – $200 million less than an out-of-court offer made six months previously. There were protests outside the New Delhi court when the award was made. Union Carbide's net profits in 1988 were $720 million. Shares in Union Carbide leapt $2 on the New York Stock Exchange when the news of the settlement was made public.

See also CHEMICAL WASTES; SANDOZ; SEVESO

REFERENCES

Crone, Hugh, *Chemicals and Society*, Cambridge University Press, 1986.

Weir, David, *The Bhopal Syndrome*, International Organization of Consumers' Unions, 1986.

Guardian, 28 June, 1 August, 13, 14, 15 August, 27, 29 November, 30 December 1985, 16 and 25 February 1989.

India Today, 31 December 1984.
New Statesman, 29 November 1985, 2 May 1986.
New Scientist, 11 April 1985.
Observer, 5 January 1986.

CONTACTS

Bhopal Victims' Support
  Committee
Oxfam
Pesticides Action Network

Red Cross
Third World First
World Development Movement

Chemical Wastes

World Resources 1987 gives an excellent description of the issue of hazardous waste: what it is, how much there is and problems of disposal.

Briefly, there are some 70,000 chemicals being traded, of which as many as 35,000 have been classified by the Organization for Economic Co-operation and Development (OECD) and US Environmental Protection Agency (EPA) as definitely or potentially harmful to human health. The chemical industry produces huge profits – $450 billion for the 24 OECD nations in 1980 – but also enormous quantities of hazardous wastes. In Europe and North America, nearly 70 per cent of these come from the chemical and petrochemical companies: in Third World countries, the figure is 50 to 66 per cent.

'Toxic' and 'hazardous' are often used interchangeably to describe types of waste, though *World Resources* prefers a stricter definition, in which 'toxic' describes a narrow group of substances that cause death or serious injury to human beings or animals, while 'hazardous' is a broader term describing all waste, including toxic waste, that presents immediate or long-term threats to people or the environment.

Most toxic and hazardous waste comes from industries that produce plastics, soap, synthetic rubber, fertilizers, synthetic fibres, medicines, detergents, cosmetics, paints, pigments, adhesives, explosives, pesticides, herbicides and chemicals. The problems connected with hazardous wastes are:

- they are being produced in increasing quantities every year;
- they have been produced for the last century, and have been disposed of by casual dumping in thousands of (often unmarked) sites;
- they are now recognized as dangerous to human health, so the

practice of 'landfilling' them in holes in the ground is becoming unpopular;
- existing landfills need to be cleaned up, both to protect the environment and prevent danger to health;
- alternative systems of disposal other than landfill are expensive, or are not available in large enough quantities to deal with the mountains of waste;
- there are so many hazardous wastes that the effects of many individual substances are unknown, and their effects in combination with each other can only be guessed at.

Growing public awareness in the developed countries has increased the difficulty and expense of hazardous waste disposal. One solution to this has been the relatively new practice of exporting unwanted waste to the Third World, where it has been stored in extremely unsatisfactory, often dangerous, conditions. This practice is becoming more difficult as it has attracted adverse publicity.

With the enormous quantities of hazardous wastes being produced every year, the only environmentally sound method of coping with the problem is either to insist that the substances are disposed of on the factory site, or that they are not produced at all. Both solutions are vigorously opposed by industry, which sees a cost burden being imposed on its production processes. On the other hand, it seems illogical that private profit should be subsidized at the expense of the public environment.

Risks of hazardous substances

In OECD countries (the 24 leading industrial countries in the West), millions of tons of hazardous substances are industrially produced, transported, stored or used each year. Although most operations are accomplished safely, there are, according to the OECD, about 20 major accidents a year in OECD countries (a major accident is one causing at least five deaths, 25 people injured, and/or 400 evacuated). It is estimated that there are a further 200 accidents each year causing significant damage to health, environment or property.

This list summarizes the most serious accidents worldwide related to hazardous substances (excluding radioactive materials) in the period 1974–87:

Site	Country	Year	Deaths	No. injured	No. evacuated
Flixborough	UK	1974	28	29	3,000
Beek	Neths	1975	14	104	0
Seveso	Italy	1976	0	193	730
Los Alfaques	Spain	1978	216	200	0
Mississauga	Canada	1979	0	8	220,000
Tacoa	Venez.	1982	145	1,000	40,000
Cubatao	Braz.	1984	508	n.a	n.a
Mexico City	Mex.	1984	452	4,248	31,000
Bhopal	India	1984	2,800	50,000	200,000
Institute	US	1985	0	140	0

Source: OECD Press Release, February 1988

Two of the incidents here are described in detail in other entries (see BHOPAL; SEVESO). The 1986 accident near Basel in Switzerland is not included in this list, as no recorded deaths or injuries occurred: but the OECD classify it as a major accident because of the environmental damage that occurred (see SANDOZ).

These accidents occurred before the chemicals concerned had become 'waste' – i.e. when they were still marketable commodities, and allegedly stored under the safest possible conditions. When their commercial use is over, however, in the majority of cases the substance retains its corrosive or toxic qualities: the problem then is how to dispose of it.

Transporting the substances contains an element of risk. In 1985, a PCB leak from a lorry closed down 100 miles of the TransCanada Highway for a week (see PCBS). In 1987, after the sinking of the ferry *Herald of Free Enterprise* in Belgium, rescue attempts were endangered by the toxic chemicals that were on board – according to the *Guardian*, 25 drums of toluene di-isocyanate (TDI), which reacts with water to create dangerous fumes; six drums of cyanide; and several other containers of different chemical waste products.

The dangers of transporting hazardous substances are recognized in the UK. Lorries carrying them display coded signs so that rescue services can modify their operations accordingly in the event of accident.

Disposal options

Disposing of the hazardous substances also involves risk. There are two favoured systems – landfill and incineration. Landfill is less than satisfactory because no hole in the ground is leak-proof over time. Nicholas Hildyard, in *Green Britain or Industrial Wasteland?*, 1986, quotes Peter Montague, project manager of Princeton University's hazardous waste programme:

There is no such thing as 'permanent' disposal of hazardous waste in the ground. There is 'long term storage' in the ground but sooner or later what we put there will move – and the place it is most likely to move to is someone's drinking water supply.

The UK favours landfill, believing that the wastes are diluted and dispersed into the soil where they are rendered harmless. Hildyard points out that, although many substances do undergo transformation in the earth, some of them – for example, tetrachloroethylene – can convert under certain circumstances into carcinogens. Others, such as chlorinated hydrocarbons, do not break down in the soil, but persist indefinitely. It is highly possible that these substances will reach local water supplies: contamination of groundwaters in the UK is not at all unknown (see WATER: UK RIVERS, ESTUARIES AND GROUND-WATERS).

The other option – incineration – is theoretically better equipped to deal with hazardous wastes. Under properly controlled conditions, and the correct combustion temperatures, incineration can destroy 99.99 per cent of organic (i.e. containing carbon) wastes. At the moment, however, only 2 per cent of hazardous wastes are incinerated in the US, because the technology is expensive, and the costs of accident or improper operation affecting local populations would be enormous. In Europe, incineration is a more common practice, but is contentious and is under increasing environmentalist attack.

A superficially attractive alternative would be to incinerate wastes at sea, away from populated areas: and this is currently done by three ships. The technology is being campaigned against by groups such as Greenpeace, however, which argue that the wastes are inadequately burned at sea, and are spread far and wide over the ocean by the smoke plume from the ships: the whole process also represents the possibility of a catastrophic accident. An explosion, spill or shipwreck would result in considerable destruction of the marine environment. If the accident happened in port, then people could also be at risk.

Experience of incineration in the UK has also raised some questions. Although the Rechem incinerator in Bonnybridge was officially cleared of causing health defects in local children (see PCBs), local farm animals suffered from a variety of abnormalities. Anthony Tucker (*Guardian*, 9 August 1988) describes how the local farming community believes airborne polychlorinated hydrocarbons (PCHs) and heavy metals to be the cause. PCHs embrace the dioxins, PCBs and difurans, and therefore include many highly poisonous compounds. They also cross the placenta in farm animals and humans, and were found in substantial amounts in fields near the controversial plant during and after the period of inquiry.

A proven causal relationship has not been established, although the circumstantial evidence looks powerful: PCHs are known to cause birth defects, including an increase in abnormalities and the likelihood of twins. At the time of the controversy, farmers had reported an abnormal number of twins in cattle exposed to the fumes of the two incinerators then operating near Bonnybridge. They also reported a broad range of disorders and diseases which did not respond to normal therapy.

Identifying hazardous wastes

Hazardous substances have been produced in quantity for more than a century, though it was not until the 1970s that their potential risk to health and the environment was appreciated. Until then, industries, or the agents they employed, dumped waste casually wherever a site could be arranged. In 1979, 10,000 drums of toxic waste were discovered beneath a rubbish dump in Amsterdam, and a national survey was ordered: within six months, 4,000 illegal dumps were discovered in The Netherlands.

By 1986, every major industrial country in the EC except Britain had carried out a survey of its old dumps. In the UK, the authorities maintain that indiscriminate dumping is likely to be small, and that public health legislation will have prevented environmental hazards:

but, as Nicholas Hildyard points out, this is likely to be optimism based on ignorance. In 1981, witnesses from the Atomic Energy Authority's Environmental Safety Group told a House of Lords Select Committee: 'We do not know how much hazardous waste is produced in the UK, who produces it, what it is, and what happens to it.' Five years later, according to Hildyard, the Department of the Environment still had no hard figures for the amount of hazardous waste generated in Britain.

This ignorance is magnified on a global scale. It is not possible to find accurate figures of how much hazardous waste is produced every year: first because the definition of what is hazardous varies from country to country, with some nations defining a substance as hazardous and others not. Even where there is agreement as to a particular chemical, defining parameters of danger may vary – in The Netherlands, 50 milligrams of cyanide per kilogram is considered dangerous, while in Belgium the figure is 250 mg per kg. Canada allows 350 parts per billion of trihalomethanes in drinking water, the US 150.

From World Health Organization literature, *World Resources 1987* has compiled a list of toxic and dangerous substances requiring priority consideration.

Arsenic and compounds
Mercury and compounds
Cadmium and compounds
Beryllium and compounds
Thallium and compounds
Chromium (VI) compounds
Lead and compounds
Antimony and compounds
Phenolic compounds
Cyanide compounds
Isocyanates
Organohalogenated compounds, excluding polymeric materials
Chlorinated solvents
Organic solvents
Biocides
Tarry materials from refining
Pharmaceutical compounds

Peroxides, chlorates, perchlorates, azides
Ethers
Chemical laboratory materials, not identifiable and/or new, with unknown effects on the environment
Asbestos
Selenium and compounds
Tellurium and compounds
Polycyclic aromatic hydrocarbons
Metal carbonyls
Soluble copper compounds
Acids and or basic substances used in the surface treatment and finishing of metals
PCBs

The definition of hazardous waste, and restrictions as to transport and disposal, are likely to be the subject of international conventions.

Both the OECD and the United Nations Environment Programme have been preparing agreements. Experience within the EC, however (see below), indicates that it may be difficult getting nations to ratify any regulations with teeth.

The second reason why hazardous waste statistics are so difficult to compile is that many nations in the Third World have no legislation for dealing with the problem, so have no knowledge of how much of their waste comes within the category.

Some attempts have been made to work out annual amounts of hazardous wastes generated globally: *World Resources 1987* quotes one global estimate of 330 million tonnes, but comments that another estimate for only 19 countries was 100 million tonnes higher.

Locating dump sites

World Resources 1987 quotes a West German official who said, 'a decade ago, most of Western Europe's toxic garbage disappeared down a black hole somewhere'. Every country in Europe – except Norway and Sweden – is faced with an abundance of dump sites, old and new, authorized or unlicensed, needing urgent attention.

In the USA, President Carter's last act in office was to sign the Comprehensive Environmental Response, Compensation and Liability Act (CERCLA) in 1980 – the Superfund legislation. The idea of the Superfund was to identify abandoned sites which were imminent hazards and clean them up: it was to be 80 per cent funded by industry, and was intended to raise $4.2 billion. After protests from the industries concerned, the eventual figure was $1.6 billion per year – a significant step forward, but nowhere near enough to clear up all the USA's 'toxic time-bombs'. The Office of Technology Assessment, a research arm of the US Congress, estimates that 10,000 sites may eventually need Superfund clean-up. This would take up to 50 years and cost $100 billion. Other estimates are lower than this, but still involve expenditure of billions of dollars.

One site was not difficult to locate – the notorious Love Canal, an uncompleted nineteenth-century waterway near Niagara Falls, which had been used as an industrial dump since the 1930s. In 1953 it was filled in, and homes, a school and a playing field built on top. In 1976, after heavy rain and snow, chemicals began seeping into the basements of homes. Children suffered chemical burns on their arms and legs, a disproportionate number of women had miscarriages or gave birth to children with birth defects. The site was declared a disaster area in 1978, and 263 families were evacuated by 1979, with another 1,000 advised to leave their homes.

Greenpeace has pointed out that the banks of the Niagara River contain, albeit poorly, more than 150 toxic waste dumps in one three-mile stretch. Among them is the Hyde Park dump, containing 80,000 tons of toxic waste, including nearly a ton of dioxin. One shovelful of this dioxin-contaminated waste, the organization alleges, could wipe out all of Lake Ontario's birds.

British rubbish

Nicholas Hildyard has described the setting up of the Hazardous Waste Inspectorate (HWI) in the UK in 1983, on the recommendation of a House of Lords Select Committee. The HWI estimate that 4.4 million tonnes of hazardous waste were generated in England and Wales in 1983. However, the Confederation of British Industry told the 1985 Royal Commission on Environmental Pollution that some 12 per cent of the estimated 100 million tonnes of industrial waste generated every year could be described as 'toxic or dangerous'. This would mean that 12 million tonnes of toxic waste were produced. The Royal Commission commented, 'there is insufficient reliable information available about industrial waste generation. Without this information, we do not consider that waste disposal authorities can properly prepare waste disposal plans for their areas'.

About 85 per cent of the HWI's identified hazardous waste is disposed of in landfills. The UK is the only country in Europe to allow 'codisposal' of waste, in which liquid industrial wastes and solid household wastes are dumped in the same site. This is a technique generally avoided in other OECD countries, because of the uncontrolled nature of the technique: usually, industrial and household waste are disposed of in separate sites.

Inefficiently-operated sites can be dangerous. *Environmental Data Services Report* no. 159 reported in April 1988 that about 1,300 landfills contain wastes that will generate gas, and are located in areas of a geological type, and sufficiently close to housing or other developments, such as to pose a public health hazard should the gas migrate off-site. Overall, about 600 sites – the great majority of which are within 100 metres of houses – are eventually likely to require additional gas controls, with about 100 requiring urgent remedial action.

The cost could be as high as £250 million. The alternative to clean-up could be methane explosions.

The HWI reckon that there are 4,202 landfills in England and Wales, of which an estimated 1,145 are licensed to take hazardous waste. In addition, there are more than 700 land-based disposal facilities, including 99 storage sites, 53 lagoons, 5 reception pits and 14 mineshafts. Not all landfills are badly run: some are excellently organized, with lined pits, logged waste deliveries and regular inspections. There are a substantial number of firms, however, that appear to be less than totally conscientious in their waste disposal practices.

The relative laxity of British disposal practice in comparison to other countries led to a booming trade in importing waste for landfilling in the UK. Imports of hazardous waste increased from 5,000 tonnes in 1984 to 25,000 in 1985, 40,000 in 1986. The government's attitude was that this was legitimate business like any other, although by 1988 the official line was beginning to change. Attracted by the high disposal costs of American rubbish in comparison to those for landfilling in Britain, a number of companies in the UK were planning to import domestic rubbish from New York. On 29 June 1988, however, Environment Minister Colin Moynihan told the House of Commons that the government was prepared to modify its policy that trade in rubbish was a legitimate enterprise. One of the worries was that 'it is difficult to see how the United States could certify free of disease the contents of many hundreds of thousands of dustbins'.

The situation in the UK is, according to the House of Commons Select Committee on the Environment, potentially disastrous. Its 1989 report on toxic waste commented: 'We feel that we must warn the Government that by continuing to ignore previous recommendations it is playing – sometimes literally – with fire . . . allowing unscrupulous operators to dump waste, almost unchecked . . . may be building up a legacy of environmental disasters for the future.'

Waste to the Third World

Britain was not the only place to receive quantities of other people's unwanted hazardous waste. The developed countries, pressed by their mountains of waste and increasing disposal costs, began to look for opportunities to export the problem. Third World countries, desperate for cash because of depressed commodity prices and the debt crisis (see NORTH–SOUTH RELATIONSHIP), seemed a logical destination.

The symbol of this trade was the *Zanoobia*, a Syrian-registered ship, which eventually returned to Italy in May 1988 with a cargo of 2,000 tonnes of fertilizer, pesticide and resin wastes. The cargo had been travelling for a year – first by another vessel to Venezuela, where the authorities insisted on its removal; then to Syria, which also refused it. In the course of their travels, eight of the *Zanoobia*'s crew were poisoned by the contents of the leaking drums and had to be taken to hospital.

Earlier shipments by other carriers had been more successful. *ENDS Report* no. 161 (June 1988) comments:

Since April, hazardous waste dumps have been discovered in Nigeria, Guinea Bissau, Guinea and the Lebanon. Plans to ship huge quantities of toxic waste and incinerator ash from the USA and Europe to these and neighbouring countries have also been unearthed. Huge profits are at stake, with governments and others in these countries being offered a few dollars per tonne to accept wastes which would cost up to £1,000 per tonne to dispose of in the industrialised world.

None of the existing dumps had been visited by western observers until this month, when the Nigerian government invited the US Environment Protection Agency, Harwell Laboratory and Friends of the Earth to a site in Koko, in Bendel State . . .

What they found on the outskirts of Koko were some 3,500 tonnes of hazardous waste contained in 10,000 drums and 30 shipping containers which had been brought from Italy over a nine-month period. The shipments were made under a forged manifest which had been substituted for an official permit to import 55,000 tonnes of relatively inert materials. The forged document included a list of 20 types of waste – including PCBs, 'obsolete' biocides and drugs, solvents, acids, plating and paint residues and 'solid residues of industrial departments' – totalling almost 100,000 tonnes.

The drums had been stacked on the dockside in Koko, then transported a short distance and dumped in an unsurfaced yard. The owner was offered a rent of £60 a month for storage, but was unaware of the contents of the drums, several of which were being used as food and drink containers in his house.

The 45-gallon drums were stacked up to four drums high, exposed to temperatures over 100 degrees F and tropical storms: almost half were leaking. Known contents included low flash-point solvents, paint and distillation residues, PCBs and acids. The fire risk is high, pollution of groundwater certain. The nearby village, only 150 yards away, draws its water supplies mainly from shallow wells.

In the resulting outcry after the discoveries at Koko, the EC increased its pressure on member states to implement two existing directives on transfrontier shipment of waste. Due to be implemented in October 1985 and January 1987, the directives had been acceded to only by Belgium, Denmark and The Netherlands. Signatory countries have to require shippers of waste to pre-notify the authorities in the receiving countries of their intentions, and provide proof that the receiving company has the technical capacity to handle the waste, as well as the agreement of the necessary authorities.

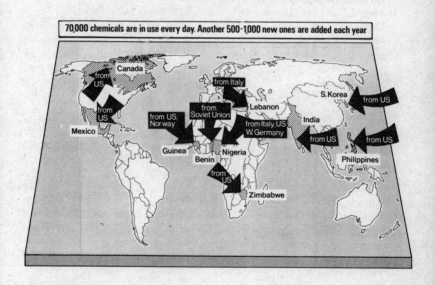

70,000 chemicals are in use every day. Another 500-1,000 new ones are added each year

Source: Gemini News Service

Once signed by all member nations, these directives will cause waste disposal problems within Europe. As the European Environmental Bureau pointed out in a conference held in December 1987, the EC has safe disposal facilities for only 10 million tonnes of hazardous waste per year, or one-third of the total generated. Twenty million tonnes of hazardous waste per year will be looking for a resting-place.

See also BHOPAL; MARINE POLLUTION; NORTH–SOUTH RELATIONSHIP; PCBS; PESTICIDES; SANDOZ; SEVESO; WATER: UK RIVERS, ESTUARIES AND GROUNDWATERS

REFERENCES

Environment Committee, House of Commons, Second Report, *Toxic Waste*, 22 February 1989.

European Foundation for the Improvement of Living and Working Conditions, *Safety in Hazardous Wastes*, EC, 1987.

Hildyard, Nicholas, 'Down in the Dumps' in *Green Britain or Industrial Wasteland?*, ed. Goldsmith and Hildyard, Polity Press, 1986.

McCormick, John, *The User's Guide to the Environment*, Kogan Page, 1985.

World Resources Institute, IIED, *World Resources 1987*, Basic Books, 1987.

Background note on First OECD Conference at high level on accidents involving hazardous substances – OECD press release, February 1988.

Brown, Paul, 'Chemicals on Ferry were to be Dumped', *Guardian*, 25 March 1987.

'Chemical Reaction that Threatens to Shake Companies', *Scotland on Sunday*, 7 August 1988.

Environmental Data Services Reports (ENDS), Nos 138, 155, 156, 158, 159, 161, 162 (July 1986 to July 1988).

Green Alliance, 'Debate on Environmental Pollution 13.1.1988: Briefing'.

Greenpeace, 'A Critical Overview of Current Waste Disposal Practice', 1986.

Greenpeace, 'International Trade in Toxic Wastes: Policy and Data Analysis', June 1988.

Tucker, Anthony, 'Burning Issue of Toxins', *Guardian*, 9 August 1988.

CONTACTS

European Community (EC)
European Environmental Bureau
Green Alliance
Greenpeace
Hazardous Waste Inspectorate
London Hazards Centre
Organization for Economic Co-operation and Development (OECD)

United Nations Environment Programme (UNEP)
US Environmental Protection Agency

Chernobyl

The accident at the Chernobyl nuclear power station in the Ukraine, USSR, has been described as the worst-ever disaster in the world. A sequence of operational errors resulted in an explosion that blew the roof off reactor No. 4, hurling radioactive debris into the air, and starting an enormous fire. Radioactive clouds trailed from the stricken plant, polluting more than 20 countries up to 2,000 km away. It is difficult to project the number of deaths from the accident, as estimates vary from a few thousand to hundreds of thousands of people: what can be said with certainty is that Chernobyl-related deaths will continue to occur for the next 50 years. In September 1986, the USSR calculated the cost of the disaster to the Soviet economy at £2 billion: by 1988, the projected cost had increased to £14 billion (the chief of the Soviet fire service, Mr Anatoli Miheev, told a London conference in September 1987 that the eventual total cost over the years may be as high as £200 billion).

Reactor design

The Chernobyl reactor which blew up was an RBMK design, cooled by water, with a graphite moderator to control the speed of the chain reaction (see NUCLEAR ENERGY). The Chernobyl plant was one of the best in the country, with efficient operational staff. It contained safety features not found in certain Western installations, including substantial steel and concrete containment walls round the reactor; modern control equipment, including sensors and measuring equipment made in West Germany; duplicate and well-protected power control cables; and a honeycomb of primary cooling circuits.

There are a number of different reactor designs, and before the Chernobyl accident, the RBMK reactor was listed, without comment, as one of these variants. If the reactor design was regarded as unsafe in the West, there are few official statements to this effect that can be traced before the accident. In its November 1985 publication *Nuclear Power Reactors*, the UK Atomic Energy Authority lists the RBMK and says merely 'many stations of this size are now under construction'. Nine years previously, the then deputy chairman of the UKAEA had stated: 'Various thermal reactor systems . . . will soon be made to work reliably and with high reliability. This includes the PWR, BWR, CANDU, MAGNOX, AGR, SGHWR, and the Russian pressure vessel and pressure tube reactors' (*Nuclear Engineering International*, April–May 1976). The speaker, Walter Marshall, subsequently became head of the UK Central Electricity Generating Board.

There are similarities between the Chernobyl plant and certain Western installations, although the Russian design is regarded in the west as a 'hybrid', in that it mixes features used in Canadian, American and British nuclear power stations. The RBMK reactor is unique to the Soviet Union, although it has been established that it was not 'primitive' nuclear technology, as was suggested in the West shortly after the accident.

There are 28 RBMKs operating inside the Soviet Union, and 27 PWRs (Pressurized Water Reactors) in Russia and other Eastern bloc countries. The RBMK is capable of producing weapons-grade plutonium, which is presumably why the design continued to be used even though anxieties were expressed about its cost. This may also explain why the USSR exports PWR technology but not RBMK reactors.

The accident

According to the detailed analysis presented by the USSR to the International Atomic Energy Authority in August 1986, human error was largely responsible for the Chernobyl accident. The plant operators were conducting an experiment with the reactor 'ticking over' at very low output – 7 per cent of its normal operating capability. The purpose of the experiment has not been stated, but it is assumed that it was concerned with the need to keep a supply of coolant water to the nuclear core in the event of an unplanned reactor shutdown.

Coolant in the RBMK is usually pumped in using power from the reactor itself; emergency pumping could be supplied by a standby diesel generator, but this takes 50 seconds – too long for continuance of safe operation – to reach full power. The engineers were trying to find out if a freewheeling turbine, previously connected to the working reactor, could keep the pumps going for a short period before the diesel generators cut in.

To simulate this event, the operators reduced the output of the reactor but failed to maintain power at the minimum safe operating level. They also turned off an automatic shutdown safety device, and the emergency core cooling system, so that the experiment would not be interrupted.

Reactors running at low output need to be carefully monitored to ensure a uniformity of neutron density. If this does not occur, the reaction can occur more quickly in parts of the core, leading if uncorrected to a runaway chain reaction. At low levels the reactor can thus become unstable and difficult to control.

Closing down the safety mechanisms was explicitly against written safety procedures. The operators compounded their errors by trying to increase the flow of coolant through the reactor. The extra water reduced the amount of steam being generated, which in turn reduced the overall pressure in the coolant circuit (this should have activated the emergency shutdown systems which had been turned off). Eventually, the pressure dropped so low that air bubbles formed in the water near the pump intake, the coolant circuit overheated, and the water flashed to steam.

Steam absorbs neutrons much less efficiently than water, so in parts of the reactor core – perhaps only a couple of fuel channels – the reaction went 'prompt critical' as the excess neutrons started a runaway chain reaction. Almost instantly, the energy generated in this area leapt by a factor of more than 100, the fuel exploded, and other explosions were set in motion. The energy released was sufficient to lift the 1,000-tonne plate of the reactor core and shatter the building housing the reactor. The radioactive core was now exposed to the air.

At 1.23 A.M. on 26 April 1986, reactor No. 4 at Chernobyl was in a state of silent running. A few minutes later, it was an inferno.

Soviet reactions

There were immediate casualties. On the evening of the accident, 129 patients were sent to Moscow hospitals, followed next day by 170 more. American surgeon Robert Gale, brought in to give medical assistance, reported that doctors had to use the 'triage' system first adopted in the First World War: patients were divided into those who were going to die, those who might live with treatment, and those who did not need immediate care. The middle group received priority attention, but surgeons needed to operate cautiously, as the affected people had absorbed so much radiation that internal organs, blood and urine had become radioactive.

Thirty-six hours after the explosion, 2,100 buses and 1,800 lorries began evacuating people within an 18-mile zone round the power station. Eventually 130,000 people were taken out of the area and relocated, in an exercise which took ten days.

At the plant itself, the first task was to stop the fire spreading to reactor No. 3 and the other two operational units. This was achieved by extraordinary heroism on the part of Soviet firefighters, working in areas which they knew to be radioactive. Many died as a result. More will perish from the long-term effects of radiation exposure.

The scientists did not know how to contain the radioactive holo-caust in unit 4, as the problem had never before been encountered on this scale. Acting intuitively, they dumped 5,000 tonnes of inert material on the reactor by helicopter – boron carbide, dolomite, clay, sand and lead. The mixture was designed to quench the fire, absorb neutrons and yet be porous enough to allow the core to be cooled by a continuous flow of gas.

After five days, the temperature inside the core started to increase again, with a resulting increase in radioactive emissions. Nine days after the accident, cold nitrogen was fed into the reactor space, successfully stabilizing the core. On the tenth day, the radioactive release was contained.

Thirty-five people died in the attempt to contain the inferno at Chernobyl: during the next 50 years, according to Dr Gale, 24,000 Soviet citizens will die from Chernobyl-caused, cancer-related deaths. As the *Observer* book, *The Worst Accident in the World* (1986), points out, however, the people living near the plant were para-doxically extremely fortunate. The disaster could have been even worse had not a number of coincidences occurred:

• the accident occurred at night, when a few hundred people were working at the plant rather than the thousands on the day shift. These would all have been exposed to a large radiation dose. The time of the event also meant that people around the plant were in their houses asleep: if they had been outside, they would have received ten times the radiation doses that they were actually exposed to.

- The fierceness of the fire sent a radioactive plume high into the air, thus minimizing fallout in the immediate vicinity; and the wind was from the south, so the radiation was blown to the less-populated areas north of the plant.
- The most fortunate occurrence was the absence of rain. If it had been raining, enormous quantities of radioactive materials would have been washed down to affect the local population.

In different weather conditions, many of the local residents would have been evacuated, not to new accommodation, but to hospitals and mortuaries. Thousands would have died in the year after the accident. As it was, the immediate death toll was surprisingly small.

The implications of Chernobyl for nuclear power

Dr Robert Gale, the American scientist who was flown in to assist in treating casualties after Chernobyl, made a speech in Bonn on 26 June 1987. Another Chernobyl-type disaster is unavoidable while present technology is operated by humans, he said. 'The likelihood of another major accident somewhere in the world is not less than 25 per cent. In the United States the probability of a core meltdown within the next 20 years is about 50 per cent.' (A firm of British nuclear consultants, Large Associates, has assessed the risk of a Chernobyl-level disaster as possibly occurring once every five years. The US Nuclear Regulatory Commission suggests that Western Europe might expect a major accident involving the release of radiation once every seven years.)

Dr Gale predicted that during the next 50 years there would be up to 60,000 extra cancer-related deaths, 1,000 birth defects and 5,000 cases of genetic abnormality as a result of the Chernobyl accident, with about 40 per cent of the deaths occurring in the Soviet Union. Other contaminated European countries would also suffer.

Estimates of death and sickness from nuclear accidents are notoriously difficult to produce. The UK National Radiological Protection Board, by way of comparison, estimates that there will be an extra 1,000 deaths in the whole of the EC as a result of Chernobyl.

The incident has slowed down, but not stopped, the onward march of nuclear power. After the disaster, plans to build nuclear power plants were abandoned in China, Austria, Finland and the Philippines, and put on hold in Belgium, Yugoslavia, Switzerland, Italy, Spain and Greece. In Eastern Europe, nuclear plant construction is officially continuing as before, although it will be some time before this can be confirmed or denied. All RBMK reactors in the USSR received major refits.

In the West, the nuclear industry has devoted much effort to distancing itself from the disaster, focusing on technical differences between Russian, American and Canadian designs to draw the conclusion that 'it couldn't happen here'. In particular, the 'positive void co-efficient' of the Russian reactor has been criticized – in which a positive relationship is assumed between formation of steam bubbles in the water coolant and a speeding-up of reactor power. Western reactors, with the exception of the Canadian CANDU, do not have positive void co-efficients.

Every reactor design has advantages and disadvantages compared to the others. The lesson of Chernobyl is not that one form of nuclear technology is preferable: it is that all nuclear reactors contain within themselves the capacity for enormous environmental disaster.

CHERNOBYL AND EUROPE

After the disaster at Chernobyl, Swedish monitoring stations first reported the cloud of radiation emitted. The Russian authorities, whether from ignorance or a desire for secrecy, did not release the news of the accident to the world for nearly three days.

Radioactive plumes from the plant continued to be emitted over a period of ten days, and were blown wherever the wind decided, from southern Italy to northern Scotland to the Lapp area of northern Sweden. Government reactions varied according to which country was involved and its attitude to nuclear power. France and Czechoslovakia – both ardent nuclear advocates – initially denied that any radiation was affecting their countries.

Some countries banned the consumption of leafy vegetables, others the drinking of milk. In the UK, the instinctive official reaction was to reassure, although this approach lost much public credibility when it became apparent that the authorities were unprepared, ill-informed

THE UK AND CHERNOBYL

1976 Lord Marshall (later head of CEGB) described Soviet nuclear systems as 'soon . . . to work reliably'.

1983 Lord Marshall: 'We do not expect big accidents to happen, the chance of their happening is extremely remote.'

1986, late April Peter Walker, Secretary of State for Energy: 'The Soviet Union, where I've been last week, is going to double its nuclear energy presence . . . In the next century countries with very big nuclear industries are going to have very big advantages. I would like Britain to have those advantages.'

26 April 1986 Explosion at Chernobyl. First radioactive cloud heads out over Poland and circles Europe.

8 May 1986 Kenneth Baker, Secretary of State for the Environment: 'The effects of the cloud have already been assessed and none presents a risk to health in the UK.'

9 May 1986 Malcolm Rifkind, Secretary of State for Scotland: 'So far as Scotland is concerned . . . we do not expect the radioactive cloud to constitute a risk to the health of individuals.'

13 May 1986 Kenneth Baker: 'I can confirm that no special precautions are needed. I repeat what I said to the House last week. It is safe to drink milk. It is safe to drink tap water. It is not necessary to take iodine tablets. In particular – as we have received so many questions on this point – I can confirm that no special precautions are necessary in giving fresh milk to infants and pregnant women.'

14 May 1986 Officials find out that radioactivity of lambs in Cumbria is exceeding the 1,000 becquerel/kilogram safe limit. No action is taken.

end of May 1986 Michael Jopling, Minister of Agriculture: '. . . we have always been a long way from the stage where we need to contemplate some sort of restriction [on sheep].'

28 April–20 June 1986 46,457 lambs sold in Cumbria for slaughter.

21 June 1986   Movement of lambs restricted in England and North Wales, because of caesium-137 contamination. Scotland follows on 24 June.

April 1987   300,000 sheep still under restriction, which is to be prolonged because of unforeseen persistence of caesium-137.

10 July 1987   Restrictions on movement of sheep in North Wales extended. Further restrictions imposed in Scotland, Wales and northern England during July and August; 550,000 animals now affected; government scientists ignorant as to how long ban will last.

16 September 1987   Restrictions imposed for the first time on movement of sheep in Northern Ireland.

21 March 1988   322,000 animals at 860 holdings in England, Scotland, Wales and Northern Ireland still covered by controls. Ministry of Agriculture admits it cannot predict when restriction will be lifted: they could continue for years.

and confused. Friends of the Earth, with good reason, described the situation as a 'shambles'.

Deposition of the radiation on the ground was crucially dependent on rainfall: the main areas affected in the UK were North Wales, Cumbria and Scotland. The radioactive cloud skirted London and the populated south-east before being washed to ground further north and west.

The picture was the same over Europe. Some areas escaped relatively lightly, others were more seriously affected. Emergency measures differed between countries, however. The BEUC (European Bureau of Consumers' Unions) examined the response of EC countries, after dividing them into most affected areas, intermediate zones and least affected areas (see table opposite).

Of the intermediate zones, it can be seen that the UK appeared to take the least action, merely issuing a warning against drinking rainwater 'over long periods'. Before, during and after the accident, a number of reassuring comments were made by official representatives, which were directly contradicted by events.

What worried many observers was the apparent direct contradiction between the reassurances (no sheep restrictions, no human

Response of European Countries to contamination from Chernobyl (X = action taken)

	Certain food banned	Warning against fresh milk	Warning against leafy vegetables	Warning to wash fresh vegetables	Ban on some food from E. Europe (before EC ban)	Ban on cattle grazing outdoors	Warning to avoid contact with rainwater	Hotlines set up
Most								
S. Germany	X	X	X			X	X	X
N. Italy	X	X	X	X	X			
France (Als)			X	X	X			X
Intermediate								
Greece		X	X	X		X		X
The Netherlands	X		X	X	X	X		X
Belgium				X		X		X
Luxembourg			X				X	
UK						X		X
Denmark				X	X	X		X
Least								
Spain								
Ireland								
Portugal								X

Source: FoE, *The Chernobyl File*, 1986

health risk) and the eventualities – indefinite sheep restrictions, projected human deaths and illnesses numbering in the thousands.

Protection from nuclear accidents in the UK is based on the premise that such an occurrence will not happen in the UK (see NUCLEAR ENERGY: OPERATIONAL SAFETY): so when it did happen, our monitoring systems and response procedures were inadequate.

Analysis of the effects of Chernobyl in the UK presents a picture much less rosy than that painted by our politicians:

- figures published by the National Radiological Protection Board showed that one-year-old children in the north of the country would be exposed on average to 0.9 milliSieverts of radiation (see RADIATION: SAFETY STANDARDS). This average lumps together low and high exposures, so some children will have been exposed to much higher levels than this. As many as a quarter of a million babies and young children in northern Britain could have received more than the recommended annual dose limit of radiation during the Chernobyl event (in south Scotland, especially Glasgow, and Cumbria).
- Many children in the affected areas now run a high risk of thyroid cancer. Thyroid cancer usually has a 1 in 20 risk of being fatal. (The other 19 should not, as is usual in official figures, be discounted. They will suffer acute pain, distress, and fear during the course of their treatment.)
- Independent scientists, using risk estimates formulated by the US National Academy of Scientists Committee on the Biological Effects of Ionizing Radiation, calculate that Chernobyl will cause 450 to 500 cancer deaths in the UK over the next 40 years, in addition to a large number of non-fatal cancers. Again, non-fatal cancer should not be discounted (1,350 to 1,500 possible cases).
- Emergency measures could have been taken which would have saved the lives of at least some of the people who are now going to die prematurely. The most obvious would have been advice to parents not to feed fresh milk to young children. The NRPB subsequently claimed not to have given this advice on the grounds of possible distress to children as a result of dietary changes.

Radiation and radiation protection

A number of radioactive substances were released from the Chernobyl incident. Some, such as tellurium-132, ruthenium-103 and ruthenium-106, were regarded as less damaging to the human body in the quantities released. Others, especially iodine-131, caesium-134 and caesium-137, were much more dangerous to human beings.

The NRPB identified four pathways by which the radiation could affect humans:

- by exposure to radiation when the radioactive cloud passed overhead;
- by breathing in material from the cloud;
- by exposure to penetrating material from the cloud that had settled on the ground or on buildings;
- by eating contaminated food.

Iodine-131, the central contaminant in the 1957 Windscale fire, was not present in such large quantities as in that disaster – although high iodine levels were monitored in Glasgow. It also has a half-life of eight days, and was not regarded as a prime threat to the UK. Caesium-134, with a half-life of two years and caesium-137 (half-life of 30 years) are the contaminants that continue to cause long-term damage to British agriculture – and presumably also to human beings.

Grazing sheep and lambs swallow the caesium from polluted grass, building up levels of radiation in their bodies that make human consumption of the animal inadvisable. If the caesium remains in substantial quantities on the ground, the process can continue for long periods of time.

In Britain, the nuclear authorities believed that the caesium would relatively quickly be absorbed by the soil. It transpired, however, that this forecast was based on an inadequate computer model of the effects of caesium. The problem with computer models is that the forecasts derived from them are only as good as the basic information they are given to work from – and the UK had used experimental data from lowland farms to set up its scenarios.

Reassurances given before and during the accident were based on forecast futures which had not taken all eventualities into account. The difficulties of working out what is likely to happen to different radioactive substances can be seen by looking at just four of them (see table).

On the sparse upland soils of places such as Cumbria, the models had little relevance. Instead of disappearing within a few weeks, the

FALL-OUT: HOW RADIOACTIVITY VARIES

	IODINE-131	CAESIUM-134/137	STRONTIUM-90/ YTTRIUM-90	CARBON-14
Stability	Half-life 8.05 days	C-134: half-life 2.06 years C-137: half-life 30 years	Sr-90: half-life 29.12 years Y-90: half-life 8 minutes	Half-life 5,730 years
Radiation	Beta and gamma	Beta and gamma	Beta	Alpha
Target	All iodine is absorbed rapidly by the body, through the stomach if ingested and through the lungs if inhaled. The target organ to which the iodine travels is the thyroid gland in the neck. It takes about six hours from ingestion to reach the thyroid, staying there for more than 120 days.	Readily absorbed from the small intestine and through the lungs. Spreads rapidly through the body tissues, concentrating particularly in muscles. About 10 per cent is excreted in two days, but the body gets rid of the bulk of caesium very slowly. About half is. removed in 110 days.	Strontium is ingested through the small intestine and absorbed through the lung if inhaled. Initially strontium replaces calcium atoms of the cells on the surface of bones, causing bone cancers. It then gradually migrates through the whole skeleton of the body, causing leukaemia if the radiation to the red bone marrow at the centre of the bone is raised.	It is taken up in the diet in the food chain or absorbed as carbon dioxide gas. C-14 is the main nuclide discharged by the British Magnox reactors, within authorized limits. The carbon dioxide exposure is least serious, because it is absorbed very quickly, mixes with the blood, but is then exhaled in minutes.

Permissible limits	For workers, 5 rems a year. In terms of radioactivity that is a limit of 2 million becquerels. The limit is divided by 50 for exposure of an adult member of the public, to give a maximum of 0.1 rem. For children, the exposure to iodine should be lower by another factor of 10, to give a limit of 0.01 rem.	For workers, 3 million becquerels a year. Limit of 50 times less for adults should be divided again by three for children.	For workers, limit is 100,000 becquerels.	For workers, ingestion of organic C-14 is limited to 90 million becquerels, and inhalation of carbon dioxide to 800 million becquerels.
Precautions	Treatment with iodine pills to swamp the thyroid with stable iodine.	There is no effective precaution. The initial excretion may be helped with diuretics to increase the activity of the kidneys.	There are no precautions which can be taken after exposure.	Because life depends on the cycle of stable carbon, there are no precautions for removing the radioactive variety.

Source: *The Times*, 7 May 1986

caesium was still strongly in evidence 18 months after arrival, and scientists are now unwilling to predict how long it will remain. A year and a half after the disaster, half a million British sheep were classified as too radioactive to be safely eaten.

In January 1988, almost two years after the disaster, the UK Country Landowners' Association – not by any means a radical organization – issued a report indicating that restrictions on the movement and slaughter of sheep in the UK may last for 30 years (initially, the government predicted that all stock would be free of restrictions within 90 days). The CLA accuses the Ministry of Agriculture of having 'earned a reputation of evasion and incompetence' on the issue. This charge could equally justifiably be levelled at the government.

See also NUCLEAR ENERGY; RADIATION; THREE MILE ISLAND

REFERENCES

Friends of the Earth (FoE), *The Chernobyl File*, 1986.

FoE, *Chernobyl and the Future, Paper Submitted to the Council of Europe*, January 1987.

FoE, *Energy Report*, 1987.

Observer special book, *The Worst Accident in the World*, Pan Books, 1986.

Patterson, Walter, *Nuclear Power* (2nd ed.), Penguin Books, 1986.

UK Atomic Energy Authority, *Nuclear Power Reactors*, November 1985.

Press reports throughout 1986–7, especially the *Guardian, New Scientist* and *Observer*, May and September 1986, and:

'Chernobyl – the Aftermath', *BEUC News*, July–August 1986.

Environment Digest, February 1988.

Johnstone, Bob, 'Low Power Sent Chernobyl Out of Control', *New Scientist*, 21 August 1986.

Lean, Geoffrey, 'The Monster in Our Midst', *Observer*, 31 August 1986.

New Scientist, Chernobyl Issue, 23 April 1987.

New Scientist, 'Curbs on sheep remain', 24 March 1988.

Webster, David, 'How Ministers Misled Britain about Chernobyl', *New Scientist*, 9 October 1986.

CONTACTS

Bureau of European Consumers' Unions (BEUC)

Campaign for Nuclear Disarmament (CND)

Cumbrians Opposed to a
  Radioactive Environment
  (CORE)
Friends of the Earth (FoE)
Greenpeace
Scottish Campaign to Resist the
  Atomic Menace (SCRAM)
World Information Service on
  Energy (WISE)

British Nuclear Fuels Ltd (BNFL)
Central Electricity Generating
  Board (CEGB)
Department of Energy (DEn)
Department of Environment (DoE)
National Radiological Protection
  Board (NRPB)

Countryside Changes in the UK

'Countryside changes' refers to the agricultural phenomenon that has taken place in Britain since the Second World War. British farmers have been encouraged to maximize their productivity, which they have done by cultivating marginal land, increasing the size of their fields and covering the earth with a potent mix of chemical fertilizers and pesticides. Food output has increased, but at a massive environmental cost.

Britain's countryside has changed, at a speed and on a scale not experienced for centuries. Environmental features that have been a part of the landscape for hundreds of years are disappearing. Meadows are being ploughed up, hedgerows ripped out, wetlands drained, ancient woodlands felled. Pesticides and fertilizers are changing the types of flowers and insects seen in our fields. The variety of the countryside is diminishing: and the tax-payer, though funding the changes, is powerless to stop them.

Past and present

In her books *The Theft of the Countryside* (1980) and *This Land is Our Land* (1987), Marion Shoard describes the gradual changes that occurred in the British countryside up to the mid-twentieth century. The landscape we see nowadays is largely the product of 6,000 years' evolution. In Neolithic times, probably about 3,800 B.C., the inhabitants of 'England' discovered that the same piece of land could grow crops more than once if it was left fallow between periods of cultivation. The population started to settle into villages, with open fields. Marion Shoard describes the Neolithic settlements as the first Agricultural Revolution.

The second Revolution occurred between 1750 and 1850. Increasing population led to an increased food demand, which made specialized livestock breeding more profitable. The new agriculture could be more economically pursued in smaller areas – so the lords of the manors closed off fields previously farmed in common with the villagers. The enclosure movement finalized a process that had been occurring for 300 years, dividing open parts of the country into a network of hedges, walls and roads.

The third Agricultural Revolution occurred after the Second World War. Previously, Britain had imported up to 70 per cent of its food needs from the colonies – but the U-Boat campaign exposed the vulnerability of a country which has to ship its basic supplies from overseas. It was decided, with massive public support, that Britain should become as self-sufficient in food as possible. Technology, legislation and large quantities of financial support were called upon to spearhead the revolution.

Changes in agriculture

The framework for change was laid down in 1947, with the publication of the Town and Country Planning Act. New development, and changes in land use, were to be subject to control by the local planning authorities. 'Development', however, specifically excluded 'the use of any land for the purposes of agriculture or forestry (including afforestation)'. Agriculture was free from planning control.

At the same time, agricultural practices were changing rapidly with the onset of mechanization. The 300,000 horses that were working British farms in 1950 have now largely disappeared, replaced by tractors, combine harvesters and other machinery. The new machines functioned most efficiently on large open fields cleared of 'obstructions' such as hedges or trees. The familiar patchwork of the English countryside began to disappear.

The 1947 Agriculture Act established the financial basis under which farmers were to work. The 'deficiency payment' scheme guaranteed farmers a minimum price for their products, regardless of what was happening on the world market. This price subsidy continued until the 1970s, when it was replaced by the EC's Common Agricultural Policy system of price support.

Other financial incentives were also in place. Since 1929, all agricultural land and buildings have been exempt from paying rates. After the Second World War, a system of capital grants was introduced, in which the tax-payer paid up to three-quarters of the cost of putting up buildings or carrying out 'improvements' – e.g. digging up hedgerows, trees and streams. Applications for grants were assessed solely from the point of view of whether or not the engineering of the scheme would work, and if it would provide maximum profit for the farmer. Environmental factors were not important.

Take these three considerations into account – freedom from planning control, guaranteed income, and financial support for development schemes – and the impetus towards change in the countryside can be easily understood. There was a lot of money to be made from ripping down the natural environment and turning it into agricultural land. Not surprisingly, this is what happened.

The countryside in 1950

The English countryside just after the Second World War was the same landscape that had captivated writers for hundreds of years. The environment had survived the Industrial Revolution, urban development and two major wars. Agriculture dominated the landscape – then, as now, over 70 per cent of the land surface was farmed. Chris Rose describes the variety of the countryside at the time in *Wildlife: the Battle for the British Countryside* (1984):

> The countryside of the early 1950s still contained many habitats essentially unaltered for centuries or even millennia. Despite the effect of wars and early trends in forestry, much of the woodland remaining was ancient, dating back far beyond the Norman conquest . . . The range of permanent grasslands was almost as rich and bewildering as the woodland: from the chalk downs of the south and east, where pasque flower, lizard orchid, yellow-wort and adonis blue butterflies were still found, to the equally alkaline northern limestones where species such as globe flower and teesdale sandwort prospered . . . Up to a hundred species could be found in a square metre of even quite average ancient grassland, a self-sown mixture gradually established over thousands of years.

Hay meadows, wetlands, heaths, peat-bogs, water-meadows, mountain pastures and commons had all survived for centuries because agriculture, river management and land drainage had been ecologically gentle. Children on spring walks could rely on finding frogs in the ponds flanking many fields; the otter was regarded as common and was hunted from Norfolk to Cornwall, from Dumfries to Kent. The countryside contained a mixture of habitats which supported a wide variety of plants, insects and wildlife.

This was to change as agriculture reorganized itself from being a stable, traditional occupation into an expanding and aggressive industry. At the beginning, this process concentrated on the existing farmed areas: hedgerows were grubbed up and copses cut down to make way for the new machinery, fertilizers began to be applied on a large scale, pesticides such as DDT came into widespread use. The application of nitrogen-based fertilizers in the UK increased eight-fold between 1953 and 1976; between 1944 and 1975 the number of approved pesticides in use on British farms increased by a factor of 12.

As productivity increased, so did profits, and farmers began to look for other cultivable areas. In the past, the 'marginal lands' – downs, heath, moor or anywhere with poor soil – had been ploughed or intensively grazed in good times, and then left to revert to scrub when times were hard. The new chemicals meant that these lands could be permanently integrated into the farm, and the financial incentives to 'improve' marginal land were large.

Wildlife and plants forced out of the fields by the new chemical regime found refuge in the marginal areas. In time, these marginal zones were taken away too.

The countryside in the 1980s

In the 1970s, environmentalists were accused of exaggerating the scale of countryside deterioration. The total figures for habitat loss and environmental change have been the subject of some controversy, as the scale of monitoring since the Second World War meant that guesstimates had had to be made. In 1984, the Countryside Commission and the Department of the Environment jointly commissioned an independent consultant, Hunting Technical Services, to carry out a two-year project monitoring landscape changes in England and Wales, with the intention of settling the argument. The project, using Landsat satellite imagery, aerial photographs and ground work, came up with the findings listed on page 96.

Areas which have contracted rapidly are semi-natural landscape and grassland. Nearly a quarter of our wilder landscape, plus almost a fifth of improved, rough and neglected grassland, have disappeared in the space of half a human generation.

The survey noted that although the total area of woodland was remaining static, internally there were changes, as conifer planting was increasing rapidly and there was a loss of broadleaved woodlands

Landscape Changes 1947 to 1982

	1947		1982		Change
	% of land	sq. km	% of land	sq. km	
England & Wales	100	151,089	100	151,089	
Semi-natural landscape	14.17	21,402	10.59	16,000	−5,402 sq. km
Farmed land under crops, etc.	28.05	42,385	35.36	52,324	+11,039 sq. km
Farm land as grassland	44.61	67,406	36.4	54,995	−12,411 sq. km
Developed land	6.13	9,268	9.70	14,655	+5,387 sq. km
Woodland	7.03	10,625	7.95	12,004	+1,379 sq. km

Source: Hunting Technical Services, *Monitoring Landscape Changes*, initial report, October 1986

(see FORESTRY IN THE UK). The consultants were also surprised to note that hedgerow removal was actually *increasing* in the 1980s.

(In 1947 there were 796,000 km of hedgerows; in 1980, 653,000; in 1985, 621,000.) It would appear that the current government has done little to stop the rate of hedgerow removal.

The (government-funded) Institute of Terrestrial Ecology, co-incidentally, had carried out a survey of environmental features between 1978 and 1984. Their findings showed an eight-year section of the overall trend identified by Hunting Technical Services, and are listed opposite.

The first official body to draw together the implications of the changes was the Nature Conservancy Council (NCC). Its analysis of environmental destruction *Nature Conservation in Great Britain* (1984), described 'the sheer scale of loss or damage to wildlife, its habitat and physical features that has taken place since 1949 . . . All main types of ecosystem have suffered appreciable loss, but, for some, the scale and rate have been catastrophic'.

The NCC report gives a breakdown of the most important losses (see page 98).

The NCC points out that other habitat loss includes intertidal flats and saltings, sand dunes, shingle beaches, lakes and rivers, and certain higher mountains.

The result of the decline in the number of different habitats around the country has been a decline in the variety of species that inhabit

ITE SURVEY RESULTS, 1978–84

Losses of rough grazing
Grassland 'improvement', often involving drainage and reseeding, eliminated:
115,261 ha of rough grassland
 14,590 ha of moorland
  8,754 ha of scrub woodland
  5,836 ha of degraded pasture
  1,459 ha of mountain grass

Losses of broadleaved woodland
24,700 ha of broadleaved woodland grubbed up
11,200 ha underplanted with conifers.
(Although 26,000 ha of broadleaved trees were planted, including small areas mixed with conifer, and 7,986 km of broadleaves were planted in lines, ITE notes that 'the new planting differed from the ancient woods' that had been felled.)

Afforestation with conifers
177,000 ha were blanketed with conifer plantations, usually on a large scale in upland grassland and moorland areas, mostly in Scotland.

Hedgerow removal
28,000 km of hedgerow were removed, approximately eight times as much as was planted. Much of this removal was in areas where cereal cropping was expanding.

them. Plants and animals in those areas taken over by agricultural intensification have suffered the greatest decline – in the lowland grasslands, heathlands and wetlands.

Of the various groups monitored so far, the butterflies and dragonflies have shown the greatest losses. There is a possibility that what has happened to these insects may be an indication of what is occurring to other, less intensively studied species. The NCC report goes on to note:

NCC Findings since 1949

Lowland neutral grasslands (including herb-rich hay meadows)
95% now lack significant wildlife interest, with only 3% left undamaged by agricultural intensification.

Lowland grasslands on chalk and Jurassic limestone
80% loss or significant damage.

Lowland heaths on acidic soils
40% loss.

Limestone pavements in northern England
45% damaged or destroyed.

Ancient lowland woods composed of native, broadleaved trees
30–50% loss.

Hedges
of around 500,000 miles of hedge existing in England and Wales in 1946–7, some 140,000 miles had been removed by 1974.

Lowland fens, valley and basin mires
50% loss or significant damage.

Lowland raised mires
60% loss or significant damage.

Upland grasslands, heaths and blanket bogs
30% loss or significant damage.

• of a total list of 55 resident breeding species of butterfly, one (the large blue) became extinct in 1979; ten more species are vulnerable or seriously endangered; another 13 have declined and contracted in range substantially since 1960;

- of our 43 species of dragonflies, three or possibly four became extinct since 1953; six are vulnerable or endangered; five have decreased substantially;
- some – an unquantified number – of our 26 species of bumblebee have been seriously affected;
- 36 breeding species of birds have shown appreciable long-term decline during the last 35 years, 30 in the lowlands and six in the uplands;
- among the mammals, the otter has become rare or disappeared in many parts of England and Wales. Bats in general have decreased and several of our 15 species, notably the greater horseshoe and mouse-eared bats, are in danger of extinction. Other species are increasingly rare, and all are now protected by legislation. Four of our 12 reptiles and amphibians are similarly endangered.
- Botanical losses are quite substantial, including ten extinctions of species since 1930. Of 1,423 native flowering plants and ferns, 149 have declined by at least 20 per cent since 1930. Three hundred and seventeen vascular plant species are regarded as nationally rare: of these, 117 have shown at least 33 per cent decline since 1930.

Destruction county by county

The national figures give little idea of the havoc that is being wreaked on individual areas. Friends of the Earth partially filled this gap in 1981, when they listed known habitat loss county by county in a publication called *Paradise Lost*. Chris Rose summarizes the list in *Wildlife: the Battle for the British Countryside* (1984):

Avon 50% of unimproved meadows in the new county of Avon were destroyed in the ten years up to 1980.

Bedfordshire and Huntingdon In Bedfordshire 70% loss in wetlands in 25 years; 14 Sites of Special Scientific Interest (SSSIs) destroyed or damaged since 1951.

Berkshire, Buckinghamshire and Oxfordshire A re-survey of 61 of the 249 flood-plain meadows in Oxfordshire identified in 1978 has shown that 12 (20%) have been lost, mainly ploughed up.

Cambridgeshire 17% of woodland lost in 35 years.

Cheshire 7% of SSSIs seriously damaged in 1980.

Cornwall In the 13 years to 1976 more hedges were lost than in the previous 75 years.

Cumbria This county has nearly half the total number of limestone pavement sites in Britain. Nationally, a survey revealed that only 3% of pavements are 100% intact, mainly because of stone removed for horticultural use.

Devon In the 20 years up to 1972, 20% of Devon's woodlands were destroyed; 67% of rough grassland and heath (outside the National Parks) lost this century.

Dorset In south-east Dorset, 38% of important botanical sites have been partly or totally changed in the last 50 years. Three-quarters of the southern heathland have been lost in the last 50 years; 32% SSSIs seriously damaged during 1980.

Durham A survey of 11 sites known to have suffered damage on or after 1957 showed a reduction in the area of wildlife interest from 3,334 acres to 637 acres (reduction of 80%) rendering the sites unviable.

Essex 9% of SSSIs seriously damaged in 1980.

Hampshire and Isle of Wight 20% of chalk grassland lost since 1966; 19.4% of heathland destroyed in 14 years. On the Isle of Wight 17.5% of chalk grassland damaged or destroyed in 14 years since 1966.

Hertfordshire and Middlesex In Herts 56% of ancient woods destroyed since 1950; 99.5% mossland destroyed or damaged by 1978.

Kent 40% of SSSIs designated since 1951 have now been damaged or destroyed.

Lancashire 99.5% of the lowland bogs have been reclaimed.

Lincolnshire At least 50% of ancient grassland lost in the last 30 years.

Norfolk Only three Broads remain substantially unpolluted and one of the three is currently under threat from enrichment from a pump drainage scheme.

Northamptonshire 20% partial or complete loss since 1960 (nine of 44 sites), 54% of sites having some loss. Of 30 proposed SSSIs, ten are under immediate threat.

Northumberland 33% loss or damage of SSSIs in last 15 years.

Nottinghamshire 90% of ponds in east Nottinghamshire have been lost in the last 25 years.

Shropshire 600 prime sites identified in county survey; 19 lost in last eighteen months.

Somerset Street Heath SSSI (Grade I NCR) – on 14 January 1981, planning permission given for peat winning.

Staffordshire 25% of SSSIs damaged in last ten years.

Suffolk 70% of Breckland Heath lost (part in Norfolk).

Sussex 25% loss or damage in last 15 years.

Wiltshire 29 out of 50 downland SSSIs have suffered some loss of scientific interest in recent years as a direct result of agriculture.

Worcestershire 35% loss of ponds in·55 years to 1971; 17% of SSSIs damaged in last 25 years.

Yorkshire Wakefield Metropolitan District lost 23.39% of woodland cover in 17 years to 1978, almost entirely due to agriculture.

Wales – Powys 7% of moorland destroyed in six years.

Scotland – Dumfries and Galloway 90% of heathland lost.

Effects of the changes

Defenders of modern agricultural practices take the view that change has always been a part of the countryside, and that opponents of current developments are, in the main, nostalgic townsfolk who want to keep the country as a weekend playground. They point to the massive increases in productivity and argue that a price has to be paid for our greater self-sufficiency in food. As *Farmer's Weekly* commented in 1978: 'Landscapes will change to meet the needs of succeeding generations. And future conservationists will inherit something new and interesting to protect.'

There appears to be an instinctive dimension to the protest against the loss of our natural countryside, an anxiety that a process of change evolving slowly for 15 or even 50 generations is having the life squeezed out of it almost overnight. Holders of this view would completely disagree with *Farmer's Weekly*: the statement may have been true 40 years ago, they would say, but not now.

There are a number of reasons why they may be correct:

Species extinction   Once a species becomes extinct, it is (by definition) impossible to re-establish. The loss of a species is not just a problem of aesthetics: there are scientific and ecological gaps created which can have serious implications for humanity (see SPECIES EXTINCTION).

Soil degradation   Modern farming relies on an intensive application of fertilizers and pesticides. *Countryside Conflicts* (1986) by Philip Lowe et al. quotes the calculations of Jennifer Rees, an agricultural economist, who notes that it is possible to grow wheat yielding 15–16 tonnes per hectare, compared with the current national average of about 6 tonnes and the average for 1950 of 3.5 tonnes. However, to do this you would need 456 kg of potash per hectare, 308 kg of phosphate, 123 kg of magnesium, 642 kg of nitrogen applied at critical points in the growing cycle, plus three applications of growth regulator and 'extravagant' use of fungicides.

The new agriculture can survive only as long as it continues to be supplied with expensive agrochemical products. The system of farming, however, changes the structure of the soil. Ms Rees comments:

Land which is intensively cropped for corn year after year becomes barren. The basic soil infrastructure is destroyed so that there is little inherent fertility remaining. It is no longer capable of supporting crops without large doses of fertilizer. In another 20 years a large acreage of British farmland will be unable to support traditional crops.

The Soil Survey of England and Wales has published reports showing that soil erosion is a much bigger problem than previously realized. The Soil Survey estimates that 27,000 sq. km of soil (about 44 per cent of all arable land) are now unstable, and that at known rates of soil loss, much of this land could be unproductive within 30 years. A 1986 report for the Soil Association also found 44% of arable lands at risk. *Soil Erosion in Britain* indicates that the problem has been increasing rapidly over the last 15 to 20 years, probably in parallel with trends towards the intensification of farm land.

Land use changes   Certain land use changes are irreversible. As an example, the ancient broadleaved woodlands, some of which have existed for 10,000 years, cannot be replaced. The 50 per cent remaining since the Second World War shelter a number of vascular plants which do not colonize elsewhere, as well as a large number of insects and a larger variety of birds than planted woods. To take another example, the limestone pavements of northern England, only 3 per cent of which are now undamaged, support an almost irreplaceable plant life.

Some bogs and wetlands cannot be restored once they are drained. Changes of land use can produce changes in other parts of the environment: draining of land, or the large-scale planting of conifers, can increase the acidification of water bodies, as ACID RAIN is transferred in greater quantities to the water.

Growth of agribusiness The changes in our countryside are unlikely to be reversed because of the new pattern of farm management and organization.

The small farmers who traditionally inhabited the countryside protected the environment for several centuries, using agricultural practices that gave back to the earth what had been taken out. The financial stimuli of the 1950s, however, encouraged the growth of larger farms as the more financially aware farmers took advantage of economies of scale. Large institutions began to invest in agriculture because of the assured returns, and the price of farm land began to rise. (The Conservative MP Richard Body estimates that price distortions in farming land in the UK has led to its being overvalued by £64 billion.)

Small farms up for sale were taken over by larger owners, and existing small farmers gradually found that, to compete, they had to use all the systems of modern farming that their larger competitors were offering. Machinery replaced the labour force, and farms were amalgamated in many areas. In 1946, there were 976,000 farm workers working the land, including full-time, seasonal and casual. In 1982, there were 338,000. There are now half as many farmers as there were after the war.

The small farmer is becoming a thing of the past, and is not responsible for the changes that are occurring in the British countryside. The culprits are the food industry, the Ministry of Agriculture, Fisheries and Food – and the National Farmers' Union.

(For References and Contacts see lists at end of COUNTRYSIDE PROTECTION IN THE UK.)

Countryside Protection in the UK

The rapid loss of countryside in Britain has occurred in spite of the existence of a number of schemes designed for countryside protection. The situation is complex for the lay observer because of jargon – SSSIs, ESAs, NCC, etc. Some of these terms are explained in the following pages.

Nature Reserves / Sites of Special Scientific Interest

In 1949, the National Parks and Access to the Countryside Act empowered the newly-formed Nature Conservancy to set up national nature reserves (NNRs) in Great Britain.

The idea of the NNRs was to identify the best parts of England, Scotland and Wales from the point of view of the animals or plants they contained, their geology, or their other physical characteristics; buy them, or come to an arrangement with their owners; and keep them in perpetuity for the benefit of the nation. Originally there was a list of 73 proposed National Nature Reserves, plus 24 in Scotland (Northern Ireland being specifically excluded from the scheme). By 1984, 195 NNRs had been established, totalling 150,000 hectares, including many of the original 97 sites proposed.

The Nature Conservancy also had the job of identifying Sites of Special Scientific Interest (SSSI) and notifying planning authorities of their existence. The SSSIs formed a national network designed to complement the NNR series, and were chosen because of their special importance in nature conservation terms. By 1984, 4,150 SSSIs had been notified, most because of their biological interest, several hundred because of their geological or physical features.

The SSSI scheme has been criticized for its lack of public involvement. The label SSSI means little to the average citizen, and can be interpreted as meaning 'Sites of Special Interest to Scientists' – i.e., boring to everybody else. This is not in fact the case, as the areas designated SSSI are invariably parts of the best countryside and wildlife habitats. If the label had been a little more imaginative, the destruction of SSSIs would not perhaps be greeted with the public apathy that frequently occurs. People can get very upset about the despoliation of some of the most beautiful parts of Britain; it is difficult to get worked up about the loss of an SSSI unless one knows exactly what that entails.

Planning applications affecting SSSIs were referred to the Nature Conservancy, with disputes between development and nature conservation interests being resolved through public inquiries. A central problem here was that agricultural and forestry developments were specifically excluded from planning law, and many SSSIs were damaged or completely destroyed by farming practices.

The work started by the Nature Conservancy was taken over in 1973 by its successor, the Nature Conservancy Council (NCC). The NCC is at pains to point out that SSSIs should be regarded as a series, and not as a number of individually interesting sites. If nature conservation is to be maintained at a minimal level in Britain, this is to be achieved by protecting all the SSSIs, not just some of them.

The designation of Nature Reserves and SSSIs has also been criticized by the environmental movement, who say that the impressive-sounding numbers of NRs and SSSIs are achieved by having many of them in northern Scotland where land is cheap but species are few; that the schemes are vastly underfunded, and therefore incapable of enforcement; and that the very fact of designating certain areas implies that undesignated areas can be developed with impunity. If the countryside is to be protected, the argument goes, the way to do so is by enforcing planning law over all developments, including agricultural and forestry use. There is little point in trying to save the best 5 per cent of the environment if the remaining 95% is allowed to collapse around it.

National Parks

There are ten National Parks in England and Wales (none in Scotland or Northern Ireland), covering an area of 5,265 square miles. They are in the Peak District, the Lake District, the Brecon Beacons, Snowdonia, Dartmoor, the Pembrokeshire Coast, the North York Moors, the Yorkshire Dales, Exmoor and Northumberland's Cheviot Hills. The 1949 Act mentioned above empowered the setting up of these parks; originally it was intended that the South Downs and Norfolk Broads should belong to the scheme, too, but the idea was dropped – leaving Londoners hundreds of miles from a National Park.

The purpose of the parks is to conserve and enhance outstanding landscapes, and to make provision for people's enjoyment of the countryside. They are run by National Park Authorities, who have local and national membership. Finance is 75 per cent provided by national government, 25 per cent by local authorities.

The designation 'National Park' is confusing because in many other countries it means a place owned by the state and open to all who wish to visit it. In Britain, however, only about 2.3 per cent of the 5,265 square miles of parks is owned by the park authorities. The Ministry of Defence, Forestry Commission and water authorities have some land, with the remainder being privately owned. If water privatization assets are uncontrolled and Forestry Commission sell-offs continue, the fraction of National Parks in public ownership will be further reduced.

According to the *Observer* (23 October 1988), the merchant bank in charge of water privatization has compiled a secret list of water authority sites with development potential, in order to facilitate the privatization process. Thames Water, for example, has 17,000 acres worth £1 billion.

In December 1988, a report by Leeds University expressed concern that the water authorities would not be able to resist development of their 435,000 acres. *Liquid Assets* warned that many areas of environmental value would be lost.

The disparate ownership of the parks leads to inevitable conflicts of interests. The National Park Authorities have negotiated management schemes with a number of owners, so that the land is run according to agreed overall objectives, and there is a degree of 'development control' which can be used to stop industrial schemes if necessary.

The Forestry Commission and the water authorities have financial priorities that do not obviously coincide with the park authorities' statutory duties, and the Countryside Commission is seeking declarations of commitment nationally from these bodies with a view to ensuring proper maintenance of the environment. A similar commitment from the Ministry of Agriculture, another big spender in the parks, would be welcome.

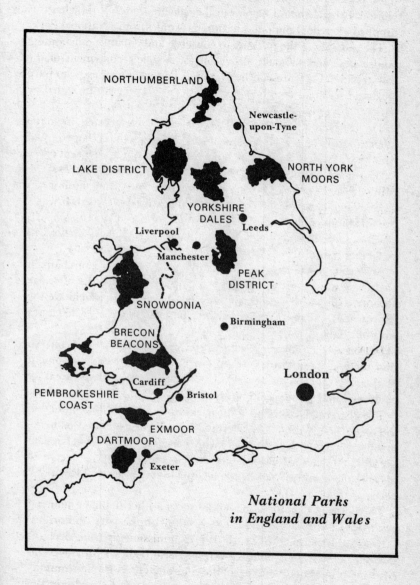

**National Parks
in England and Wales**

Source: Countryside Commission

Land ownership and management in the National Parks
(% per park)

Park	Owner/manager									
	Park Authority	National Trust	Forestry Commiss.	Ministry Defence	NCC	Local Authority	CEGB	Water Authority	Private	Other
Brecon Beacons	7.0	3.0	8.0	0.1	0.6	—	—	4.0	76.7	0.6
Dartmoor	1.4	3.7	1.8	14.0	18.0	—	—	3.8	57.3	—
Exmoor	4.2	10.0	2.0	—	—	0.2	—	1.4	78.4	3.8
Lake District	3.8	24.8	5.6	0.2	—	—	—	6.8	58.8	—
North York Moors	0.6	0.8	16.6	0.5	—	0.9	—	0.1	76.7	3.8
Northumberland	0.2	0.7	18.9	22.6	—	—	—	1.2	56.4	—
Peak District	4.2	9.7	0.5	—	0.1	—	—	13.0	72.5	—
Pembrokeshire	0.5	4.7	1.2	4.5	0.5	0.5	—	—	88.0	0.1
Snowdonia	1.0	8.7	15.6	—	1.5	—	1.1	0.9	69.8	1.4
Yorkshire Dales	0.1	1.3	0.2	0.4	—	—	—	0.1	97.8	0.1

Source: *National Parks Today*, Winter 1987

The contradictions of National Park policy can be seen in some of the developments that have been sited in these 'extensive areas of beautiful and relatively wild country'. They include Trawsfynydd nuclear power station, Snowdonia; Fylingdales Ballistic Missile Early Warning System (North York Moors – to be replaced by a 105 foot high pyramid); and Eldon Hill and Topley Pike limestone quarries (Peak District).

Areas of Outstanding Natural Beauty (AONB)

The popularity of the National Parks can be judged by the 90 million visitors they attract every year, and this despite the fact that they are situated away from the bulk of the population in south-east England. Their location has been criticized on the grounds of being too remote, and it has also been pointed out that most parks protect the upland areas of England and Wales – the two lowland areas originally selected, the Broads and the South Downs, being left off the final list – leaving the lowland areas of the country at the mercy of agricultural development.

The 1949 Act allowed for another designation as well as National Park: the AONB (Area of Outstanding Natural Beauty). Thirty-four AONBs cover roughly the same proportion of land as that allocated to the national parks – about one-tenth of the area of England and Wales – and take in a larger allocation of lowland countryside. Some well-known AONBs include the Cotswolds, the Wye Valley, the Malvern Hills and the Chilterns.

Marion Shoard in *The Theft of the Countryside* (1980) has pointed out that the reasons for bestowing National Park status on some areas while withholding it from others do not stand up well to scrutiny. AONBs are established in places like the Cornish coast, where an attempt at National Park designation has failed, or in locations where the countryside is beautiful but does not include areas of large, unenclosed roughland.

Although AONBs are not supposed to be inferior to National Parks, the distinction is important, as AONBs do not receive the money, staff, legislative protection or other special treatment that the parks enjoy. The parks get funding from central government but, with the exception of specific projects, AONBs have to be financed by local authorities. AONBs do not provide the public with the widespread access to the countryside that was envisaged in the 1949 Act, and it is arguable as to exactly how much environmental protection they do afford: a study on development control in the East Devon AONB showed that the chances of getting permission to build a house were higher inside the AONB than outside it. Shoard concludes that the AONBs 'looked like a damp squib from the beginning'.

Heritage Coasts occupy a similar mediocre position in the environmental hierarchy. In 1979 these covered some 1,084 km of coastline in England and Wales, including the 92 km Northumberland coast and the 63 km north Norfolk coast. As with AONBs, they receive grant aid only for specific projects, and are generally underfunded and inadequately supported.

National Scenic Areas

There are no National Parks or AONBs in Scotland, which instead have National Scenic Areas, a kind of hybrid of the two. The 40 proposed areas cover one-eighth of Scotland. In *Crisis and Conservation* (1984), Pye-Smith and Rose point out that the scheme has attracted criticism from Scottish observers because much of the designated land is owned by absentee landlords. The NSA scheme appears to subsidize absentee landowning by exempting designated areas from capital gains tax, effectively giving large cash sums to people who, it could be argued, were not the most deserving of public subsidy. If this kind of money is to be allocated to environmental protection in Scotland, it could perhaps be used more effectively by channelling it to entire communities, rather than by giving it to single families.

Environmentally Sensitive Areas

In August 1986, the Ministry of Agriculture labelled six areas of England and Wales as 'environmentally sensitive areas' on grounds of landscape, historic importance and the value of wildlife habitat. Farmers were to be offered £6 million of incentive payments over the years to continue the more traditional methods of land management and maintain the beauty and wildlife value of their farms.

The ESAs cover important areas of wetland and marshland (the Somerset Levels and the Norfolk Broads); upland moor and mountain (the Pennine Dales and the Cambrian mountains); chalk downland (the South Downs) and coastal heath and moorland (West Penwith). A further two or three ESAs are to be designated in Scotland and Northern Ireland.

The ESA scheme received a mixed response. Some farmers welcomed it, others were annoyed at being included in the project, others again were angry at being excluded. The environmental movement was relieved that the government was finally beginning to realize the need to integrate agriculture and conservation – but intensely frustrated at the restricted nature of the approach. The Nature Conservancy Council and the Countryside Commission had originally identified 46 potential ESA sites in England and Wales, totalling 2,865,000 hectares. This was whittled down to a shortlist of 14 sites, which was in turn cut to six, for financial reasons. By the end of the 1980s this had increased to 19.

Friends of the Earth commented: 'Until farmers everywhere become eligible for special payments to maintain practices which benefit conservation, most of the countryside. ... remains exposed to environmentally damaging agricultural development. This provides further justification for an extension of planning controls.'

The argument for planning controls

'Planning controls' are the centrepiece of the conservationists' approach to environmental protection. Currently, agricultural or forestry projects, and buildings which are intended for their use, are outside the scope of the planning laws. The intention of this exclusion was to encourage the growth of the farming industry after the Second World War (see COUNTRYSIDE CHANGES IN THE UK). In the post-war period, agriculture was not thought a necessary candidate for planning control – its role in the countryside had, up to this point, been environmentally beneficial.

The laws do produce some strange results. A shed that houses knitting machinery needs planning permission; the same shed housing agricultural machinery does not. Richard Body, himself a farmer, points up the apparent idiocy of current regulations in *Farming in the Clouds* (1984):

The destruction of our countryside can be stopped by applying planning restrictions on agriculture similar to those imposed upon businessmen. Two new buildings may look identical to the passer by: one will need planning permission, but not the other. If I put five parrots in a cage that should only one, I will be prosecuted; but not if I put five hens in it. I can pollute the atmosphere as a farmer, but not as a businessman. My friends in the Thames Water Authority tell me that they commit an offence if they ask an employee to take a hook to trim the sides of our river by himself, but I, as a farmer, can ask Billy who works for me to do exactly the same job and I am innocent of the crime.

Proposers of rural planning controls cite the success of the urban wildlife movement as an indication of what can be done. Most of the green space in towns is publicly owned and managed on our behalf by civil servants. Even privately-owned land is subject to planning controls. As soon as the urban conservation movement realized this, and started political pressure for more environmentally benign management of the green areas, results began to be achieved. Local authority money, previously used to suppress nature and destroy habitats, began in the 1980s to be used more positively.

The argument in favour of stricter rural planning has been accused of authoritarianism (why should farmers be told what to grow in their fields?), but there appears to be no logical reason why people should be told how to manage their land in the town and not in the country. As an example, a system has been proposed whereby farmers should notify local planning authorities if they want to remove important landscape features – an obvious interest to all in the vicinity. The system has not been adopted, although some changes are now in train (1989).

Countryside management may be significantly changed by the shifting attitude of the EC towards farm quotas. Previously, farmers' choice was limited by the incentive payments that were paid on certain crops and not on others; these may soon be withdrawn, and farmers will be looking for other means to augment their income. It does not seem illogical that these incentives should be redirected into countryside conservation if that is what the public wants. This is a possibility: by October 1988, some 2,000 farmers had applied to take 150,000 acres out of cereal cultivation, under the government's 'set-aside' scheme, designed to reduce grain surpluses. The success or otherwise of this scheme remains to be seen: the set-aside land may revert to a more natural state – or it may become eligible for development at a later date.

Common land

Over the centuries, England has experienced a number of different systems of land management. The first written records, in the seventh century A.D., show a country owned in small lots by free peasant proprietors, owing allegiance to a local overlord and then the local king. Considerable areas were 'common' land – i.e. the property of a village or a larger community, and in their possession for a number of centuries. If the local lord wanted to appropriate this common land, it was on the understanding that certain historical rights, such as the right to gather nuts or mushrooms, were still to be enjoyed by the local community. What individuals owned was theirs to keep; what the villages possessed was theirs by right.

The invasion of William the Conqueror changed all this. William claimed all the land in England for the monarchy: from henceforth land could not be owned as an absolute right, but by permission of the king. The country was divided among 180 of William's supporters, who in turn released smaller land areas to their friends and relations. Although the principle of 'common lands' was still respected (the new ruling class thought that abolition would provoke a violent reaction) the philosophy of common ownership was now under threat.

The process of enclosure began in 1483, when Edward IV authorized woods to be fenced off to protect young trees from grazing animals. By the Civil War (1642 to 1650) half of England's agricultural land had been enclosed. The process was finalized by the Enclosure Acts in the eighteenth and nineteenth centuries, when millions of acres, previously open to all, were fenced in and adapted for agricultural purposes.

It was usually the lord of the manor who took over the common land, either with the aid of the law or frequently using private force. In 1865 the Commons Preservation Society (now known as the Open Spaces Society) was formed with the intention of halting the accelerating loss of the commons. Shortly after its formation, the society managed to prevent the takeover of Hampstead Heath, Wimbledon Common, Berkhamsted Common and Epping Forest – all areas that arguably would have disappeared by now had it not been for the spirited resistance of the protestors.

Legislation soon followed. The Commons Act of 1876 legitimized many recreational commons; in 1899 the public were granted limited rights of access to some areas, which was extended in 1925 to all urban commons.

Things have not gone much further, however. An estimated 1.5 million acres of Britain are common lands, most now privately owned but with restrictions placed upon their use because of the ancient rights of the 'commoners' – common people of the area. Only about one-fifth of these commons are legally open to the public. The remainder are frequently subject to pressures from their 'owners' – ownership occasionally being the subject of vigorous dispute – wishing to make an economic use of the land. As a result, commons can suffer from neglect and conflict.

In 1958, the Royal Commission on Common Land stated that, 'as the last reserve of uncommitted land in England and Wales, common land ought to be preserved in the public interest'. The Commission recommended that all common land should be registered; that it should be legally open to the public; and that owners, commoners and local authorities should set up management and improvement schemes.

Only the first recommendation was adopted, and common land had to be registered in a three-year period after 1965. Unfortunately, this was not a long enough time for all common land to be identified, and as a result some was lost from the public domain for good. The legal complexities covering ownership of some commons meant that a number have been enclosed since then, as local authorities were unable or unwilling to enforce the law. In 1983, in a further attempt to clear up the uncertainties involved, the Countryside Commission and a number of interested organizations set up the Common Land Forum.

The Common Land Forum published its conclusions in 1986, recommending a five-year period for owners, commoners and local authorities to set up management schemes for the commons, after which they would all be open as of right to the public, subject to certain minor restrictions. The government greeted the recommendations with cautious approval, and is now being pressured to back its stance with legislation. If the recommendations do become law, a major step forward will have been taken to safeguard many of Britain's beautiful areas. The alternative is the continuing loss of countryside that has, or should have, been available to the public for hundreds of years.

Access to the countryside/footpaths

This Land is Our Land (Marion Shoard, 1987) gives a breakdown of who owns the countryside in the United Kingdom. In 1986, the

Forestry Commission, with nearly 3 million acres, was Britain's largest owner of land. Substantial areas were also owned by the Ministry of Defence, the water authorities, local authorities and the nationalized industries. In total, however, this represents less than 13 per cent of the land surface of the UK – a percentage likely to shrink after the privatization of the water authorities, and possible sell-offs of Nature Reserves and Forestry Commission land. The financial institutions, pension companies, insurance companies, and the like, own about 1 per cent of the land. The remainder – more than four-fifths of the entire countryside – is owned, as it has been for the last thousand years, by private individuals.

A small number of titled families – dukes and marquesses, viscounts, earls, barons, baronets and the royal family – own nearly a third of the land in Great Britain. In Scotland, whole islands, deer forests or even ranges of mountains may belong to one individual, who holds complementary parcels of land in England or Wales. If this person decides to put a wall around the entire area, and stop the rest of the population from entering, there is nothing that can be done to prevent this happening.

Trespass is a civil, not a criminal offence (unless the intention of the trespass is to commit a criminal act), so the sign saying 'Trespassers will be prosecuted' is not actually correct. On the other hand, the costs of a civil case can be high, in the unlikely event of a case going to court. The important point about ownership of land in Britain, however, is that, once warned by the landowner, an individual has no alternative but to leave the area. People have no rights at all to walk over the countryside when it belongs to someone else – and it usually does.

There is one important exception. There are about 120,000 miles of public footpaths and bridleways – to give them their correct name, public rights of way – along which ordinary citizens are legally entitled to roam. The network of paths has been in existence for centuries, but was set into a proper legislative framework by the 1949 National Parks and Access to the Countryside Act. Local councils were told to establish what were the public rights of way in their area, map them and then ensure that they were properly maintained.

Landowners have legal responsibilities if their land includes a right of way. These are: to allow walkers free passage along the footpath; not to obstruct a footpath with wire, fencing or other obstacles; to maintain the stiles along the path; not to grow crops over the footpath, and to restore the path if it is ploughed up; and not to keep any animal in a field adjoining a footpath if they know that it is likely to be dangerous. County councils have a statutory duty to maintain paths and to clear them of obstacles.

The only means to revoke a public right of way is to prove that a footpath is no longer needed for public use. One way to do this is to make it impassable. Local surveys by the Ramblers' Association have found up to a third of footpaths in some counties to be impeded by obstacles. If this occurs, the obstruction should be reported to the county council, who should then be strongly encouraged to take action. The public right of way network is not fixed in concrete: around 1,500 formal proposals to alter it are made every year. Organizations such as the Ramblers' Association have saved many a footpath from destruction.

Over 18 million trips to the countryside will be made on a typical summer Sunday, according to a 1984 Countryside Commission survey. Walking, says the Sports Council, is Britain's most popular sport. In the 1970s, some conservation organizations took the view that the protection of the countryside would be best achieved by setting up a small number of nature reserves, and discouraging 'the crowds' from gaining access. Although this philosophy helped to save a small number of natural areas, it was a narrow-minded approach that failed to protect the countryside at large.

The 1980s ideal is to get as many people as possible into the countryside, so that they can appreciate it for what it is, and strengthen the popular movement for its protection. Public footpaths are one of the most powerful weapons in the conservationists' armoury, and they should be safeguarded wherever possible.

See also FORESTRY IN THE UK; PESTICIDES; SPECIES EXTINCTION; WATER

REFERENCES

Barr et al., *Landscape Changes in Britain*, Institute of Terrestrial Ecology, 1986.

Body, Richard, *Farming in the Clouds*, Maurice Temple Smith, 1984.

Countryside Commission, *Common Land, the Report of the Common Land Forum*, 1988.

Hodges, R.D., and C. Arden-Clarke, *Soil Erosion in Britain*, Soil Association, 1986.

Hunting Technical Services, *Monitoring Landscape Change*, DoE/Countryside Commission, 1986.

King, Angela and Sue Clifford, *Holding Your Ground*, Maurice Temple Smith, 1985.

Liquid Assets, pub. Leeds University/Council for the Protection of Rural England, Royal Society for the Protection of Birds, December 1988.

Lowe, Philip, et al., *Countryside Conflicts*, Gower/Maurice Temple Smith, 1986.

Nature Conservancy Council, *Nature Conservation in Great Britain*, 1984.

Open Spaces Society, *Our Common Right, the Story of Common Land*, 1987.

Pye-Smith, Charlie and Chris Rose, *Crisis and Conservation*, Penguin Books, 1984.

Rose, Chris, 'Wildlife: the Battle for the British Countryside', in Wilson, Des, (ed.), *The Environmental Crisis*, Heinemann, 1984.

Shoard, Marion, *The Theft of the Countryside*, Maurice Temple Smith, 1980.

Shoard, Marion, *This Land is Our Land*, Paladin, 1987.

Baines, Chris, 'Conservation Comes to Town', *BBC Wildlife*, June 1987.

Countryside Commission News, September–October 1986.

Environment Digest No. 18, November 1988.

'Farmers Prove Sensitive about New Environment Subsidies', *New Scientist*, 21 August 1986.

Friends of the Earth Press Release, 14 August 1986.

National Parks Today

Observer, 23 October 1988.

Vulliamy, Edward, 'Farmers to be Paid for Conservation', *Guardian*, 15 August 1986.

CONTACTS

The Council for National Parks
Council for the Protection of Rural England
Countryside Commission
Fauna and Flora Society
Friends of the Earth (FoE)
Institute of Terrestrial Ecology
Nature Conservancy Council
Open Spaces Society
Ramblers' Association
Royal Society for the Protection of Birds (RSPB)

Soil Association
World Wide Fund For Nature UK (WWF UK)

Country Landowners' Association
Department of Environment (DoE)
Ministry of Agriculture, Fisheries and Food (MAFF)
National Farmers' Union

Cycling

There are now 15 million bicycles in Britain. Cycle sales trebled between 1973 and 1983, with more cycles currently being sold than cars. Cycling has a number of advantages over other systems of transport: it is cheap, quiet, non-polluting, doesn't cause traffic jams or waste energy. One thousand six hundred miles of cycling can be achieved for the energy equivalent of a gallon of petrol.

Cycling would also appear to be admirably suited to British travel habits, where half of all car journeys are five miles or less. In our cities, this distance could be achieved as quickly on a bike as in a car, at minimal expense, and be better for one's health. The cycle is also the most democratic form of transport, as 90 per cent of adult men and 68 per cent of adult women are capable of riding a bike: half the adult population, on the other hand, are unable to drive a car.

The increase in cycling popularity is reflected in a rising number of kilometres travelled: 3.24 billion kilometres in 1973, and 5.04 billion in 1984. Cycle flows into central London increased by more than 70 per cent between 1977 and 1983. One-eighth of all journeys to work in Cambridgeshire are by bike, and a tenth of all journeys in Humberside, Norfolk and Lincolnshire.

The growth in cycling in the UK has not been as rapid as the growth in cycle sales, however. The reason for this appears to be the perceived dangers of urban cycling: in 1987, 280 cyclists were killed, 4,851 were seriously injured, and 21,000 slightly injured. This figure represents almost 10 per cent of all road user casualties. If cycling is to reach its maximum potential – and there is a long way to go before this occurs – these accident rates would have to be reduced.

A number of schemes have been put forward to this end. Some cities are introducing cycle-ways which are specifically for cyclists only (or in some cases shared by cyclists and pedestrians). The best known of these was the GLC's plan to build a network of 1,000 miles of cycle-lanes throughout London. By March 1985, 250 miles of the network had been built, approved or proposed.

Other cities have been building cycle routes, notably Nottingham (the Greater Nottingham Cycle Network) and Southampton. Initiatives such as the Greater Manchester Cycling Project should ensure that others follow suit. A 15-mile cycle route has been built from a disused railway line between Bristol and Bath. A cycle network has been proposed for West Yorkshire, detailing 230 miles of short cycle routes on disused railway lines and canal towpaths, linked by stretches of quiet roads. The whole network could be constructed for the cost of 130 yards of urban ring road.

Useful though cycle routes are, they will not solve the problem of road traffic casualties among cyclists: it is not possible or desirable to separate cycles completely from other traffic. Two-thirds of adult cyclist accidents are caused by motorists, from a combination of inattentiveness, carelessness, speeding, illegal parking or drunk driving. To make the roads safe for cyclists, the cycling campaigners have put forward a programme called the Four Es:

Engineering   Road construction should include cycle-lanes, and measures such as advanced stop lines at traffic lights (to facilitate right turns), cycle phases on traffic lights, and larger central reservations at busy crossing points. Traffic speeds and volumes in residential areas could be restricted with road humps. Such measures would be extremely cheap in comparison to normal road construction costs, and would save lives.

Enforcement   This involves enforcement of speed limits – especially in residential areas; random breath tests (which have reduced drink-related road deaths in Finland by a third, and achieved accident savings in Australia, New Zealand, Scandinavia and 38 States of the USA); stricter punishment of illegal and dangerous parking; and greater enforcement of cycle safety laws, particularly riding without lights at night.

Education   Safety programmes should be aimed at all road users, rather than, as currently, just at cyclists. If 70 per cent of adult cycle accidents are caused by motorists, the figures are not going to be radically improved unless their attitudes towards cyclists are changed.

Encouragement More government encouragement of cycling is needed – and that means financial commitment rather than just moral exhortation. The UK Department of Transport spent £160,000 in 1983 and 1984 on cycling, approximately £200,000 in 1985. This compares poorly with the £3,000 million budget for roads (see TRANSPORT POLICY IN THE UK).

The potential for cycling as a means of transport should not be underestimated. Better planning for bikes has been encouraged in the Netherlands, Denmark and Germany, with the result that cycling has become much more popular in those countries. As an example, Groningen, in The Netherlands, has planned its road system so that car entry into the centre of town is restricted: 50 per cent of all journeys in Groningen are now made by bike.

See also AUTOMOBILE POLLUTION; ENERGY

REFERENCES

Department of Transport Traffic Advisory Unit, Leaflet 14, 1986.

Friends of the Earth, *Why We Have to Control the Car*, 1984.

Friends of the Earth, *Transport*, 1984.

Friends of the Earth, *Cycle Planning, Your Questions Answered*, 1985.

Greater London Council, *Towards a Cycle Network*.

Caudrey, Adriana, 'Fast Living, Fast Death', *New Society*, 1 August 1986.

Knight, L., 'Steer past financial potholes when you get on your bike', *The Times*, 27 May 1989.

CONTACTS

Cycle Campaign Network
Cyclists' Touring Club
European Cyclists' Federation

Friends of the Earth (FoE)
London Cycling Campaign

Deforestation

'Deforestation' is the term used to describe the disappearance of forests from large parts of the world's surface. Figures produced by the United Nations Environment Programme (*Environmental Data Report*, 1987) show a world loss of 290 million hectares (three-quarters of a billion acres) of forests and woodlands between the early 1960s and the early 1980s.

Exact statistics as to the extent of the world's forests, and the rate at which they are being depleted, are difficult to establish because of varying interpretations as to what a forest is (see below), and the enormous area which the forest surveys cover. There is agreement as to the general trend, however: deforestation has been occurring steadily over the course of this century, with a rapid acceleration since the Second World War.

Forest areas in the more temperate parts of the world appear to be stable or even slightly increasing – with the exception of Central Europe, where large tracts of forest are dying, presumably as a result of air pollution (see ACID RAIN). The brunt of deforestation has been borne by woodland and tropical forests in the Third World. In some regions, the rate of forest loss has accelerated so quickly that the result is complete deforestation; whole countries face the same fate by the end of the century.

If the current rate of clearance continues, all the world's primary (i.e. undisturbed) rainforest will disappear or be damaged within the next 30 years, with the same fate befalling all rainforests about half a century later.

The disappearance of a single tropical forest is an environmental tragedy because of the loss of an enormous number of species, some possibly unique. The global trend of destroying tropical forests, however, has extremely serious, potentially catastrophic, consequences, for:

- the 200 million people living in or near tropical forests;
- regional climate, as weather conditions become radically changed (the effects on global climate can only be hypothesized);
- forest animals, plants and insects, which will become extinct in millions;
- the inhabitants of the world, who will lose a genetic storehouse of species that has to date provided the bulk of our agricultural and medical progress.

The world's forests can be classified in various types:*

(1) Temperate forest

These grow in areas which are warm enough and low enough to support forests but not as hot as the tropical areas. They include:

Deciduous woodland   Mainly found in lowland areas, and including scrub and herbs as well as trees. A number of varying species.

Coniferous woodland   Generally found on higher ground, with fewer species. Much modern coniferous forest, especially in Europe and Australasia, contains non-native species or is extensively managed.

Mediterranean woodland   Including both coniferous and deciduous woodland, found in Mediterranean countries of Europe and North Africa.

Temperate rainforest   Found in parts of North America, Australia and northern Asia. A richer habitat than the drier temperate forests.

(2) Tropical forest

'Tropical' describes the 40 per cent of the world's land area between the Tropics of Cancer and Capricorn, and 'tropical forest' is a general term for forests found in tropical monsoon regions of the world (this geographical definition is relaxed enough to include the forests of northern India and Nepal). Within the classification there is an enormous variety of forest types, including swamp forest, cloud forest, coastal mangrove, deciduous woodland, etc.

Almost two-thirds of tropical forests are seasonal or all-year rain forests, also known as tropical moist forests, with the remainder being drier open woodlands. The latter cover about 800 million hectares.

Tropical rainforests cover some 7 per cent of the world's land area, about 900 to 1,200 million hectares (2.2 to 3 billion acres); 58 per cent

* Adapted from Nigel Dudley, *The Death of Trees*, 1985.

of them are in South America, with Africa (19 per cent) and Asia and Oceania (23 per cent) having the rest (see map, below).

The main countries with tropical forests are Brazil, which contains almost 33 per cent of the total; Zaire and Indonesia (each with 10 per cent); Papua New Guinea, Colombia, Venezuela, Gabon, Peru and Burma, each with over 200 square kilometres of tropical forest. Three countries – Brazil, Zaire and Indonesia – together possess more than half of all the world's tropical forests.

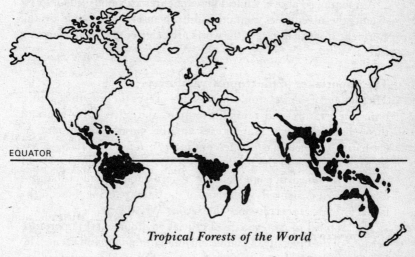

EQUATOR

Tropical Forests of the World

Source: Friends of the Earth

Problems of definition

A range of different estimates have been published as to the extent of forest cover generally, and the area under tropical forest. An important factor in this uncertainty is the problem of defining what is or isn't a forest. Surveyors use definitions such as these:

Open woodland Trees covering at least 10 per cent of the ground, permitting growth of a continuous dense grass layer.

Closed forests Broadleaved, coniferous or bamboo formations, not cleared for the previous 20 or 30 years, with such a dense canopy (i.e., 'roof' of leaves) that a continuous grass layer cannot become established on the ground.

Forest fallow Land overgrown with open or closed woodland after a 'slash and burn' operation (see below).

Plantation   Forests established commercially on land previously un-
forested, or planted to replace an indigenous tree species.

The uncertainties in the surveys arise from the difficulty of establishing the minimum 10 per cent cover, the difference between open
and closed formations, and the problems of distinguishing between
tree and shrub formations. These difficulties are exacerbated by the
practical problems of mounting a survey which covers the entire
globe.

As mentioned above, while different figures are published for forest
extent, the inventories contain within themselves the same overall
story: the tropical forests of the world are being eroded at an alarming
rate.

The importance of the tropical rainforests

The climate of the wet tropical areas encourages the growth of plants:
both temperature and rainfall are high, and often fairly constant
throughout the year. Rainforests are the natural vegetation. As
Catherine Caufield has pointed out in *In the Rainforest* (1985), a few
thousand years ago the rainforest belt covered 5 billion acres – 14
per cent of the earth's land surface. Approximately half of that has
already been destroyed, with most of the damage being done in the
last 200 years, especially since the Second World War.

The tropical rainforests are of crucial environmental importance
because of the diversity of plants and animals that inhabit them. The
Ice Ages destroyed vast areas of forest in the more temperate zones
but not nearer the equator: many rainforests maintained their
existing populations and provided shelter for those species that
managed to escape from the freezing northern wastes.

As the temperature never sinks below zero in the tropical forests,
plant species do not need to concentrate their energy on survival
during a cold winter, but can go for maximum growth. The intense
competition for survival means that species do not tend to dominate,
as in parts of the north, but proliferate in a shoulder-to-shoulder
existence.

By comparison with the bare north, the rainforests are teeming
with life:

• According to the World Wildlife Fund, a recent study of one hectare
of Peruvian rainforest – about the size of a large garden – found

41,000 different insect species living in the forest canopy, including 12,000 types of beetle.

- Tropical forests have 5 to 20 times more species of tree than temperate forests. Together, Canada and the USA have 700 tree species: the island of Madagascar alone has 2,000.
- Caufield describes how one square mile of rainforest near the Colombian city of Quibido has 1,100 species of plants (Great Britain has 1,430 altogether). Tiny Panama has as many plant species as the whole of Europe.
- The world is commonly assumed to contain some 5 million species, of which 1.75 million are properly recorded by science. About 155,000 of the 250,000 known species of plants are to be found in the rainforests, 80 per cent of all insects, nine-tenths of the world's primates (monkeys and related animals).
- Research carried out by Terry Erwin of the Smithsonian Institution led to the estimate that each species of rainforest tree supports over 400 unique insect species. These figures indicate that there may be 20 million or more insect species in the tropical forests, many more than previously suspected (Erwin now thinks the figure is more likely to be 30 million).
- Many of the plants, animals and insects are likely to be endemic (i.e., found in one place, and nowhere else). Destroy one rainforest, and an uncountable number of species will be lost: destroy all of them, and the total will run into millions. The number of lost species would be a very significant proportion of all the species on the planet.
- Half of the world's main crops were originally discovered in the tropical forest, including coffee, tea, sugar, bananas, rice, maize, cocoa, oranges, lemons and peanuts. Our domestic chickens were bred from the red jungle fowl of Indian forests. Twenty-five per cent of US drug prescriptions have ingredients derived from rainforest species – but only a fraction of these sources has been investigated. For example, 1,400 forest plants may have anti-cancer potential. If this untapped reserve disappears, then a major source of advances in nutrition, food supply and medicine will disappear too.

Reasons for deforestation

There are two general reasons behind global deforestation: survival, and economics.

Survival refers to the population growth, pressure to clear land for farming and government-inspired settlement schemes that have led to much deforestation in tropical America – particularly Brazil. Impoverished peasants and urban dwellers have been encouraged, or forced by economic circumstances, to migrate along the Trans-Amazonia Highways and settle in a 'pioneer' area. There they burn and cut enough forest to provide a homestead and stay there as long as the soil will allow – frequently a matter of a few years. Then the cycle starts again.

'Slash and burn' as the technique has become known, has destroyed large areas of forest in the Amazon Basin. Paradoxically, this apparently brutal system of forest clearance leaves seeds, tree stumps, microhabitats and nutrients still in the soil. As the pioneers move on, the forest can begin to re-establish itself and it is possible that primary forest species may return after 50 years or so. 'Slash and burn' is not a technique to be encouraged – but its long-term effects do not appear as catastrophic as those of full-scale ranching (see below).

In other areas of the world, the trees are destroyed because the inhabitants need to burn them for fuelwood. In 1985, the Tropical Forestry Action Plan, published by the Food and Agriculture Organization (FAO) of the United Nations, stated that 180 million Africans faced acute scarcity of firewood in 1980. This figure amounted to nearly 40 per cent of the estimated population of Africa. By the year 2000, when the FAO reckons another 175 million people will be severely affected, 65 per cent of Africa's population will be experiencing shortage of firewood.

In *The Greening of Africa* (1987), Paul Harrison describes how deforestation is most serious in the more densely populated areas of west, east and southern Africa. East Africa's closed forests are being cleared at an annual rate of 0.8 per cent per year; Burundi's are declining by almost 3 per cent a year, and in West Africa 4 per cent of the closed forest is being razed annually. The level of threat varies widely between regions (see map). The FAO estimates that 16 of the 45 countries in sub-Saharan Africa face fuelwood deficits on all or part of their territory, which could only be met by cutting trees faster than they are growing: another 18 could not even meet their demands by overcutting, and had to go short.

Economics In terms of forest area, more than 50 per cent of deforestation is caused by fuelwood gathering and settler expansion.

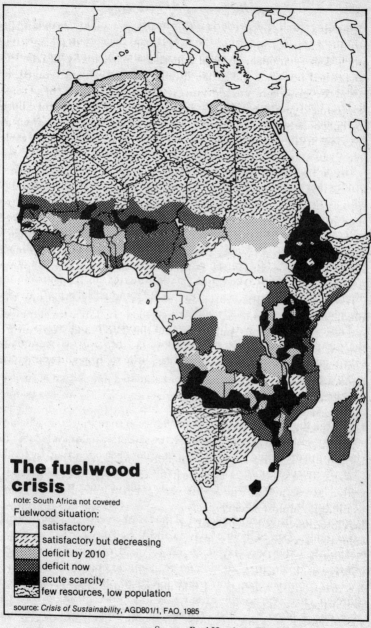

The fuelwood crisis

note: South Africa not covered

Fuelwood situation:

- satisfactory
- satisfactory but decreasing
- deficit by 2010
- deficit now
- acute scarcity
- few resources, low population

source: *Crisis of Sustainability*, AGD801/1, FAO, 1985

Source: Paul Harrison, *The Greening of Africa*, 1987

According to *World Resources 1986*, nearly 1.5 billion people in 63 countries (or 60 per cent of the people who depend on fuelwood for cooking and heating) are cutting wood faster than it can grow back. At present fuelwood consumption rates, the estimated wood deficit will double by the year 2000.

The United Nations Environment Programme lists 1.6 billion cubic metres of wood being used as fuelwood and charcoal per year between 1981 and 1983; the other category listed, 'Industrial Wood', has an annual production figure of 1.4 billion cubic metres.

Globally, these figures represent an approximate 45 per cent production of industrial wood to a 55 per cent use for fuelwood and charcoal.

Looking at the regional figures, however, the picture is rather different. North America and Europe provide about 750 million cubic metres of industrial wood, some 45 per cent of the world total, yet produce only 200,000 cubic metres of wood for fuel (15 per cent of the world total). Africa, Asia and South America are responsible for producing only 24 per cent of the world's industrial wood, and 80 per cent of the world's fuelwood.

These figures are used by the timber industry to deflect criticism: the disappearance of the world's forests, they say, is caused by overpopulation and ignorance, and has little to do with commercial logging practices.

However, the argument:

- Ignores the close interconnection between many logging schemes and the settler drives that follow – the settlers would not be able to penetrate the tropical forests, had they not been opened up by roads for the purpose of logging. The FAO estimate that 70 per cent of all clearances are possible only as a result of the roads and infra-structure built for logging.
- Ignores the historical depletion of the forest reserves by the logging companies, especially in Malaysia and West Africa.
- Minimizes the role played by First World countries and multi-nationals, in creating an aid and economic system in which Third World countries chop down their forests to provide much-needed foreign currency, in the absence of any other means of raising revenue – often as a direct result of Western trade tariffs and embargoes. It also neglects the per capita usage of wood in the

Third and First Worlds: as Erik Eckholm points out in *Down to Earth* (1982), the average American consumes as much wood in the form of paper as the average resident in many Third World countries burns as cooking fuel – and this ignores the many other uses for wood which the American will have.

- Avoids the fact that fuelwood losses come mainly from open and dry forests, especially in Africa, not from the closed tropical moist forests.

- Is based on a non-sequitur – the situation is so bad, it implies, that our industrial contribution is neither here nor there. In fact, the industrial cut, though smaller in proportional terms, represents an enormous area of tropical forest: 50,000 sq. km of closed tropical forest is logged annually. Loggers take only 4 to 10 per cent of the trees as these are the commercially attractive species, but leave the land area severely degraded and often unable to recover. Less than 10 per cent of the wrecked forests are replanted. Sustainably managed logging in countries such as Malaysia is virtually non-existent.

There is often a connection, also, between the economic reasons for deforestation and the 'survival' drive that follows. Catherine Caufield describes in *In the Rainforest* (1985) how Central American rainforests are destroyed over enormous areas – to provide cattle ranches for the North American hamburger market.

Latin American beef is half the price of the USA counterpart, so it is imported in accelerating quantities to the North. The rainforest is cleared by large landowners, run as a cattle ranch for five to eight years until the soil gives up, and then left, as the ranch moves elsewhere. The land, occupied for millions of years by rainforest, is now useless, as the internal regeneration processes that kept the rainforest alive have been destroyed. The good news: five cents off the price of hamburgers in the USA. The bad news: more than one-quarter of the Central American rainforest destroyed since 1960.

This vast sterilization of land has consequences for the peasants that have been trying to live off it. Figures produced by the FAO show that, in Latin America as a whole, 93 per cent of the land is owned by 7 per cent of the landowners. According to Caufield, various forms of peasant agriculture support 100 people per square mile. Cattle ranching supports one person per 12 square miles. The displaced workforce has to go somewhere if it is to survive. In most Latin American countries, the simplest way to establish title to unoccupied land is to cut down the trees. In legal terms, deforestation is improvement of the land.

Around the world, say the World Wildlife Fund, between 11 and 15 million hectares of tropical forest are lost every year, an area larger than Austria. Six million hectares of this is rainforest, the rest being the drier variety. Every month, an area half the size of Wales is felled; every minute, an area the size of twenty football pitches disappears. Clearly, unless this trend is halted, the tropical forests are doomed.

New data on Amazonian burnings, released in 1988, indicate that the situation is worse than previously imagined. Satellite data from Brazil's Space Research Centre showed that, in the 1987 August to October burning season, nearly 80,000 square miles of forest was devastated by fire, representing about 4 per cent of the entire Amazon region and equal to an area five times that of Switzerland. About 40 per cent of the land destroyed was virgin forest. The fires were virtually all illegal – the Brazilian Forestry Service has 900 wardens to guard an area larger than Europe – and tended to follow by the sides of roads.

What is disappearing*

Ivory Coast   Forest almost logged out (1965 – 15 million hectares; now, one million hectares).

Malaysia   Peninsular Malaysian forest resources will be exhausted by 1990.

Congo   68 per cent of rainforest scheduled to be logged.

Thailand   Will lose 60 per cent of the 1981 forest by year 2000.

Nigeria   Complete deforestation expected by year 2000.

Guinea   Will lose one-third of forest by year 2000.

Madagascar   Will lose 30 per cent of forest by 2000.

Ghana   Will lose 26 per cent of remaining forest by 2000.

Indonesia   200,000 ha logged a year; 10 per cent of the 1981 forest will be destroyed by the year 2000.

Honduras   Will lose over 50 per cent of remaining forest by 2000.

Nicaragua   Will lose over 50 per cent of remaining forest by 2000.

* According to World Wildlife Fund. For a more comprehensive list, see Norman Myers, *The Primary Source*, 1985.

Ecuador   Will lose over 50 per cent of remaining forest by 2000.

Guatemala   Will lose one-third of remaining forest by 2000.

Colombia   Will lose one-third of remaining forest by 2000.

Brazil   Will lose 8 per cent of remaining forest by 2000 (an area of 63 million ha – two and a half times bigger than Portugal).

What has disappeared

World   40 to 50 per cent of all tropical forests destroyed.

Philippines   55 per cent forest loss between 1960 and 1985.

Thailand   45 per cent forest loss between 1961 and 1985.

India   All primary (i.e., original) rainforest destroyed.

Bangladesh   All primary rainforest destroyed.

Sri Lanka   All primary rainforest destroyed.

Haiti   All primary rainforest destroyed.

China   50 per cent loss of forest in S. Province of Xishuangbana.

The consequences of deforestation

Species extinction, and the impact of this on the world's scientific, agricultural and medical progress has been described above. The argument is usually phrased like this to appeal to the self-interest of the reader. Higher moral questions, such as whether we have the right systematically to exterminate competing species, and what effect this will have on ourselves, are very rarely addressed. It can be said that the world will become a much greyer place as the variety of life-forms decreases, and that this may have an impact on our general behaviour – though this argument is certainly in the realms of hypothesis.

On a more down-to-earth level, deforestation has significant consequences. The forests fix soil to the earth; when the trees are removed, the soil blows away or is removed by rains. This erosion of the soil makes the area useless for farming; clogs up local watercourses, to the extent of silting up major canals and dams; and leads to floods in the rainy season, as the soil is no longer able to retain the rains in sufficiently large quantities (this is one of the main reasons why the Chipko movement was founded in India – erosion, soil loss, and floods after over-intensive tree-felling). In extreme cases, the deforested area will become a desert (see DESERTIFICATION).

Deforestation will also have an effect on local climate. In the Amazon Basin, several estimates show that water coming in from the Atlantic Ocean accounts for about half of the precipitation (i.e., rain, mists, etc.) in the region, with the rest coming from water vapour recycled by trees. Amazonian rain can be recycled over three times this way, with some forest downpours containing 90 per cent forest-generated rain. If the trees are cut down, the rain cycle is interrupted.

Forests absorb more of the sun's energy than open land: deforestation can disrupt local weather patterns by warming air that was previously kept cool. Deforested zones experience greater fluctuations in air and soil temperature than the forest that they have replaced. Humidity is another factor that is altered.

The impact of forests on world climate is still largely unknown, although research is urgently necessary. The widely-held idea that trees are the 'green lungs' of the planet, producing the world's oxygen, is, according to current knowledge, a myth, as the world contains much larger oxygen sources. There is a possibility, however, that the disappearance of trees over large areas may increase carbon dioxide build-up in the atmosphere. As the WWF comments: 'Their role in maintaining the global climate is poorly understood, but removing the forests must be the worst possible way of finding out how crucial they are.' The scale of the 1987 Amazon burnings (see above) has been compared by scientists 'to the outburst of a very large volcano' – producing an estimated one-fifth of the world's carbonic gases, along with large quantities of carbon monoxide, ozone, methane, and nitrogen oxides. This, coupled with the disappearance of large numbers of trees which could be absorbing carbon dioxide, will have a marked impact on the GREENHOUSE EFFECT.

Attempts to stop deforestation

In the 1980s, the environmental movement and the international community have realized the threat to the tropical rainforests.

- In 1982–3, the World Wildlife Fund and the IUCN (International Union for the Conservation of Nature and Natural Resources) launched a Tropical Forest Campaign. By 1986, 40 per cent of WWF's programme of international project expenditure involved tropical forest conservation.
- In 1985, an International Task Force composed of the World Bank, the World Resources Institute, the IUCN and the United Nations Development Association launched *Tropical Forests: a Call for Action*, proposing a global plan to prevent deforestation, save the tropical

forests and avert the fuelwood crisis by increasing the number of plantations and better managing exploited forests. The plan called for 56-nation involvement at a cost of $8 billion. In 1987, the founder members met planners from six countries, the OECD and UNEP at Bellagio, Italy, and announced that an annual $1 billion commitment had almost been realized. The plan has come under intense criticism from the environmental movement for being underfunded and badly directed – but it indicated at least a willingness to grapple with the problem.

- In 1986, after ten years of discussion, the International Tropical Timber Organization (ITTO) was established in Yokohama, Japan. This runs the International Tropical Timber Agreement (ITTA), an economic treaty between 18 producer and 22 consumer nations which together control over 90 per cent of tropical timber trade and tropical forests. One of the stated aims of the ITTA is conservation. The formation of the ITTO can be seen as a positive step, but the dilatory progress of the organization to date is beginning to attract criticism.

- In 1940, the total area of nature reserves and national parks worldwide was the same size as Madagascar, and only 2 per cent consisted of tropical moist forest. Today the total area is larger than India, Bangladesh, Pakistan and Sri Lanka, and tropical forests account for 8 per cent. There are now about 560 tropical forest parks and reserves covering 78 million hectares – although this is about only 4 per cent of all tropical forests, with many reserves and protected areas being too small to be effective.

- Certain countries – notably China – have started large reforestation schemes. Again, though not by any means large enough to affect significantly the downward spiral of world forest protection, these projects are encouraging signs.

- Some countries are willing to exchange foreign debt for a promise to protect certain forest areas. 'Debt-for-nature' swaps have taken place in Bolivia (Amazon Basin) and Costa Rica (Guanacaste National Park). Some conservation groups are exploring the possibility of direct aid to threatened parks (e.g. the Korup area of Cameroon).

All the above schemes can be seen as a recognition of the seriousness of the problem. An interesting British initiative is the Friends of the Earth consumer campaign launched in 1987. FoE has lobbied retailers, manufacturers, importers, architects, local authorities and other users of tropical hardwoods to adopt a Code of Conduct, ensuring that Britain trades only in well-managed, ecologically sound timber products. Some 50 local authorities are investigating ways in which they can help.

The European timber trade bears a significant responsibility for the disappearance of tropical rainforests, as Nectoux and Dudley show in *A Hard Wood Story* (1987). Europe accounts for 40 per cent of global trade in tropical timber imports by volume, and 32 per cent by value, ranking close behind Japan. European companies, especially French, German and Dutch, still directly control much of the logging and wood processing in West Africa. Many make little provision for replanting; the profits often do not stay in the host country; some projects have even been funded with aid money from Europe.

In addition to this, EC trade barriers discriminate against imports of processed tropical timber, but encourage imports of raw materials. (The effect of import barriers is as harsh or harsher in the other two main markets – the USA and Japan.) Producer countries are refused the economic advantages of adding value to their own product, and produce in bulk to compensate. This leads to extremely wasteful practices. The amount of timber wasted during extraction in SE Asia alone, for example, is estimated to be double the total for global tropical hardwood exports.

In 1989, WWF launched an attack on Japan for its role in the tropical timber trade. The world's leading tropical timber importer, Japan, consumed more than 20.6 million cubic metres of the commodity in 1987 – an increase of 25 per cent on the 1986 figure and more than in either the US or European Community. Japan's policies of unsustainable logging in the Malaysian states of Sabah and Sarawak threaten the continued existence of some of the most biologically valuable forest in the world: 68 per cent of Japan's land area is forested; 96 per cent of Japanese plywood is made from tropical timber.

The consumer countries – Japan, Europe and North America – have an advantageous arrangement, whereby their forests are managed sustainably, and their exotic hardwood needs are met by destroying the environment in a distant part of the world. As long as they believe that this will not have environmental consequences for their own countries, and public opinion is unmoved, the situation looks likely to continue.

Friends of the Earth's campaign strategy depends on alerting consumers to the dangers posed by buying environmentally unacceptable tropical timber, and allowing them to make choices by consulting their *Good Wood Guide*. Currently, only 5 per cent of the UK's tropical timber imports come from sustainably managed concessions. If FoE's *Good Wood Guide* is successful, consumers will start exerting the type of pressure that the large manufacturers understand – economic. In the absence of significant consumer pressure, the large multinationals will continue a process that is halfway to completion. To the next generation, the tropical rainforests could be a subject of merely historical interest.

See also DESERTIFICATION; NORTH–SOUTH RELATIONSHIP; POPULATION; SPECIES EXTINCTION

REFERENCES

Caufield, Catherine, *In the Rainforest*, Heinemann, 1985.

Dudley, Nigel, *The Death of Trees*, Pluto Press, 1985.

Eckholm, Erik, *Down to Earth*, Pluto Press, 1982.

Harrison, Paul, *The Greening of Africa*, Paladin, 1987.

Independent Commission on International Humanitarian Issues, *The Vanishing Forest*, Zed Books, 1986.

Longman, K. A. and J. Jenik, *Tropical Rainforest and its Environment*, Longman, 1987.

Myers, Norman, *The Primary Source*, W. W. Norton, 1985.

Nectoux, François and Nigel Dudley, *A Hard Wood Story*, FoE Trust, 1987.

Nectoux, François and Yoichi Kuroda, *Timber from the South Seas*, WWF International, 1989.

United Nations Environment Programme, *Environmental Data Report*, UNEP/Basil Blackwell, 1987.

World Resources Institute, IIED, *World Resources 1986*, Basic Books, 1986.

WWF, *Conservation of Tropical Rainforests*, *WWF Special Report*, 1987.

WWF International, *Tropical Rainforests* (information brochure), 1987.

WWF International, *WWF calls on Japanese government to curb tropical timber trade*, Press Release, 13 April 1989.

Environment Digest No. 18, October 1988.

FoE International, *ECO*, vol. 45, no. 1, Yokohama, November 1987.

Moore, Peter, 'What Makes Rainforests so Special?', *New Scientist*, 21 August 1986.

Prior, Juliet and Janet Tuohy, 'Fuel for Africa's Fires', *New Scientist*, 30 July 1987.

Third World First, *LINKS 19, Reclaiming the Earth*, 1983.

CONTACTS

Conservation International
Friends of the Earth International
Green Deserts
Greenpeace International
Intermediate Technology (IT)
International Union for the Conservation of Nature and Natural Resources (IUCN)
Oxfam
Rainforest Action Network
Rainforest Information Centre
Sierra Club
Survival International
Third World First
United Nations Environment Programme (UNEP)
United Nations Food and Agriculture Programme (FAO)
World Resource Institute
WWF (was called World Wildlife Fund, now World Wide Fund for Nature)

Desertification

'Desertification' describes the deterioration of much of the world's dryland regions. The problem is global in scale, currently affecting nearly one-quarter of the world's land area in all five continents.

Desertification refers to a loss of productivity of the land, classified as moderate loss (25 per cent), severe (25–50 per cent), to very severe (over 50 per cent). In certain cases, the end result is the creation of a desert where before there had been thriving agriculture.

The phenomenon is caused by poor land management and environmental pressures, by human rather than natural factors. It currently affects almost 250 million people; and the situation is getting worse, rather than better. According to the United Nations Environment Programme (UNEP), one-third of the earth's land area, and as many as 850 million of the world's poorest people, are at risk. Climate change (the GREENHOUSE EFFECT) may exacerbate the problem.

The solutions to desertification appear to be well established, and a programme for tackling the problem was agreed in 1977. The initiative has not been successful, however, because of the political complexities involved, both in the international community, and in the affected countries themselves.

Reasons for desertification

The world has five main desert zones (see map): the desert basins that run from north-western Mexico to the south-western United States; the Atacama Desert in south-western South America; the great desert belt running from the Sahara in Africa through the deserts of Iran, the USSR, Pakistan, India, Mongolia and China; the Kalahari desert in southern Africa; and most of the continent of Australia.

Desertification does not occur in these desert areas, but in the arid and semi-arid lands nearby. (Arid land has 200–250 mm, or 8–10 inches, of rain per year. Semi-arid has 250–600 mm, or 10–23 inches,

Areas threatened by desertification
Source: UNEP, *Sands of Change*, UNEP Environment Brief, No. 2, 1987

Takla Makan

Arabian

Sahara

Kalahari

Atacama

existing desert

high risk

moderate risk

of rain per year.) Desertification can start almost anywhere, but fertile land at the edge of existing deserts is at particularly high risk. In the Sudan for example, the edge of the Sahara has moved southwards about 100 km between 1958 and 1975.

There are a number of reasons for desertification, although Alan Grainger in *Desertification* (1982) identifies four main types:

> overcultivation
> deforestation
> overgrazing
> unskilled irrigation

The problem is compounded by increasing population.

The United Nations Environment Programme identifies 18 inter-dependent factors, which can be simplified into the basic phrase 'pressure for land':

- Countries need to grow cash crops (or are convinced that this is a need): this displaces traditional agriculture, which moves to marginal land. The marginal areas, previously unused, either decline in productivity or remain at a basic productive level until a climatic shock such as drought finishes off the process of degradation.
- Low livestock prices force producers into rearing more cattle, which overgraze the rangelands. The soil is stripped of vegetation and nutrients, becoming a dry dust which will blow away in the wind.
- Forests are removed either as a cash crop or to make room for increasing cattle or grain farms. Desertification commonly follows DEFORESTATION, because water runs off the bared hills too quickly, taking much of the topsoil with it. The eroded remains are unable to maintain a viable agriculture.
- Irrigation schemes are started to service the new crops, but are inefficiently planned and result in waterlogging of crops, or salinization (i.e. salting-up) of the soil. Continual evaporation from the soil can bring salt up from the subsoil, leaving it on the surface of the ground, which becomes unusable.

Any of these factors can be compounded by, or caused by, a large increase in local population such as is happening over large parts of the globe (see POPULATION). It is not drought that causes desertification – many of the newly desertified areas have had recurring droughts throughout the centuries, without the consequences that are occurring now – but the way in which the land is managed. The most well-known modern example of this process in the West is the formation of the Dust Bowl in the Mid-west of the USA in the 1930s. This was caused by the agglomeration of farms, the removal of hedgerows and over-intensive agriculture – not by natural causes.

The phenomenon of desertification is not new: it played a role in the downfall of the Sumerian, Babylonian and Roman civilizations.

Key Facts

- About 3,500 million hectares of land – an area the size of North and South America combined – are affected by desertification. A quarter to a half of this land has suffered productivity losses of at least 25%.
- Every year about 6 million hectares of land are irretrievably lost to desertification, and a further 21 million hectares are so degraded that crop production becomes uneconomic.
- The rural population affected by serious desertification (i.e., 25 to 50% loss of land productivity) rose from 57 million people in 1977 to 135 million in 1984.
- The situation is likely to become extremely critical in the rain-fed croplands by the year 2000, and to be little better elsewhere.
- Desertification causes annual losses of about $26 billion compared to the $4.5 billion a year needed to control it – about three-quarters of what is needed is being spent, but the remaining quarter is crucial.
- Although more money is needed, the most successful attempts to control desertification have been cheap, local, small in scale and run by those personally affected.
- The technical solutions, such as reforestation, improved farming techniques and better land use, are well known and have been successfully applied in many areas.
- In spite of this, the battle is being lost . . . a massive new effort to control desertification is required if declining productivity, erosion, famine and political chaos are to be avoided.

Source: UNEP, *Sands of Change*, UNEP Environment Brief No. 2, 1987

Much of the Sahara Desert, for example, was at one time well vegetated and highly populated, with flourishing forests and plains supporting a good variety of wild game. What is new, however, is the scale on which it is occurring, and the threat that is posed for the future.

Areas affected

A World Map of Desertification was prepared at the time of the United Nations Conference on Desertification (1977). This showed that 2 per cent of Europe, 19 per cent of America, 31 per cent of Asia, 34 per cent of Africa and 75 per cent of Australia were at risk from desertification. The highest risk areas included parts of California, Chile, Argentina, north-east Brazil, large parts of Africa, Iraq, Pakistan, Turkey, Spain and north-west Australia.

Desertification around the world

	Range-lands	Crop-lands	Irrigated land	Forest and woodland	Ground-water
Sudano-Sahelian Africa	●	●	●	●	●
Southern Africa	●	●	●	●	—
North Africa	●	●	●	●	●
Western Asia	●	●	●	●	●
South Asia	●	●	●	●	—
Asian USSR	√	√	√	√	?
China, Mongolia	√	●	√	●	?
Australia	—	—	●	—	—
Mediterranean Europe	—	●	√	√	—
South America	●	●	●	●	●
Mexico	—	●	●	●	●
North America	√	√	√	√	●

● desertification accelerating   — static   √ improving

Source: UNEP, *Sands of Change*, UNEP Environment Brief No. 2, 1987.

In human terms, desertification is a tragedy mainly affecting those who can least afford it: people in low-income developing countries, in areas already climatically, geographically and economically disadvantaged. Agriculture in these countries is often the main source of jobs, income and Gross National Product, so the effects of desertification can lead to famine and political turmoil. After the drought of the early 1970s, every government fell in the affected Sahel countries.

A large number of people are at risk. Severe desertification currently affects more than 135 million, but some 850 million people live in the world's dry lands, of which more than 500 million are rural dwellers. More than half of these are already affected by at least moderate desertification. UNEP identifies three susceptible areas – rangelands (i.e., grazing for livestock), croplands watered by rain, and croplands watered by irrigation.

The rangelands are the worst affected of dryland areas, with 80 per cent of the total 3,700 million hectares already suffering from desertification. The rangelands have a comparatively small population – 66 million (see diagram below). Of the other areas, 60 per cent of rainfed cropland and 30 per cent of irrigated croplands are at least moderately affected by desertification.

rangeland
total area 3700 million hectares   80% at least moderately desertified
total population 66 million

| 23 | 25 |

at risk from moderate desertification
at risk from severe desertification
(millions)

rainfed cropland
570 million hectares 60% at least moderately desertified
total population 260 million

| | 82 | | 90 | |

irrigated cropland
131 million hectares 30% at least moderately desertified
total population 175 million

| 40 | 20 |

Populations at risk

Source: UNEP, *Sands of Change*, UNEP Environment Brief, No. 2, 1987

Effects of desertification

For the rural poor in the affected areas, survival depends on the success of a few crops or the sale of a few animals. As productivity of the land falls, their living conditions worsen. Crops fail, water sources dry up, animals die and fuelwood becomes more difficult to obtain. Grass becomes exhausted, farmers move on to areas previously considered infertile, water sources become polluted with silt and salt. The area becomes too degraded for continued use, and the people move elsewhere.

Migration is the only solution for the affected populations. During the Sahel drought of the early 1970s, nearly a million 'environmental refugees' fled from Upper Volta (now Burkina Faso). Half a million fled from Mali. The victims of desertification in Central America and Haiti moved to the United States; in India, they went to the Punjab; in Brazil, where in the north-east desertification threatens an area the size of Western Europe, they flock to Rio de Janeiro and São Paolo, cities which are already grossly overcrowded.

The Sahel   The Sahel (Arabic for 'shore'), also described as the Sahelian region, is the area of semi-arid lands bordering the southern Sahara: Mauritania, Mali, Burkina Faso, Niger, Chad, Senegal, Ghana, Cameroon, Nigeria and the Central African Republic. It first came to world attention in the drought of the early 1970s, when between 50,000 and 250,000 people died.

The intensity of the drought, according to some observers, may have been exacerbated by the expansion of the groundnut (i.e., peanut) cash crop in Niger and other Sahelian countries in the 1960s. The amount of fallow land in the agricultural zone shrank rapidly: nomadic pastoralists had to increase their grazing in the marginal lands of the north. This caused further desertification, and increased the nomads' exposure to the effects of the drought.

Since 1977, desertification over much of the area has worsened, especially in Chad, Mali, Mauritania, the Niger and Senegal, even though some $200 million has been spent on reforestation. More specific projects, such as sand dune stabilization, have had some success.

The area is one of the poorest in the world, with per capita incomes of less than $400 per year. Life expectancy is below 50 years. Most Sahel countries have large debts and severe shortages of foreign exchange. Populations are increasing by 2–3 per cent annually, with widespread migration to the cities. By the year 2000, urban populations in Chad, Mali, the Niger, Mauritania, Senegal and Burkina Faso are expected to be 11.8 million, a 224 per cent increase over 1975.

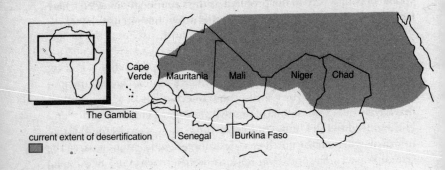

The Sahel

Source: UNEP, *Sands of Change*, UNEP Environment Brief, No. 2, 1987

The Sahel is an example of the circular nature of desertification. Pressure for land leads to over-intensive use, which leads to land loss: as a result, the pressure increases on the remaining agricultural areas.

Future prospects

The Sahel disaster of the early 1970s prompted the United Nations Conference on Desertification in Nairobi, Kenya, in 1977. Erik Eckholm, in *Down to Earth* (1982), provides a lucid commentary on the reasons for the conference and its outcome. Development experts rushed in famine relief to the Sahel in 1972 and 1973, but realized at the time that deeper forces than a drop in rainfall were undermining the region. Development patterns over recent decades were obviously out of kilter with the zone's ecological limits: the result was a degeneration of natural resources, and a rising vulnerability to drought.

The UN conference brought together technical experts and senior diplomats who made a number of recommendations. Central to these was the need to spend $48 billion in developing countries over the next 20 years, to rehabilitate all damaged irrigated lands, half the affected rangeland, and three-quarters of rainfed croplands. Two million hectares of sand dunes were to be stabilized too.

The year 2000 was set as the goal for halting desertification, but that target is now, a decade after the UN conference, seen as impossible to achieve. The international community has not responded as urgently to the problem as the situation demanded: there has been some investment in the affected areas, but often of the wrong type and in insufficient quantity.

As Eckholm says, governments in the developed and developing worlds prefer short-term, instant schemes to the long-term plans necessary to stabilize rainfed croplands. A new irrigation project can be shown to the investors: a stabilization scheme is 'only' the maintenance of something that is already there.

In addition to this, desertification is not just a problem that can be solved with knowledge and money: it is linked to basic patterns of national life, and its solution requires difficult political and cultural reforms. There is also an international dimension. It is difficult for the African countries to make long-term plans when their income depends on the uncertainties of the international commodities markets. As Paul Harrison comments in *The Greening of Africa* (1987), 'In the long run, speedy advances in Africa will require changes in the world economic order' (see NORTH–SOUTH RELATIONSHIP).

It is difficult to forecast, ten years after desertification surfaced at international level, whether the problem will be adequately solved and if so, when. As an environmental issue, it has a low priority in the industrialized countries: there are not many books about the issue in comparison with the wealth of material in other areas, and the campaigning organizations are underfunded and stretched by the scale of the problem and its long-term nature.

The United Nations Environment Programme says that the battle is being lost, and a massive new effort is called for. Analyses of the situation since 1977 indicate that it is worsening, with the possibilities of even greater devastation. In 1982 Dr Tolba, executive director of UNEP, wrote: 'There is no doubt that the process of desertification is accelerating, with millions of hectares of arable land being lost every year.' Desertification can be countered, given an international commitment to its solution. This commitment has not yet become a reality.

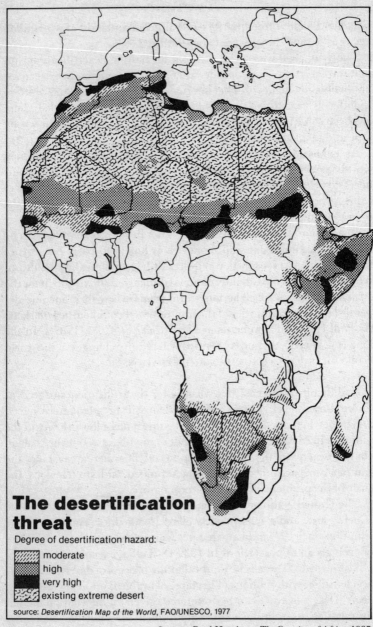

The desertification
threat

Degree of desertification hazard:

- moderate
- high
- very high
- existing extreme desert

source: *Desertification Map of the World*, FAO/UNESCO, 1977

Source: Paul Harrison, *The Greening of Africa*, 1987

See also DEFORESTATION; NORTH–SOUTH RELATIONSHIP; POPULATION

REFERENCES

Eckholm, Erik, *Down to Earth*, Pluto Press, 1982.

Grainger, Alan, *Desertification*, Earthscan, 1982.

Harrison, Paul, *The Greening of Africa*, Paladin, 1987.

International Commission on Humanitarian Issues, *The Encroaching Desert*, Zed Books, 1986.

UNEP, *Environmental Data Report*, Basil Blackwell, 1987.

UNEP, *Sands of Change*, UNEP Environment Brief No. 2, 1987.

World Resources Institute, IIED, *World Resources 1986*, Basil Books, 1986.

CONTACTS

Green Deserts

International Institute for Environment and Development (IIED)

Oxfam

Save the Children

United Nations Economic Programme (UNEP)

United Nations Food and Agriculture Organization (FAO)

War on Want

Energy

ENERGY CONSERVATION

Conventional systems for producing and using energy deplete the earth's natural resources and cause large-scale problems with pollution. Energy conservation makes energy go further, saves money, produces greater efficiency and protects the environment.

Energy loss

Current systems for producing energy are extremely wasteful. Britain's power stations, for example, lose more energy than is gained from the entire output of North Sea gas. Less than 40 per cent of the energy released by burning fuel in these stations is actually converted into useful electricity, the rest being transmitted into exhaust gases or cooling water. Eight to 10 per cent is lost during the transmission and distribution of the electricity.

The energy flow chart for the UK shows how much is wasted in converting primary energy into useful energy. Thirty per cent of the initial fuel is lost in the conversion and distribution process, needed to turn the base substances into items such as petrol, diesel oil, coke, etc.; an additional 30 per cent is lost when the processed fuel is used in badly insulated buildings, gas-guzzling vehicles and inefficient appliances.

Of the initial energy source, only two-fifths is finally used.

The reason for this is historical. Most of the buildings and machinery that we use now were designed some time ago, when coal and oil were regarded as so cheap as to be not worth conserving. This attitude is changing rapidly.

Oil used to be regarded as a basic cheap necessity that could be taken for granted, like water or sand. This perception changed with the oil price rises in the 1970s: and as oil prices rose, so did those of

Energy flow in the UK 1985

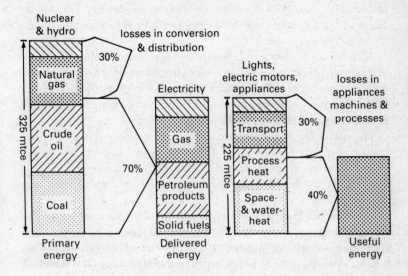

Source: Michael Flood, *Energy Without End*, FoE, 1986

other basic fuels like coal and gas. Countries began to realize that energy efficiency, and energy conservation, could save them millions of dollars. From an environmental point of view, this realization had fortunate consequences. The best way to minimize pollution is not to produce it in the first place.

The general philosophy in Britain has not reflected changing attitudes towards energy conservation that can be detected elsewhere round the globe. The UK agrees with the principle that energy conservation is a good thing, but not to the extent of putting large amounts of money into it. Most companies, for example, place capital investment for energy conservation at the bottom of their list of priorities. This lack of financial commitment is also shared by the government.

Conservation as an alternative to construction

The benefits to be gained from an efficient programme of energy conservation are enormous. Britain's total energy bill is approximately £40 billion (1988 Department of Energy figure), of which about 20 per cent, according to the government's own analysis, could be easily eliminated. The savings involved would be more than £8,000 million per year. (Government scientists at the Energy Technology Support Unit reckon that the energy cut, and the financial savings, could be twice this size.)

Apart from a public relations campaign encouraging people to insulate their houses and switch off lights, however, the UK government has not succeeded in prioritizing energy conservation. The year of the 'Monergy' campaign launch, 1986, saw an increase of 2.7 per cent in the use of primary fuels.

The reason for this lack of success is partly connected with the price of fuel, and partly structural. When oil prices quadrupled in the 1970s, economic pressure forced the UK to be prudent with its use of the fuel. With the oil price fall in the 1980s, the motivation was removed.

Our current complacency is, however, very short-sighted. The collapse in oil price was due to a number of temporary causes – the Iran–Iraq war, the collapse of OPEC, the strange enthusiasm of the UK for offloading oil at bargain prices at a time when the world oil price was falling – and will not continue in the long term. Oil is a commodity with very small available reserves (see below) and prices will certainly rise again.

The second reason for the failure of the government's conservation initiative is structural, and connected with the way our energy utilities are organized: it is not in the interests of the three big energy sectors – electricity, gas, and oil – to limit the outputs of their product. The corporate interests of all three sectors lie in greater, *not* reduced, national energy consumption.

If the Central Electricity Generating Board, for example, foresees an increase in energy demand over the next ten years, its only suggested remedy is to build a power station. It is not perceived as the job of the CEGB to meet extra demand by better conserving the existing supply; and in its publications and public statements, the institution judges its corporate success on the increased electricity output it can achieve. The same criterion – size of output – is used to judge the success of the oil companies and the gas business.

In the USA, however, things are seen differently. US power stations are commercial organizations that have to justify expenditure to their shareholders. Construction of a billion-dollar power station is an expenditure that needs to be carefully justified. The assumption is not made – as it is in the UK – that this construction is automatically a good thing.

In many States (New York, Massachusetts and California, for example) utilities are also required by their supervisory boards to present an analysis of all investment options, including energy conservation, before building new plant. Choosing the 'Least Cost Option' can be environmentally beneficial: in many cases it makes more commercial sense to meet an excess of energy demand over supply by conserving energy rather than bearing the cost of a new power station. This approach treats energy conservation as an energy source – i.e., a certain amount of investment will produce specific financial returns. In many cases, the return achieved from conservation is more than the return achieved from conventional sources. The environmental benefits are also considerable.

- *State of the World 1986* describes how the Pacific Gas and Electricity Company of northern California has provided $168 million to its customers in zero-interest loans in order to install specific conservation systems. It expects to spend $1 billion over the next decade, save at least $3 billion dollars in plant construction, and reduce peak power use by 1,900 megawatts.
- The Florida Power and Light Company aims for a similar peak reduction between 1982 and 1992: it has performed energy audits on 300,000 homes and encouraged the replacement of 50,000 inefficient air-cooling and heating systems. It aims to reduce peak power demand by 2,100 megawatts between 1982 and 1992 – 16 per cent of the company's current generating capacity.
- The federally-owned Bonneville Power Administration invests in energy conservation as a more cost-effective alternative to new sources of supply and says: 'Our energy efficiency programmes mean that we do not anticipate needing any new power plant until 2003. Without this conservation effort, we would need new capacity as soon as 1990.' As an example of conservation producing financial returns, Bonneville cites its co-funding of conservation measures with its local aluminium smelters – high-demand electricity users whose viability, and therefore electricity use – fluctuated as the world price of aluminium rose or fell. The conservation measures meant that the plants used less electricity, but were more efficient,

and therefore less likely to close in adverse market conditions. Their electricity use became more constant and predictable – thus more profitable from the utility's point of view.

- A 1983 study by the Investor Responsibility Research Center found that 72 per cent of the USA's utilities have formal energy conservation programmes. The 120 utilities surveyed said that their peak load can be reduced by 30,000 megawatts during the next decade, saving $19 billion in avoided construction, for an outlay of only $6 billion. The programmes combine energy audits, home weatherproofing schemes, and cash rebates for the purchase of energy-efficient appliances.

This kind of energy conservation is already producing large financial savings: it makes better economic sense to use power stations as fully as possible, rather than have plant standing idle, waiting for the period of peak demand. The initiative did require a certain departure, on the part of the power utilities, from their traditional role. In the UK, however, the idea of the Central Electricity Generating Board, or its privatized successors, funding customers to conserve electricity is inconceivable.

Our electricity sector has a very traditional response to climbing demand for energy: build more power stations. The only solution to meeting peak demand is to have a 'reserve supply' of power stations, with a total capacity to produce far more electricity than is routinely needed. This is an expensive solution to the problem. The cost of building a large power station is currently between £1,500 and £2,000 million.

Possibilities for conservation

Energy efficiency　In the UK, one kilowatt-hour of electricity costs around 5.6 pence if it comes from the mains, nearly £100 from a transistor battery. If this kind of information were more widely known, people would be less enthusiastic about buying batteries.

'Energy efficiency' is a concept that would-be purchasers apply to cars (how many miles does it do to the gallon?) but to few other appliances. Over the working life of a refrigerator, for example, the consumer will pay more money for electricity than the fridge cost in the first place.

Refrigerators vary in energy efficiency, and some use as little as one-eighth the electricity of others. If the consumer knew which were the more energy-efficient machines, then the total price of using the machine over its working life could be considerably reduced.

On a national scale, there would be large-scale energy savings. According to evidence presented to the House of Commons Environment Committee, Britain's fridges and freezers have an electricity consumption equivalent to the output of two or three Sizewell B nuclear power stations. Even a 10 per cent reduction in this electricity demand would be enormous. This could be achieved by a system of energy-labelling for fridges, and better industry standards. The Association for the Conservation of Energy looked at three energy sectors in 1988 – lighting, domestic refrigeration, and industrial electric motors. If only the most energy-efficient of these appliances were used – by selection from those models already on the market – then the national electricity saving would be in the order of 11 per cent, or four Hinckley 'C' nuclear power stations.

Energy efficiency in household appliances is already improving. The new jug kettles, for example, are more energy-efficient than the traditional electric kettle. Average efficiency of household appliances in the US has increased by 20 to 30 per cent in the last five years, and in Japan it has increased by 50 per cent.

There is still a long way to go, however. The American Council for an Energy-Efficient Economy reckon that newly developed highly efficient devices have not yet found their way into most homes or long-term energy planning scenarios. If gradually introduced, these technologies could free up power supplies for under 2 cents per kilowatt-hour – less than one-fifth of the generating cost of new power plants.

Combined heat and power Consumption of electricity can be made more efficient – and the same is true of its production. One of the best-known ways of improving conventional power stations' efficiency is by using their waste heat for local industry or local housing. Hot water is piped direct from the power station into factories and homes, for a very small extra cost.

Combined Heat and Power (CHP) stations generate electricity less efficiently than conventional power stations: but, because the heat they produce is also used, their overall efficiency can be as high as 70 to 80 per cent, or twice as efficient as electricity-only plant.

CHP is a proven technology. In *Energy Without End* (1986), Michael Flood points out that outside the UK, CHP-district schemes are commonplace, with major installations in Berlin, Budapest, Copenhagen, Hamburg, Helsinki, Milan, Munich, Odense, Oslo, Paris, Rotterdam, Stockholm, Vienna, Warsaw, Moscow and New York.

CHP, and district heating schemes, are not unknown in the UK. According to Flood, CHP currently provides about 15 per cent of the electricity for UK industry. District heating supplies space-heating (i.e., heats rooms and water-heating) for 1 per cent of the population. Several thousand schemes are already in operation, although only a few provide heat as a by-product of electricity generation.

A 1979 Department of Energy paper concluded that CHP could be the cheapest long-term method of providing heat and power for industry, and heat for buildings in cities. Energy Paper No. 35 stated that the technology 'could eventually provide 30 per cent of Britain's space and hot water needs and save up to the equivalent of 30 million tonnes of coal per year'.

CHP has not made the advances that would be expected in the UK, given that the country is well suited to its potential (two-thirds of the population living in towns and cities with high heat load densities). The sixth report of the House of Commons Energy Committee, published in 1985, laid the blame for this on the electricity industry:

Witnesses made the point in evidence that CHP/DH would not succeed as long as the heat production, distribution and sale were looked on as second-ary activities to electricity generation. At the heart of the problem facing those who are attempting to get such schemes off the ground is the continued existence of this attitude of 'product and by-product' in the electricity supply industry . . . As long as this attitude prevails amongst the institutions with the real power to promote CHP, then this orphan technology will be prevented from coming into its inheritance.

Recycling   John McCormick's book *The User's Guide to the Environment* (1986) provides a very useful overview of the rationale for recycling. The 'consumer society' sprang up after the Second World War, and with it our habit of buying something, using it once and then throwing it away. The process, as McCormick points out, involves a continual depletion of natural resources, and an overuse of energy supplies. Throwing away an aluminium beer can or a copy of *The Times* has been likened to pouring away the equivalent of a beer can half filled with petrol.

In addition to saving resources and energy, recycling is less polluting. The production of iron, steel and aluminium produces more air pollution than their recycling. And recycling of all types reduces land and water pollution. Nearly 90 per cent of all Britain's municipal waste is buried in landfill: this has caused problems of leaching (i.e., leakage) into nearby water bodies (see CHEMICAL WASTES).

Recycling covers a number of different areas:

- *Paper* More than one-third of the world's annual commercial wood harvest is turned into paper, of which one-quarter is recycled. This figure could be doubled in the next fifteen years. Britain currently recycles about one-third of its paper, not as much as the world's leaders – Japan, Mexico, Spain and The Netherlands, which recycle 40 to 50 per cent – but average in European terms.
- *Glass* *The Recycler's Guide to Greater London* (1986) makes the point that Britain recycles only 13 per cent of its bottles, even though its 210,000 tonnes of glass recycled in 1985 was a record figure. Recycling is not the most efficient way of using glass – reusing bottles, as is common for milk and some brands of beer, is more efficient than recycling – but is much more useful than just throwing them away. Britain's Bottle Bank scheme was launched in 1977: a 1985 Directive from the EC requiring member states to increase the amount of refillable and recycled containers in use should continue the momentum.

  Denmark has an interesting system. Aluminium cans are not allowed to be sold, nor are non-standard bottles. All drinks have to be marketed in one of thirty bottle types, which are returnable for a deposit. Any shop which sells bottled drink has to accept returned bottles, whether or not the shop was the point of sale. This system significantly reduces the amount of glass thrown away as refuse – and the amount of broken glass turning up in the countryside and on beaches.
- *Aluminium* The US Environmental Protection Agency estimates that re-using aluminium cans saves 95 per cent of the energy used for making new aluminium and causes 95 per cent less air pollution. Twenty tons of aluminium can be recycled for the same amount of energy needed to make one tonne of new metal from bauxite – and

aluminium can be recycled over and over again. In the UK, can collection schemes are starting up, with all-aluminium cans having a scrap price of about 1p each. In Britain 3,800 million cans are used annually for drinks packaging alone (half of which are pure aluminium): aluminium can collection could be a useful source of fundraising for charitable organizations.

● *Rubbish* The Warmer Campaign has been pressing vigorously for an increase in the use of rubbish as fuel. Every year, Britain dumps 30 million tonnes of rubbish in holes in the ground: it could be used instead to generate electricity, create heat for industrial purposes, or heat hospitals, schools, public buildings or even whole districts. The UK currently recycles around 6 per cent of its waste to provide energy. Other countries do more than this.

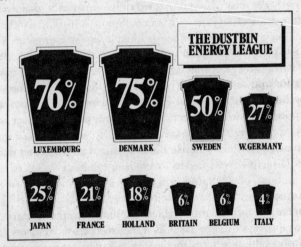

Some international comparisons: percentage of national waste used to produce energy.
Source: *The Warmer Bulletin*, September 1985.

The point has been made that in environmental terms waste recycling can be more efficient than combustion: the Warmer Campaign has included recycling as one of the options in its technology. Whether recycling is included in the scheme or not, producing energy from waste is a much more useful system than just dumping it in the ground, provided that harmful substances are not transmitted into the air in the combustion process. Waste combustion can be economically attractive. Incineration incorporating Combined Heat and

Power came top in a feasibility study for the London Boroughs of Greenwich, Lewisham and Southwark, which currently send 240,000 tonnes of rubbish a year to be landfilled. The rubbish incineration scheme was even cheaper than landfilling.

Conservation possibilities for Britain

In 1981, EC comparisons of how much energy was used for a unit of productive value showed Britain to be one of the worst performers in the Community. In 1984, a comparison of energy/Gross Domestic Product ratios by the International Energy Agency showed the UK as 11th out of 12, a position which had only slightly improved by 1989.

Some suggestions for improved UK energy have been made above: energy efficiency, Combined Heat and Power, recycling of materials, energy conservation funded by electricity generation utilities. There are other possibilities:

Third-party financing   Much used in the US, this involves an energy-conservation firm approaching a company, doing an energy audit, paying for and installing energy conservation systems, guaranteeing the savings to be achieved, and bearing the financial burden should it not produce the desired effect. The company pays back the cost of the service over an agreed time-period.

The number of companies offering this type of service increased tenfold in the USA in the period 1983–5.

Increased machine efficiency   According to figures presented by Earth Resources Research at the Sizewell Inquiry, industrial electric motors account for 25 per cent of the UK's national electricity use – and they lose almost half the energy they use in producing the final mechanical drive. Application of controls and variable drives could lead to much increased efficiency.

Home Energy Surveys   Experience in the USA and Denmark has shown that, given the right information and incentives, householders will take measures to improve the energy efficiency of their homes. The information needs to be provided by a qualified energy auditor. Forty per cent of Danish homes have to date been surveyed. The scheme is wholly self-financing, but needed financial commitment from the government when it began.

In the UK, over 20 million homes consume £10,000 million worth of fuel every year. The Association of Metropolitan Authorities has pointed out that, while most houses have some loft insulation, less than one-sixth of the total have it sufficiently to match current proposed standards. Up to 20 per cent of a house's heat is lost through an inadequately insulated roof.

Improved grant schemes for low-income householders   The USA has operated a federal grant scheme for low-income householders, which gives an average of $1,600 per dwelling – at no cost to the consumer – to allow comprehensive energy conservation measures to be installed. The rationale behind this is that it makes economic nonsense to provide financial assistance for fuel bills without making similar assistance available for conservation. In the UK, the DHSS provides fuel allowances for approximately 2.25 million homes, at an estimated £1,400 million a year. As no attempt is made at improving energy conservation in these houses, beyond a small grant for loft insulation – soon to be withdrawn – this fuel allowance goes, literally, up the chimney.

ENERGY SUPPLY

'Energy supply' is frequently thought of as 'electricity supply'. This, however, describes only part of the picture. 'Energy' in the context of 'world energy supply' means the wherewithal to clothe, feed, warm, transport, accommodate and provide for the population of the globe. The raw materials that power this chain of events are referred to as 'primary energy supply' – oil, coal, natural gas, hydroelectricity, nuclear power, biomass (wood, charcoal, dung, crop wastes, etc.), and renewable energy sources such as solar and wind power.

World use of energy is enormous, with rapidly increased demand over the last few decades, and a likely further rise for the foreseeable future. Total world energy consumption more than doubled between 1930 and 1960, and more than doubled again between 1960 and 1984.

Energy production and usage directly affects the environment by depleting natural resources, releasing gases and metals on combustion, causing waste disposal problems and giving rise to large-scale marine or land contamination. All the major sources of primary energy production have environmental consequences, though some are much more environmentally harmful than others.

Increasing consumption of energy, and shifts in reliance on specific energy sources, are occurring in most countries of the world. Technologies previously considered as 'alternative' are now being seen in a much more favourable light, and are being adopted on a commercial scale.

World energy use

There are wide variations between different bodies as to the estimated size of world energy consumption. According to the United Nations Environment Programme's *Environmental Data Report*, the world in 1960 consumed 115,009 petajoules of energy. By 1986 this had increased to 288,367 – a rise of 150 per cent in 26 years.

The rise was not caused solely by population growth. Over the 24 years, there was a 44 per cent increase in per capita energy consumption. Individuals are consuming more, at the same time as the number of individuals is climbing very fast.

In the industrialized world, this demand is being met by three main sources of energy supply – oil, coal and natural gas, which between them provide more than nine-tenths of world energy supply, again according to UNEP figures. Hydroelectricity is responsible for 2.6 per cent, and nuclear power 1.3 per cent (these figures are low, in comparison to others that have been published: *Energy Without End*, for example, allocates 77 per cent of energy use to coal, oil and gas; 14.5 per cent to biomass; 5.7 per cent hydroelectric; and 3.3 per cent nuclear).

Of the big three, according to UNEP, oil provides nearly half, coal almost a third, and gas one-fifth of world supply.

Total world energy production, 1983

Oil 45.1%   Coal 30.2%   Gas 20.7%   Hydro 2.6%
Nuclear 1.3%

Source: UNEP, *Environmental Data Report*, 1987

Figures for world energy supply are confusing, as they often refer to different energy sectors. Energy *consumption* is different from energy *production*, as there is frequently an energy loss between the two. The data for *commercial* energy consumption differ from that for *world* consumption, as the former is a part of the latter. Figures for world *electricity* supply are different from world *energy* supply, for the same reason.

Most global figures for energy production also ignore the part played by biomass, because wood, crop wastes and dung are frequently gathered rather than bought, so are difficult to quantify. Biomass plays a significant part in the economies of several developing countries, however, contributing 90 per cent of the energy consumption of countries such as Malawi and Mozambique, and more than a third of the consumption of Brazil, India and Peru.

Michael Flood, in *Energy Without End*, estimates that biomass provides about one-seventh of the world's primary energy. Biomass is thus important, because – apart from the obvious reason that it keeps millions of people alive and warm – an energy source on this scale means that depletion rates of oil, coal and gas are less than they would be otherwise. Biomass can also have environmental implications (see DEFORESTATION).

In energy terms, as in the use of most of the world's resources, the inhabitants of the developed world take the lion's share. According to the World Bank, the US leads the world in per capita energy consumption, with each individual consuming 400 times the commercial energy used by the smallest consumer, the average Ethiopian;

Per capita commercial energy consumption, in kg of oil equivalent, selected countries, 1985

USA	7,278	Argentina	1,468	China	515
USSR	4,885	Mexico	1,290	Pakistan	218
FRG	4,451	Algeria	1,123	India	201
UK	3,603	Malaysia	826	Kenya	103
Japan	3,116	Brazil	781	Ethiopia	17

Source: World Bank, *World Development Report*, 1987

World energy resources

Supplies of oil and gas are running out. This was appreciated with some intensity in the developed world during the 1970s, when two massive oil price rises concentrated minds on energy conservation and fuel switching. In the late 1980s, however, the drop in oil prices has reversed that feeling of urgency.

UNEP estimates that we are using up available reserves of oil at a rate of 3.2 per cent per year, and natural gas at a rate of 1.7 per cent per year. This means that the world will run out of exploitable oil in 31 years, and of gas in 58.

This is acknowledged as a tentative figure. Other sources give different projections, but within the same short-term range. The conservation commission of the World Energy Conference estimated in 1986 that the world will be running out of oil and gas by the year 2020, unless new and large supplies are discovered (they also thought that supplies of uranium would become critical at the same time).

World Resources 1986 reckons that oil production could continue at its present level until some time between 2025 and 2050, but would then drop off sharply; and natural gas should be able to maintain its current output for several decades.

The Worldwatch Institute calculate that ultimate depletion of world oil resources is between 50 and 88 years away.

There is a possibility that large oil and gas fields are yet to be discovered, although in the case of oil, more than three-quarters of the world's sedimentary areas have been explored. Although the exact date of oil and gas depletion remains the subject of discussion, the principle remains – they are going to run out, probably in the first half of the next century.

The world does have abundant supplies of coal – but it may not be wise to burn them, because of the increasing carbon dioxide build-up in the atmosphere. Carbon dioxide release is unavoidable when coal, oil, or gas is burnt: and the quantities emitted so far, together with pollution from other sources, are already large enough to cause an increase in the world's average temperature (see GREENHOUSE EFFECT).

International concern about the world's climate has grown remarkably during the 1980s. The Montreal Agreement of 1987 (see OZONE LAYER) was the first reflection of global anxiety about what is happening to the world's upper atmosphere. As knowledge increases, it becomes more likely that the use of fuels like coal and oil, which contribute towards the greenhouse effect, will be voluntarily phased out.

This means that there are serious problems with all three principal sources of primary energy. Oil and gas are in relatively short supply, and the use of coal may be discouraged around the world for climatic reasons. Fuels derived from coal – such as the 'new' coal gas -- are still in the development stage, and have not yet passed the test of commercial application or environmental acceptability.

The two smaller energy sources are not about to step into the gap. Hydroelectric power has been successful in smaller installations, and has been used in countries such as Iceland where there are a number of fast-flowing rivers. On the other hand, not all countries have this kind of natural resource, and hydro power has come under criticism. The environmental degradation, and inefficiency in operation, of

---

The language of energy

Abbreviation	Item measured	Explanation
Mtce	National energy	= million tonnes of coal equivalent. A million tonnes of coal theoretically produces a certain amount of heat. Other forms of energy are measured in coal equivalent, or sometimes oil equivalent. 1 tonne of coal is equivalent to 0.59 tonnes of oil, 700 cubic metres of gas.
J	energy	= joule. Mtce is rather imprecise because there is a wide range of heat content in coal. The joule is an internationally recognized, and precisely defined unit of energy – though rather a small one. There are 26.6 million billion joules in a million tonnes of coal. This would usually be written as 26.6 PJ.

PJ	energy	= petajoule = a million billion joules.
W	rate at which energy is supplied	= watt. 'Power' is the rate at which energy is used or delivered. A watt is a joule per second.
kW	rate at which energy is supplied	= kilowatt = a thousand watts. A single-bar electric fire delivers one thousand watts of energy, or one kilowatt.
MW	rate at which energy is supplied	= megawatt = a million watts. A large power station can supply 500 to 600 MW from one turbine. Three such plants grouped together means the station has a capability of 1,500 to 1,800 MW.
GW	rate at which energy is supplied	= gigawatt = a thousand megawatts.
kWh	energy use over 1 hour	= kilowatt-hour. If the electric fire burns for one hour, it supplies 1 kWh of electrical energy. kWh is usually used to indicate the cost of a system for producing electricity. Cost comparisons between different systems of electricity production are usually made by comparing the cost in pence per kWh.
GWh	energy use over 1 hour	= gigawatt-hour = a million kilowatt-hours. A million one-bar electric fires burning for one hour supply 1 GWh of energy.
TWh	energy use over 1 hour	= terawatt-hour = thousand million kilowatt-hours.

Source: adapted from Michael Flood, *Energy Without End*, 1986 mega-schemes funded in the Third World by the large financial agencies has made multilateral agencies more wary of hydro power.

Nuclear power has been discredited in all but a few countries as too expensive and too dangerous (see NUCLEAR ENERGY).

Thus, within the lifetime of the current generation, there is a likelihood that the sources of energy commonplace today will have run out or become unusable. The nature of world energy production will have to change. Certain countries have already recognized this, and are investing in energy technologies such as energy conservation, solar power, wind energy and fuel cells.

Energy in the UK

1. Inland consumption of primary fuels (in million tonnes of coal or coal equivalent)

	1960	1970	1980	1986
Coal	198.6	156.9	120.8	113.5 (33.9%)
Petroleum	68.1	150.0	121.4	112.6 (33.6%)
Natural gas	0.1	17.9	71.1	83.6 (24.9%)
Nuclear electricity	0.9	9.5	13.4	21.3 (6.4%)
Hydroelectricity	1.7	2.3	2.0	2.4 (0.7%)
Electricity imports	—	—	—	1.7 (0.5%)

2. Fuel used for electricity generation (in millions of tonnes of coal or coal equivalent)

	1981–2	1982–3	1983–4	1984–5	1985–6
Coal	85.22	80.77	82.29	42.78	86.05
Oil (firing)	8.21	6.66	6.64	38.33	5.29
Oil (lighting up)	1.61	1.66	1.67	7.00	1.76
Natural gas	—	—	—	0.66	0.21
Nuclear	12.22	15.33	16.47	19.08	19.68
Hydro	1.90	2.20	1.95	1.48	1.95
Other	0.23	0.17	0.14	1.37	0.17
Total	109.39	106.79	109.17	110.17	115.12

Source: DEn, *Digest of United Kingdom Energy Statistics*, 1987

RENEWABLE ENERGY

'Renewable energy' refers to those systems that can produce power without depleting the earth's natural resources. The technologies include solar, wind, tidal and wave energy, hydroelectricity, geothermal (i.e., heat from the earth's core), and some others.

The difference between conventional and renewable energy is that one is based on finite reserves, so will eventually run out; the other has the potential to continue indefinitely. There is a secondary difference, which is connected to the first: the conventional systems transfer a substance – coal, oil, or uranium – from one place in the environment into another, where it is refined, used, and dumped. Large amounts of pollution are deposited on land, in the air and in the sea. Renewables leave the natural resource as much as possible in its original state so that it can be used again.

Standard economic analysis has traditionally worked against the renewable option. A technology which is new, under-researched and underfunded is compared against an energy system that has had years of research and billions of pounds put into it: if the new technology cannot produce a basic unit of electricity as cheaply as the existing system, it is regarded as useless. This approach does not allocate an economic cost to the fact that the new system may be producing electricity with little damage to the environment, while the old favourite is responsible for wholesale degradation.

Even under this restrictive comparison, renewable energy is now a practical proposition. Hydroelectric power, for example, is already producing twice as much power around the globe as nuclear. Wind-power has been developed to the stage where it can deliver electricity more cheaply in certain circumstances than coal, oil or nuclear, and is being used for this purpose in the USA and Denmark. Wave-power is being produced in Norway at a price that also competes, though full-scale commercial introduction has not yet begun. Solar power is being used already to heat water in homes in Greece, Australia and the Middle East.

Renewable energy systems are usually smaller than their conventional alternatives, and less wasteful. It is a central tenet of the renewable philosophy that energy should be conserved wherever possible. This apparent statement of the obvious is not accepted by adherents to traditional technologies.

Renewable technologies

Wind energy   With the exception of hydroelectric power, wind energy is the most well-established of the new technologies. Until relatively recently, its development had been impeded by a lack of research and investment, but in the early 1980s, California decided to give tax relief to investors who produced renewable energy to be sold to the electricity utility.

The result was an enormous growth in the number of wind energy stations. In 1981, the state had 144, with a capacity of 7 megawatts. Four years later, there were 4,500, with a capacity of 1,014 megawatts.

In the initial rush, some of the schemes were impractical, but the technology improved so quickly that 500 megawatts per year were being installed by 1987 (*Guardian*, 24 April 1987) even after the tax breaks finished. The drop in world oil price temporarily removed the financial advantage of wind-power, but it will return.

In the UK, the Wind Energy Group was formed – a large industrial lobby, consisting of Taylor Woodrow, British Aerospace and GEC – which states confidently that wind energy can provide power more cheaply than coal or nuclear stations. In January 1983, at the start of the Sizewell Inquiry, the cheapest reliable wind turbine of a useful size would have cost around £2,500 per kilowatt. Today, British manufacturers say that, given a flow of orders, they can supply wind turbines with guaranteed performance and reliability for £800 per kilowatt or less.

The Californian experience bears this out. In four years, costs fell by more than two-thirds. If machines no better than those currently in use in California were to be used in the UK, they would produce electricity at a cost of little more than 2p per kilowatt-hour – two-thirds of the CEGB's rather optimistic estimate of the cost of electricity from Sizewell B nuclear power station.

The Danish government, which has profited by exporting wind machines to California, has announced that 10 per cent of national electricity needs will be met from renewable energy, including wind-power, by the year 2000.

The UK has expressed interest in wind technology. Research is now being funded to the tune of £4.3 million a year. This is less than one-thirtieth of the £145 million going into nuclear research (*Hansard*,

28 November 1988) but an improvement on the past. A number of wind stations have been opened for research purposes. The most recent, a 3-megawatt turbine built by the Wind Energy Group in the Orkneys, will produce enough power to supply 2,000 homes – the largest output of any turbine in the world. Official estimates are that up to 20 per cent of Britain's energy needs can be supplied by wind-power: this possibly underestimates its true potential.

Doubts about wind-power used to centre on reliability, though experience has shown that the problem of wind availability can be overcome by careful siting of the machines. The remaining problem, however, is aesthetics. Thousands of machines are needed to produce large-scale electricity, and there have been complaints in California about visual intrusion. Visual impact could be minimized by building the turbines offshore, screening them with trees, or attempting to place them in hidden locations.

In *Energy Without End* (1986), Michael Flood makes the point that conventional electricity systems are themselves extremely unattractive objects: oil rigs and coal-mines are not things of beauty, and neither are the 10,000 route miles of high voltage overhead cable supported by more than 40,000 large unsightly pylons. If we have become used to these, then maybe we would be able to accommodate the 6,000 large and medium-sized wind turbines that Flood reckons would be enough to meet one-fifth of Britain's electricity needs.

Alexi Clarke in *New Scientist* (May 1989) reckons that 10,000 to 20,000 medium- and large-sized turbines would meet between 10 and 20 per cent of the UK's energy needs. This sounds a lot, says Clarke, but he compares this also with the 40,000 electricity pylons, of which half are as tall (45 to 51 metres) as medium-sized turbines.

Wave energy   In 1982, the UK research programme into wave energy was wound down. An official government survey said that there was 'only a low probability of any design achieving an energy cost below 8p a unit in 1982 money values'.

In 1986, Norway unveiled its two prototype wave stations at Tofteshallen, which were producing electricity at 2.5p per unit (using the British system for calculating electricity cost). This is cheaper than power produced by coal, oil or nuclear-powered systems. Norway has now sold its technology to Portugal, Indonesia and Puerto Rico. The technology is still at an early stage – one of the stations at Tofteshallen was destroyed in a storm in December 1988.

In 1987, the UK government announced that Britain's first wave station would be built at Islay in the Inner Hebrides. The station, costing £230,000, will generate electricity at 4 to 5p per unit. This cost may be almost halved when serial production takes place.

The total resources of the Western seaboard have been estimated at more than twice Britain's current output of electricity. The UK has one of the best wave climates in the world. Given adequate funding, wave energy could provide a substantial section of British electricity production.

Tidal energy The Norwegian and British wave systems work through water rushing up a hollow column and powering a turbine. Tidal

Comparative tidal scheme performance (Estimates)

	Mean tidal range m	Barrage length m	Installed capacity MW	Annual energy output Gwh	Cost of energy p/kWh
Severn–Inner line	7.0	17,000	7,200	12,900	3.7
Severn – Outer line	6.0	20,000	12,000	19,700	4.3
Morecambe Bay	6.3	16,600	3,040	5,400	4.6
Solway Firth	5.5	30,000	5,580	10,050	4.9
Dee	5.95	9,500	800	1,250	6.4
Humber	4.1	8,300	1,200	2,010	7.0
Wash	4.45	19,600	2,760	4,690	7.2
Thames	4.2	9,000	1,120	1,370	8.3
Langstone Harbour	3.13	550	24	53	5.3
Padstow	4.75	550	28	55	4.2
Hamford Water	3.0	3,200	20	38	8.5
Loch Etive	1.95	350	28	55	11.7
Cromarty Firth	2.75	1,350	47	100	11.8
Dovey	2.90	1,300	20	45	72.
Loch Broom	3.15	500	29	42	13.9
Milford Haven	4.5	1,150	96	180	10.0
Mersey	6.45	1,750	620	1,320	3.6

Source: A. C. Baker, ICE Symposium Paper, October 1986

systems are much larger in scope, and involve impeding water flows in whole estuaries. As the tide ebbs, the motive power is used to produce electricity via a series of turbines.

There are six tidal stations in operation round the world, in China, the Soviet Union, Canada and France. The technology is proven and could produce enormous quantities of power. Schemes are being considered in the UK for several places, including the Severn estuary, the Mersey, Solway Firth, the Wash and Morecambe Bay. The Severn is the largest, with a potential of producing 5 per cent of our current national consumption of electricity at around 3p per unit.

The Royal Society for the Protection of Birds is extremely anxious about tidal schemes, as the area between low and high tide is an important feeding ground for any species of bird. Tidal schemes remove the availability of this habitat by more than 50 per cent, and the RSPB opposes the development of tidal power on the grounds that it would mean the death of thousands of waders and wildfowl. Seventeen per cent of Europe's pintail are threatened by the development of the Mersey barrage. Other threatened species include teal, dunlin and redshank.

Hydroelectric   Fifty large hydroelectric schemes and 20 smaller ones (mainly based in Scotland) together produce about 2 per cent of Britain's national electricity output. They also provide the cheapest electricity – according to the Central Electricity Generating Board, at 0.7p per unit. Many of the best British sites for large hydro schemes have already been developed.

Hydro power is very energy-efficient, with up to 90 per cent of the potential energy being converted into electricity. The schemes can pose problems in terms of river management, however, by reducing the water flow. Rivers also routinely carry silt downstream, which builds up in the hydro reservoir, reducing the amount of water available to drive the turbines. Each hydroelectric scheme has a finite life dependent on the rate at which its reservoirs silt up. This can be avoided by having a silt-clearing facility, but often the reservoirs are simply too large for this to be possible.

Hydro power is an extremely useful system for producing electricity. In *The Energy Question* (1982), Gerald Foley estimates that in Europe, some 80 per cent of the total potential for this technology has already been exploited; in America, about 60 per cent. Development in South America, Africa and Asia, however, is only about 20 per cent of potential – and as these areas are poor in coal and oil, this is a likely source of energy for the future.

There are limiting factors, however. Water is used for many purposes other than electricity generation, and it is not always practical to sacrifice irrigation, navigation and fishing in favour of electricity production. Hydro power can flood large areas of land, making them unusable; and many Third World countries feel that the high capital costs of large dams are not justified when they have so many other pressing problems to deal with.

The Gaia Atlas of Planet Management looks at the impact of the Aswan Dam in Egypt, a huge project that supplies enormous quantities of electricity. While the advantages of the scheme cannot be denied, disadvantages include the destruction of the offshore sardine fishery, the silting up of Lake Nasser, problems of waterlogging and soil salinity, and the spread of the water-based parasitic disease schistosomiasis. Thorough impact assessment schemes could have minimized many of these effects.

Solar energy   *Passive* solar energy is already saving fuel bills around the world. The heat from the sun warms buildings, thus reducing the need for fires or central heating. Passive solar features, including conservatories and glazed courtyards, trap heat very effectively. Houses can be designed to use this heat source: the Pennyland Estate in Milton Keynes has over 100 well-insulated passive solar houses, with large south-facing windows and good insulation. Heating bills have been reduced by 40 per cent, compared with equivalent-sized houses built to normal standards. The Milton Keynes houses cost 1 per cent more in construction costs, which was paid back in saved fuel bills in just two years.

Active solar systems trap heat from the sun and use it to heat water, which can be used to heat buildings. The UK receives enough heat from the sun in a year to provide most of the hot water and central heating necessary for a well-designed building. To date, this has proved impractical in the UK on a house-by-house basis because of the high costs. In order to survive in a small market, manufacturers have had to increase their profit margins.

Active solar heating is used in many countries, however. A large district-heating scheme in Uppsala, Sweden, has part of its heat requirements met by 4,500 square metres of solar flat plate collectors. Surplus heat is stored in rock, and then used to warm 550 dwellings. Uppsala is roughly at the same latitude as the Shetland Isles.

A number of countries are using active solar power. Michael Flood points out that Japan currently uses 3 million solar water heaters, and that several solar power stations operate successfully in California. Solar heating is used to heat water in several parts of Greece, Australia and the Middle East.

Solar *cells*, also known as photovoltaic cells, are in common use. In 1983 about 60 million solar-powered calculators were sold, using 10 per cent of world output of solar cells. As the cost of the technology fell – by 60 per cent between 1975 and 1982 – so manufacture and application increased. Solar cells are now used for refrigeration, water pumping, telecommunications and lighting. If technical advances and mass production bring the cost down further in the early 1990s, solar electricity will compete directly with grid electricity and the potential market will be enormous.

Fuel cells   Fuel cells work by running a battery on a continuous flow of hydrogen and oxygen as fuel. These combine in the presence of a catalyst to create water, at the same time producing an electrical charge. The direct chemical conversion to electricity means that fuel cells are theoretically very energy efficient. They are also clean, silent, compact and non-polluting.

Fuel cells powered the Apollo missions to the moon. They also provide power to the space shuttles, and are being investigated as a source of energy for submarines. Expensively researched and produced for the space missions, they have until recently not been considered practical for everyday use.

In the late 1970s, the Americans and Japanese launched development projects to produce fuel cells as a source of energy for small-scale installations. A 40 kilowatt, a 200 kilowatt, and two 4.5 megawatt prototypes have been built. One of the 4.5 megawatt plants, by Tokyo Bay, has been producing electricity for the national grid for more than a year.

The Japanese are so attracted by the technology that they plan to have 35,000 megawatts of fuel cell power station capacity in utilities and industry by the year 2005. This is a larger energy source than all the fossil-burning and nuclear-fuelled plant added to the British

Renewable energy technologies which produce electricity

Technology	Category	Economics (Estimated power costs p/kWh)*	Prospects in UK	Constraints on widespread deployment in UK
Hydropower: large-scale central generation	●●●●	Already deployed by the generating boards.	Almost fully exploited.	Most available sites already developed. (4.3 TWh)
Hydropower: small scale (up to 5 MW)	●●●	Depends on site.	Uncertain: under study at present.	Rates and extraction charges. Environmental impact.
Tidal Power	●●●	Unit cost from 3.0, depending on estuary	23 TWh/y (11 Mtce/y) from those estuaries with estimated costs of 5p/kWh or less.	High capital costs and large lead times of large projects. Public acceptability.
Wave-power: large open seas (2 GW)	●	9–14 (1982)	Limited by poor economies of present devices. Still scope for improvement.	Economics. Technology not yet proven and developed.
Wave-power: small, shore mounted (1 MW)	●●●	Could be competitive now in some locations.	Total resource limited by available sites.	Availability of sites. Commercial devices not yet developed.

Wind-power: on land	●●●	2.5–3.2 depending on site.	Uncertain, but potential of 15 GW, or 10% of present electricity generation.	Public acceptability. Rate of installation.
Wind-power: offshore	●	4–7	Offshore technology not yet proven technically and economically.	Technology yet to be proven in the harsher environment.
Geothermal hot dry rock	●●●	3–6 (1985)	Technology is not yet proven technically and economically.	Undeveloped technology. Risk of failure to create a productive well.
Photovoltaics	●	8 to 64 from system costing £1 to £8 per peak watt.	Very limited without a major breakthrough on costs.	Cost. Mismatch between supply (summer) and demand (winter).

KEY

Economically attractive	Promising but uncertain	Long shot
●●●●●	●●●	●

Source: *Financial Times*, 25 January 1988

network in the last 20 years. Moderate estimates also suggest between 10,000 and 25,000 megawatts in the US by 2010.

Fuel cells operate in small units, making them unacceptable to the UK, which likes its electricity production produced by very large stations. Plants of this size are too small to interest generating authorities.

Geothermal energy   Geothermal energy uses heat buried deep inside the earth as a system for boiling water. The UK's test project, at the Camborne School of Mines in Cornwall, has drilled 2 kilometres into granite. Cold water is piped into the rock, which returns at a temperature of 150 degrees C.

More than 20 countries are producing energy from natural steam, with the world's largest geothermal field in California. The world's installed geothermal capacity was 3,500 megawatts in 1986 and may more than double by 1990.

Deep-drilling for geothermal energy is still in its infancy. Problems centre round water loss, and the need to dig deeper into the earth's core to find hotter water. The UK Department of Energy was considering withdrawing its grant from Camborne in 1986, but research is continuing, co-funded by the EC.

Biomass   Biomass (i.e., energy from wood, crop residues, dung or plants) is traditionally used in many countries. It is the main fuel for some 2 billion people, and the only source of energy for cooking in rural areas of the developing world. Industrialized countries also use a proportion of biomass in their energy mix, Canada and Sweden getting 8 per cent and 10 per cent of their energy needs from the fuel, mainly wood.

Fuelwood burning is an essential for millions of people. The rate of wood extraction is causing environmental disturbance, however: according to *World Resources 1986*, a 1983 study showed that over a billion people lived in areas of wood scarcity in 1980, and could only meet their energy needs by further depleting wood reserves. This figure is projected to double by the year 2000, unless remedial measures are taken (see DEFORESTATION).

Biomass is being adapted to other uses. The best known is in Brazil, where 2 million vehicles run on alcohol produced from sugar, and another 8 million on gasohol (a mixture of alcohol and unleaded .

petrol) – although this has also encountered environmental problems relating to land use and air pollution. In the EC, the suggestion has been made that surplus food could be converted into bioethanol and blended with petrol. It remains to be seen whether this is a particularly energy-efficient system for coping with an agricultural surplus.

The Department of Energy has issued an assessment of renewable energy in Britain (see pages 172–3). It should be treated as a very conservative view.

Estimated expenditure on Research and Development by the UK Department of Energy in 1988–9 was to be:

	£ million
Nuclear Energy	144.57
Hydroelectric Power	0.15
Wave Power	0.15
Wind Power	4.30

Source: *Hansard*, 28 November 1988

See also ACID RAIN; GREENHOUSE EFFECT

REFERENCES

Association for the Conservation of Energy (ACE), series title *Lessons from America*:
'1. Home Energy Ratings'
'2. US Gas and Electricity Utilities and the Promotion of Conservation'
'3. Third Party Finance'
'4. Comparison of Investment Programmes: Energy Demand Vs Supply'
'5. The Regulation of Gas and Electric Utilities in the USA'
'6. The Promotion of Energy Conservation in Low Energy Households – US Experience'.

ACE, *A Lesson from Denmark: A Study of the Danish Home Heat Survey Scheme*.
ACE, *Regenerating the Inner City: the Energy Dimension*.
ACE, *Energy in the 80s: Report No. 5 – Home Energy Audits*.
ACE, *Conservation saves need for power stations*, Press Release, November 1988.
Castle, Kim, *The Recycler's Guide to Greater London* (2nd ed.), London Energy and Employment Network, 1986.
Department of Energy, *Digest of United Kingdom Energy Statistics*, 1987.

Elkington, John, *Sun Traps*, Penguin Books, 1984.

Earth Resources Research, *Greenhouse Gas Control in the UK*, research document for Greenpeace UK, 1988.

Flavin, Christopher, 'Moving Beyond Oil', in Worldwatch Institute, *State of the World 1986*, 1986.

Flood, Michael, *Energy Without End*, FoE Trust, 1986.

Foley, Gerald with Charlotte Nassim, *The Energy Question*, Penguin Books, 1982.

FoE, *Critical Decision, a Report on the Sizewell Inquiry*, 1986.

Hansard, 28 November 1988.

House of Commons, *Fourth Report from the Environment Committee, Session 1983–4, vol. 2*.

McCormick, John, *The User's Guide to the Environment*, Kogan Page, 1985.

Myers, Norman (ed.), *The Gaia Atlas of Planet Management*, Pan Books, 1987.

UNEP, *Environmental Data Report*, Basil Blackwell, 1987.

World Bank, *World Development Report 1987*, Oxford University Press, 1987.

Association for the Conservation of Energy, House of Commons presentation, November 1988.

Clarke, Alexi, 'How green is the wind?' *New Scientist*, 27 May 1989.

'Coal comes back as a gas', *New Scientist*, 29 April 1989.

Cook, Frank, 'Norway is Beating Britain to Rule the Waves', *Guardian*, 29 December 1986.

Cross, Michael, 'Hope against Hiccup for Fuel Cells', *Guardian*, 27 February 1986.

de Groot, Peter and David Hall, 'Power from the Farmers', *New Scientist*, 9 October 1986.

Environmental Data Services, Report 164, September 1988.

Fells, Ian, 'The Trials of Privatising Electricity', *New Scientist*, 11 February 1988.

Flood, Michael, 'Norway Rules the Waves', *New Scientist*, 18 December 1986.

'Hot-Rocks Trail Goes Tepid', *New Scientist*, 9 October 1986.

'Norway waves goodbye to wave power machine', *New Scientist*, 14 January 1989.

Rose, David, 'Rethink on Wave Power at Islay Station Backed', *Guardian*, 6 June 1987.

Tucker, Anthony, 'Britain Locked Out of Fuel Cell', *Guardian*, 11 April 1986.

Tucker, Anthony, 'Energy Gives Way to Lethargy', *Guardian*, 9 October 1986.

Tucker, Anthony, 'Tilting at Wind Bills', *Guardian*, 24 April 1987.

Warmer Bulletin.

CONTACTS

Association for the Conservation of Energy
Centre for Alternative Technology
Friends of the Earth (FoE)
Greenpeace
Warmer
Wind Energy Group

Food Additives

Food additives are chemical preparations which are added to food with the intention of making it last longer, taste different, have a different texture or a more attractive colour. Between 3,700 and 4,000 additives are available for use in the UK today, of which fewer than 350 are covered by detailed legal control. The remaining 90 per cent of additives are not subject to regulatory supervision and have not been tested for safety on a research basis verifiable by the general public. The UK uses a number of additives that have been banned in other countries.

Adulteration becomes acceptable

Food additives were recognized as a problem in the last century, when black lead was used to colour tea leaves, alum to make bread look white, and red lead added to cheese. Groups such as the Anti-Adulteration Movement pressurized the government into passing food protection laws between 1860 and 1875. At the turn of the century, there were about 50 additives being used in food.

Between 1875 and 1925, the modern chemical industry developed, producing new dyes and additives. These standardized food, giving it a long shelf-life, so that it could be sold on the mass market. At the end of the Second World War there were fewer than 1,000 different food products. Now there are ten times that many, with three-quarters of all food being industrially processed. The number of additives which service this market has increased ten-fold since 1955.

Additives are used for a number of different reasons. Melanie Miller, in *Danger! Additives at Work!* (1985) lists 24 different types of additives, but divides these into four general groups:

TYPES OF FOOD ADDITIVES

Preservatives   Used to slow the growth of harmful bacteria, and
to stop the food going 'off'.

Approximate number: 63

Texture modifiers   Used to change the texture of the food, making
it thicker, firmer, more airy, jelly-like, etc.

Approximate number: 70

Colour and flavour modifiers   Used to change the smell, colour or
flavour of food.

Approximate number: 3,640

Processing aids   Used for a variety of purposes, mainly to help
change the food from its natural to its processed state.
Include acids, anti-caking agents, anti-foaming agents,
improvers, solvents, conditioners.

Approximate number: 91

The figures are approximate, as additives can have a number of
different purposes and should not necessarily be included in just one
group. Over 95 per cent of additives are primarily used to adjust the
colour, texture or flavour of food. More than 3,500 flavours are added
to our foods: they are not regulated by government, and manufacturers do not have to name or identify flavourings on food labels. This
is a large loophole in the laws covering additives.

Identifying additives in food
Opposite is a typical list of ingredients from a packet of pork sausages.
The contents are listed in order of quantity, with the largest quantities occurring first, and the smallest last. This label tells us that the
principal ingredient here is pork, followed by water, then rusk, beef,
etc. By law, pork sausages have to be at least 65 per cent meat, but
only half of this has to be lean meat: the rest can be gristle, lips, meat
forced from the carcass, etc. So even this hierarchical structure of
ingredients does not give us the full story about what we are eating.

Identifying additives in food

Reading the Label

E223 is the code for sodium metabisulphite. It is a *preservative* which inhibits the growth of micro-organisms, slowing decay and preventing poisoning from microbial growths. Its anti-oxidant properties may help prevent large amounts of fats in the sausages turning rancid during their long shelf life. Preservative-free sausages are available.

Classified as an *emulsifier*, this additive (Code E450) allows added water to be bound into the sausages to increase their weight and give a firmer texture.

SAUSAGES INGREDIENTS LABEL

Ingredients: pork, water, rusk, beef, wheat, flour, soya protein, salt, di-, tri-, and polyphosphates: E450, spices, preservative: E223, flavour enhancer: monosodium glutamate, anti-oxidant: E301, colour: Red 2G, flavouring

---

E301 is the code for sodium L-ascorbate. It is an *anti-oxidant* and colour preserver; it prevents fats going rancid and stops colours and flavours fading.

MSG (621) stimulates the taste buds of your tongue and increases the sensation of flavour – so it is called a *flavour enhancer.*

Red 2G (128) is an azo dye – giving colour to the sausage, disguising the amount of fat or rusk. In foods exposed to light it is used in preference to other red dyes because it does not fade when exposed to light. Red 2G has no E in front of the number because it has not been approved by the EC yet.

'Flavouring' is a term that covers the vast majority of food additives – more than 3,500. Flavourings are not regulated; there is no permitted list. They do not have to be named or identified on food labels. This is a big loophole in the laws controlling additives.

Source: Melanie Miller, *Danger! Additives at Work!*, 1985

The chemical names towards the end of the list have a familiar sound, but slip away from comprehension. They are important, however: we need to know the answers to such questions as:

- What is an anti-oxidant?
- Why are some numbers 'E' numbers, and others not?
- Why is monosodium glutamate written in full, and not as a number?
- Why are there more polyphosphates than spices?
- What *is* polyphosphate?
- What's the difference between flavouring and flavour-enhancer?

Answers in brief

- Anti-oxidants stop fats and oils oxidizing (i.e. mixing with oxygen in the air) and going rancid. The physiological action of anti-oxidants is under investigation in many countries: the anti-oxidants, E 310, E 311, E 312, E 320, E 321 are not permitted in baby food and can cause problems for sensitive people such as asthmatics and aspirin-sensitive subjects. BHA and BHT (E 320 and E 321) are controversial additives which may cause rashes and hyperactivity, cause cancer in animals, and are banned or heavily restricted in certain countries.
- 'E' numbers are those additives which are acceptable to the EC. At the time of Britain's entry into the EC, the UK list of permitted additives differed considerably from those of other European countries. The EC pressurized Britain to stop using a large number of additives (unsuccessfully). As a compromise, the UK was granted an exemption to continue using certain additives, provided that the food was not exported to the EC. Those additives with numbers but no 'E' prefix have either been banned by the EC, or are still awaiting approval. Melanie Miller lists 102 such additives in her book.
- To comply with EC Directives, food sold in the UK has to carry a description of its contents, including the class and 'E' number, or name, of the additive used. In Britain, where many additives do not have 'E' numbers, non-E additives are often written in full. Monosodium glutamate is not an EC-approved additive.
- Di-, tri-, and polyphosphates are used to bind water in food: a way of making the product cheaper. There is more of this substance than spices in the product because of the amount of water that is to be retained in the sausages.

• Flavour enhancers have no real taste in themselves: they are used to stimulate the taste buds, to make them more responsive to the taste that is being experienced. Not approved by the EC, flavour enhancers are now being considered for approval in Europe.

A good deal can now be learned from labels, and people with children, allergies, skin problems, migraines or just a general desire to avoid chemical adulteration of food, would benefit from access to a list of additives. Melanie Miller's book – which has been drawn on extensively so far in this entry – lists additives, giving information about restrictions for children, restrictions of permitted quantities, non-EC approved substances, and WHO recommendations.

Maurice Hanssen's trail-blazing *E for Additives* (1984) gives a full description of additives' origin, function, adverse effects and occurrence in particular products. In the introduction, he lists 40 additives that the Hyperactive Children's Support Group recommend should be avoided. In the companion book, *E for Additives Supermarket Shopping Guide* (1986), he lists 79 additives that he personally would prefer to do without.

Janette Marshall's *Shopping for Health* (1987) gives information about whether additives are of synthetic or natural origin; lists 77 additives that people should beware of, and 74 that are suspected of causing health problems; details additives to be avoided by people on low-sodium diets; and has a list of substances acceptable to vegetarians or vegans.

The London Food Commission's *Food Adulteration* (1988) lists particular additives and groups of additives, accompanied by health risks involved. This includes 12 of the more common additives that are suspected of causing cancer or gene damage.

The list of E numbers on the next page is adapted from the Soil Association publication, *Look Again at the Label* (1984), and is *not* an exhaustive list (in addition to E 160(a), for example, there are five other E 160 additives followed by different letters). For a fuller picture of additives, the reader should refer to Millstone and Abraham's excellent book *Additives – A Guide for Everyone* (1988).

ADDITIVE LIST

A number of different additive lists have been published. There is some variation between the lists (E 153 Carbon is considered safe by some people, for example, though it is banned in the US as a suspected carcinogen). Certain substances are treated with caution in most lists. These include:

- artificial colourings, e.g. E 102 (tartrazine), all of which are banned, for example, in Norway;
- anti-oxidants E 320 (BHA), E 321 (BHT), which cause cancer in animals;
- anti-oxidants E 310, E 311, E 312 (gallates), irritants, banned from UK baby food;
- E 150 (Caramel) provides most colouring used in foods: certain formulations may decrease the white blood-cell count;
- Nitrates and Nitrites (E 249–E 252) not permitted in baby food in the UK and restricted in most European countries.

The list below gives minimal data: for further information, lists mentioned on the previous page should be referred to.

Key

! = Treat with caution. C = May cause cancer or gene damage. H = May cause hyperactivity or allergies. B = Banned in baby foods. R = Recommended for banning from baby foods (Food Advisory Committee, 1987). ? = Suspect. S = Safe.

Colourings			Preservatives		
?R	E 100	Curcumin	S	E 200	
S	E 101	Riboflavin	S	E 201	
S	E 101a	Riboflavin-5-phosphate	S	E 202	Sorbates
!HR	E 102	Tartrazine	S	E 203	
!HR	E 104	Quinoline Yellow	!H	E 210	
!HCR	107	Yellow 26	!H	E 211	
!HR	E 110	Sunset Yellow	!	E 212	Benzoates
!HR	E 120	Cochineal	!	E 213	

Colourings – *cont.*

!HR	E 122	Carmoisine
!HCR	E 123	Amaranth
!HCR	E 124	Ponceau 4R
!HCR	E 127	Erythrozine
!HCR	128	Red 2G
!R	E 131	Patent Blue V
!HCR	E 132	Indigo Carmine
!HCR	133	Brilliant Blue
SR	E 140 ⎫	Chlorophyll
SR	E 141 ⎭	
!HR	E 142	Green S
?HCR	E 150	Caramel
!HR	E 151	Black PN
!CR	E 153	Carbon
!HCR	154	Brown FK
!HR	155	Brown HT
S	E 160a	Beta-carotene
?H	E 160b	Annatto
SR	E 160 ⎫	Relatives of
SR	E 161 ⎭	Carotenids
SR	E 162	Beetroot Red
SR	E 163	Anthocyanins
SR	E 170	Chalk
SR	E 171	Titanium Dioxide
SR	E 172	Iron Oxides
?R	E 173	Aluminium
?R	E 174	Silver
?R	E 175	Gold
!HR	E 180	Pigment Rubine

Preservatives – *cont.*

!H	E 214 ⎫	
!H	E 215	
!H	E 216	
!H	E 217	Complex benzoates
!H	E 218	
!H	E 219 ⎭	
!HC	E 220	Sulphur Dioxide
!H	E 221 ⎫	
!H	E 222	
!H	E 223	
!H	E 224	Sulphites
!H	E 226	
!H	E 227 ⎭	
!C	E 230	Biphenyl
!C	E 231	2-Hydroxbiphenyl
!	E 232	Sodium Biphenyl-2-yl Oxide
!	E 233	used on citrus and banana skins
S	234	Nisin
?	E 236	Formic Acid
?	E 237 ⎫	Formates
?	E 238 ⎭	
!C	E 239	Hexamine
!C	E 249	Potassium Nitrite
!HC	E 250	Sodium Nitrite
!HC	E 251	Sodium Nitrate
!C	E 252	Potassium Nitrate
S	E 260 ⎫	
?	E 261	Acetates (Vinegar)
S	E 262	
S	E 263 ⎭	
?	E 270	Lactic Acid
S	E 280 ⎫	Propionates (not
S	E 281	recommended for
?	E 282	migraine sufferers)
S	E 283 ⎭	
S	E 290	Carbon Dioxide
S	E 296	Malic acid
S	E 297	Fumaric acid

Key

! = Beware! C = May cause cancer or gene damage. H = May cause hyperactivity or allergy. B = Banned in baby foods. ? = Suspect. S = Safe.

Anti-oxidants, emulsifiers, stabilizers, miscellaneous

S	E 300	} Ascorbates		S	355	Adipic Acid
S	E 301			S	363	Succinic Acid
S	E 302			?	370	Heptonolactone
S	E 304			S	375	Vitamin B
S	E 306	} Vitamin E		S	380	} Citrates
S	E 307			S	381	
S	E 308			?	E 385	Salt of EDTA
S	E 309			S	E 400	} Alginates (seaweed)
!B	E 310	Propyl Gallate		S	E 401	
!B	E 311	Octyl Gallate		S	E 402	
!B	E 312	Dodecyl Gallate		S	E 403	
!HBC	E 320	BHA		S	E 404	
!HBC	E 321	BHT		S	E 405	
S	E 322	Lecithins		S	E 406	Agar
?	E 325	} Lactates		?C	E 407	Carrageenan
?	E 326			S	E 410	} Natural gums
?	E 327			S	E 412	
S	E 330	} Citrates		S	E 413	
S	E 331			?	E 414	Acacia Gum
S	E 332			S	E 415	} Natural gums
S	E 333			S	E 416	
S	E 334	} Tartrates		?B	E 420	Sorbitol
S	E 335			?B	E 421	Mannitol
S	E 336			?	E 422	Glycerol
S	E 337			!C	430	} Stearates
S	E 338	} Phosphates		!	431	
S	E 339			?	432	} Polyoxyethylenes
S	E 340			?C	433	
S	E 341			?	434	
S	350	} Malates		?C	435	
S	351			?	436	
S	352			S	E 440	Pectin
S	353	Metatartaric Acid		?	442	Ammonium Phosphatides

Anti-oxidants, emulsifiers, stabilizers, miscellaneous – *cont.*

!	E 450	Polyphosphates	?	513	Sulphuric Acid
S	E 460 ⎫		?	514	Sodium Sulphate
S	E 461 ⎪		S	515	Potassium Sulphate
S	E 463 ⎪		S	516	Calcium Sulphate
S	E 464 ⎬ Celluloses		S	518	Magnesium Sulphate
S	E 465 ⎪		?	524	Caustic Soda
S	E 466 ⎭		?	525	Caustic Potash
?	E 470 ⎫		S	526	Calcium Hydroxide
?	E 471 ⎪		?	527	Ammonium Hydroxide
?	E 472 ⎪		S	528	Magnesium Hydroxide
?	E 473 ⎪		?	529	Quicklime
?	E 474 ⎪		?	530	Magnesium Oxide
?	E 475 ⎪			535 ⎫	
?	E 476 ⎬ Fats, soaps, fatty acids.		!	536 ⎭ Ferrocyanides	
?	E 477 ⎪		?	540	Calcium Hydrogen Phosphate
?	E 478 ⎪				
?	E 481 ⎪		!	541	Phosphate
?	E 482 ⎪		?	542	Bone phosphate
?	E 483 ⎭		!	544 ⎫	Polyphosphates
?	491 ⎫		!	545 ⎭	
?	492 ⎪		S	551 ⎫	Silicates
?	493 ⎬ Sorbitans		S	552 ⎭	
?	494 ⎪		?C	535	Talc
?	495 ⎭		!	554 ⎫	Silicates
S	500 ⎫		!	556 ⎭	
S	501 ⎪		?	558	Bentonite
S	502 ⎬ Carbonates		S	559	Kaolin
S	503 ⎪		S	570 ⎫	Stearate
S	504 ⎭		S	572 ⎭	
?	507 ⎫		?	575	Glucono delta-lactone
?	508 ⎪		S	576 ⎫	
?	509 ⎬ Chlorides		S	577 ⎬ Gluconates	
?	510 ⎭		S	578 ⎭	

Flavour enhancers

!	620	Glutamic Acid	!	622 ⎫	Other glutamates
!B	621	Monosodium Glutamate	!	623 ⎭	

Flavour enhancers – *cont.*

!B	627	Guanylate	S	904	Shellac
!B	631	Inosinate	!C	905	Mineral Hydrocarbons
!B	635	Guanylate and Inosinate	S	907	Wax
!	636	Maltol 'Fresh bake'	S	920	Amino-acid derivative
!	637	Ethyl Maltol – sweetener	!	924	Bromate
?C	900	Dimethicone	!	925	Chlorine
S	901	Beeswax	!	926	Chlorine Dioxide
S	903	Carnauba Wax	!	927	Azoformamide

Risks and benefits of additives

The food industry lobbies hard for the use of additives, arguing that they protect public health, give a wider variety of choice and enable food to be produced more cheaply. There is a certain amount of truth in all three statements: meat, for example, has to be preserved if it is to be kept for any period of time, or the result would be fatal attacks of food poisoning; choice has expanded with the growth of additives, although it may not always be an expansion of healthy food; and a new additive can reduce the cost of an already established food process.

As to colouring, say the food lobby, manufacturers have tried in the past to reduce the use of this, and the result has been a drop in sales; it is the consumers, not the manufacturers, who lead the demand for luminous peas.

Our preference for artificial colours is not always shared by other countries: the French, who have the reputation of enjoying their food, have uncoloured (khaki) canned peas, instead of the bright green that we know. Norway banned the use of artificial colours in food in 1978. Sweden has severely restricted the use of colours in food. Austria does not allow the use of colouring in processed fruit.

There is evidence that the climate of opinion is changing in Britain. Some food manufacturers reformulated their products before the EC label deadline in 1986, to avoid giving consumers the idea that they were buying a chemistry set instead of a frozen meal. *E for Additives* was reprinted eleven times in the year after its publication, as people caught on to the idea of tracing E numbers from labels. The supermarket firm Safeway published a list of 51 'contentious' additives that it was proposing to remove from its own-label brands. The food industry has voluntarily agreed not to include colouring in baby foods.

The special protection given to babies points to the risk being incurred by the rest of us. Babies and young children have delicate immune systems, and need to avoid harmful substances such as the anti-oxidants E320 (BHA) and E321 (BHT). Fourteen other additives are explicitly forbidden for use in baby food, with more in the pipeline.

Adult immune systems vary between individuals, and certain additives produce adverse reactions. Thousands of people will react to E102 (tartrazine), with skin rashes, breathing difficulties, hay fever or blurred vision. Some parents have cured hyperactivity in their children by limiting the additives in their diet. Four additives have been linked to cancer in humans, with more causing cancer in animals: no figure is yet available for the number of deaths a year in Britain which may be the result of consuming additives.

The Ministry of Agriculture, Fisheries and Food is reassuring. Their publication *Food Additives – the Balanced Approach* points out:

- that some additives (e.g. E440, Pectin) have natural origins;
- that a few people have adverse reactions to additives, but more appear to react adversely to natural foods;
- that it is illegal under the Food Acts to put anything into food that will injure health;
- and that additives are safe as they have all been rigorously tested.

The reassurances are not as firmly based as they would appear. The fact that an additive is 'natural' is not always a guarantee that it is safe; and many 'natural' additives are synthetically produced anyway. As to the second point, no one knows whether more people react adversely to natural products than to additives: the research into additives is less than comprehensive, and a reasoned comparison with natural foods is not yet possible. The reassurance also ignores the fact that people who are allergic to eggs don't eat them: it is more difficult to avoid an additive.

The third reassurance is true but relies on disputed definitons as to what will injure health. Research into additives (the fourth point) has neither been rigorous, nor authoritatively proved that the additives concerned are 'safe'. The cancer-causing properties of an additive are tested by feeding it to animals, yet animal tests are successful in detecting human carcinogens less than 50 per cent of the time: and bad laboratory practice has been established in a number of testing establishments (see PESTICIDES).

Most damaging, however, is the fact that additives are nearly always tested in isolation, without other additives being present. An adult in the UK can consume up to 60 different additives in one meal, which will combine with one another in their effect on the body. The results of this have not been established, and neither has the effect on the UK citizen of consuming, on average, almost a fifth of a pound of additives each week.

ADDITIVE-FREE LIVING

Three-quarters of Britain's food contains additives of one sort or another. 'Hidden' adulteration occurs, too. Bleaches used in British white bread don't have to be declared, although some manufacturers make bread with unbleached flour. Chemicals which are added to the food before they get to the food manufacturer don't have to be listed as additives (see PESTICIDES). Parents with hyperactive children may be avoiding foods containing tartrazine, only to find it turning up in the unwrapped fresh cakes they can buy from the baker. The additives E320 and E321, avoided by people who are additive-conscious, are used in animal feedstuffs and may be absorbed by eating meat fat.

The way to avoid additives is to eat organically grown food (produced without fertilizers, pesticides, hormones or antibiotics); to avoid processed foods where possible; and to check labels rigorously. 'Flash' labelling should be mentioned here – this refers to the practice of flashing, for example, NO ARTIFICIAL PRESERVATIVES on the label even though the product contains artificial colouring or flavouring. ONLY NATURAL ADDITIVES should be checked to ensure what additives are being referred to – sugar and salt are natural, but not necessarily to be sought after as additives.

Organic food can be checked as to its authenticity, as can free-range eggs and meat. The government is being pressurized towards clarifying the labelling of our food (see FOOD IN THE UK). It would be useful if products containing additives banned in baby food carried a label UNSUITABLE FOR BABIES, but this is not happening at the moment because of pressure from the food industry. (Some common foods, a well-known mayonnaise for example, and certain brands of crisps, have contained, or still contain, additives which are regarded as unsuitable for young children.)

The Food Additives Campaign Team (FACT), representing a cross-section of 20 national organizations, presented a 12-point manifesto in December 1985. The London Food Commission has similar objectives. They include measures to:

- make the Food Advisory Committee, which gives recommendations about additives, truly independent (at the moment it is dominated by people who work in the food industry);
- remove the secrecy from this committee (evidence on safety and necessity of additives is currently covered by the Official Secrets Act);
- remove all additives which are suspected of causing cancer;
- test the 'cocktail effect' of mixing different additives together;
- take additive testing out of the hands of the food industry and give it to independent government laboratories (tests to be financed by the food industry);
- enforce labelling of all additives on all foods, instead of selective labelling on certain foods as at present;
- make labels carry warnings if they contain additives known to cause any kind of harm to people; foods containing additives banned for children should carry explicit warnings.

See also ANIMALS; FOOD IN THE UK; PESTICIDES

REFERENCES

Hanssen, Maurice, *E for Additives*, Thorsons, 1984 (rev. ed., 1987).

Hanssen, Maurice, *The New E for Additives*, Thorsons, 1987.

Hanssen, Maurice, *E for Additives Supermarket Shopping Guide*, Thorsons, 1986.

London Food Commission, *Food Adulteration*, Unwin, 1988.

Marshall, Janette, *Shopping for Health*, Penguin Books, 1987.

Miller, Melanie, *Danger! Additives at Work!*, London Food Commission, 1985.

Millstone, Erik and John Abraham, *Additives, a Guide for Everyone*, Penguin Books, 1988.

Ministry of Agriculture, Fisheries and Food (MAFF), *Food Additives, a Balanced Approach*, n.d.

MAFF, *Look at the Label*, 1985.

Soil Association, *Look Again at the Label*, 1984.

Walker, Caroline and Geoffrey
  Cannon, *The Food Scandal*,
  Century Arrow, 1985.

Cannon, Geoffrey, 'E is not for
  Additives', *Guardian*, 16 May
  1986.

CONTACTS

Food Additives Campaign Team
Hyperactive Children's Support
  Group
London Food Commission
Soil Association
Vegan Society
Vegetarian Society

Food and Drink Federation
Food Manufacturers' Federation
Ministry of Agriculture, Fisheries
  and Food

Food in the UK

The link between diet, health, environment and the method of food production can be explored by looking at the connection between diet and coronary heart disease. In the UK, more people die early deaths from heart disease, strokes and cancer, than in any other country in Europe. Heart disease is our single most common cause of death.

Our national diet appears to be responsible for this, linked of course to other factors – smoking, lack of exercise, and stress, for example. Every year, around 180,000 people die from coronary heart disease, which kills 30 per cent of all men and 20 per cent of all women in the UK. One Briton dies from this cause every three minutes.

In the USA, changing dietary patterns and increasing interest in exercise led to a 25 per cent drop in heart death rate between the late 1960s and the early 1980s. Heart disease deaths have fallen in many countries, including Canada, Belgium, Australia and The Netherlands. There has been no significant fall in the UK.

The reason for this disparity is Britain's continued reliance on highly processed foods; over-consumption of sugars, salt, saturated fats and alcohol; and under-consumption of starches and fibre. We are what we eat: and what we eat isn't particularly healthy.

The 'balanced' diet
Current nutritional policy in Britain rests on the notion of the 'balanced' diet, developed in the 1930s and 1940s. Nutritionists wanted to abolish 'deficiency' diseases which were caused by not eating the right protein, vitamins and minerals. (Rickets, for example, is caused by a deficiency of Vitamin D, and scurvy by not getting enough Vitamin C.)

Foods were classified in groups: certain foods gave energy, others were a source of protein, others provided vitamins and minerals. The idea was to eat a wide range of foods, which would give a balanced input of everything that was needed. Under this concept, large quantities of sugar could be consumed, provided that they were topped-up by other parts of the diet that supplied protein, vitamins and minerals.

The theory was successful, in that it greatly reduced the numbers of deficiency diseases in Britain. Unfortunately, it did not consider the long-term consequences of over-consuming harmful substances such as sugar. Eating a chocolate bar after breakfast, lunch and tea could be defended, provided that it was part of a 'balanced' diet; it was not realized, however, that doing this every day was likely to lead to health problems in middle age.

The British over-consume a number of substances which are likely to cause illnesses later in life. This is true of the nation as a whole and not just a few individuals. As an example, *The Food Scandal* (Walker and Cannon, 1985) describes how too much cholesterol in the blood is an established cause of heart disease. Only about 5 per cent of people in the UK have very high cholesterol counts, however; and the majority of deaths (about 90 per cent) occur in the enormous number of people who have 'average' blood cholesterol levels. In the UK, the 'average' cholesterol level is enough to be fatal. In 1989, this was confirmed by research indicating that 80 per cent of middle-aged men and all middle-aged women in Britain would be in the 'at risk' category according to American guidelines for acceptable blood cholesterol levels (*New Scientist*, 11 March 1989).

Cholesterol in blood is caused by high levels of saturated fat and cholesterol in food, aggravated by smoking and lack of exercise. If we want to reduce the number of heart deaths in the country, we need to change the type of food that we eat.

THE NACNE REPORT

The National Advisory Committee on Nutrition Education (NACNE) was set up in 1979 to consider the national diet. It included representatives of government departments, the academic community, the food industry and nutrition specialists. Drawing on existing nutritional research, and consulting acknowledged national experts, in 1983 it published *Proposals for Nutritional Guidelines for Health Education in Britain*, which it described as 'a collaborative national effort that seeks to identify what is wrong with the diet of the

British population as a whole'. It was the first major reassessment of the national diet since the war, and its findings were explosive.

NACNE pointed out that 39 per cent of British men and 32 per cent of women were overweight, increasing the risks of coronary artery disease, high blood pressure, diabetes and gall bladder disease. The average weight for height of the population is continuing to rise: this suggests that the problem of overweight is increasing rather than diminishing.

NACNE also overturned the advice normally given to overweight people – to eat less of each item that they consume. Rapid loss of body weight is achieved by losing body water rather than excess body fat: body fat is best reduced by steadily losing 1 to 2 pounds per week, rather than crash dieting. The most efficient way to do this is not by eating less food, but by changing the type of food that is consumed. The amount of input stays the same, but the quality changes.

A healthier diet involves eating less fat (which is normally 'hidden' in meat and meat products) and sugar (used in processed foods). These should be replaced with fresh fruit, vegetables and cereal fibre (e.g. wholemeal bread). Regular exercise should also be regarded as essential to a healthy dietary regime.

Looking at the national diet, and not just the diet of overweight people, NACNE came to similar conclusions. The report recommended that we should reduce:

- sugar consumption by 50%;
- salt consumption by 25 to 50%;
- consumption of fats by 25%;
- and intake of alcohol by one-third.

In addition, we should:

- increase consumption of fibre by 50%.

These recommendations were explosive because, if they were to be carried out, they attacked the food industry in its most lucrative sector – processed foods. The profit margins on selling potatoes as potatoes are not particularly large; if, however, they are cooked, mashed, shaped, bulked up with sugar, additives, preservatives and salt, and sold under a million-pound advertising campaign as, say, Crunchy Spudlisnaks, then the profit can be enormous. Unfortunately, however, NACNE's view was that potatoes were better for you than Spudlisnaks.

The food lobby is powerful and influential: the top five companies have a turnover of £24,000 million a year. The government had been worried about NACNE before the report was published; because of pressure from the food industry, it had had to be redrafted a number of times. After the report was finally released, the administration distanced itself from its recommendations, and disbanded NACNE in 1984.

The international scientific consensus has come to similar conclusions to the NACNE report. In the USA, the 1977 McGovern Report (*Dietary Goals for the United States*) recommended cuts in fats, sugars and salt, and increased consumption of fibre. Between 1968 and 1978 20 expert committees on heart disease prevention or dietary goals had been published, in the USA, Canada, Germany, The Netherlands, and other countries. All accepted that heart disease is diet-related. All proposed changes in diet. A total of 50 international reports since 1968 have linked nutrition to disease.

In Britain, Caroline Walker, the secretary of the NACNE report working group, teamed up with journalist Geoffrey Cannon to write *The Food Scandal*, which explains the NACNE report in ordinary language and extends the arguments in it. The publicity and notoriety surrounding NACNE has had an effect on public consciousness about food. In 1984, the official Committee on Medical Aspects of Food Policy (COMA) published *Diet and Cardiovascular Disease*, linking heart disease to consumption of saturated and processed fats; in 1986, the British Medical Association's *Diet, Nutrition and Health* again linked our food and our health. By 1986, sales of brown and wholemeal bread in the UK accounted for 25 per cent of all bread consumed, compared with 10 per cent in 1976.

The public gives every impression of being concerned about diet, and wants clear information about which foods are healthy and which are not. This could be achieved by legislation enforcing clear labelling of food products in order to enable the consumer to spot the hidden fats in processed foods.

What to eat, what to avoid

As a generalization, the more highly processed a food is, the less likely it is to be good for you. If we are to cut down our consumption of fats, sugars and salts, and increase our input of starches and fibre, it is better to eat fresh 'whole' food – real apples, real potatoes, wholemeal bread, fresh vegetables. It would also be useful to cut down our consumption of dairy and meat products.

Descriptions and sources of principal dietary components are listed below.

Fats, saturated and unsaturated Fats come from dairy products, meat and certain types of vegetables. *The Food Scandal* describes how fats and oils are made up of fatty acids, of which there are over 20. Fatty acids have a complicated chemical structure, consisting of chains of carbon atoms, to which atoms of oxygen and hydrogen are bound. If a lot of hydrogen atoms are bonded to the carbon, then the fatty acid is *saturated* (i.e., saturated with hydrogen). With different chemical structures, more carbon atoms are free of hydrogen, and the substance is *unsaturated* (i.e., not saturated with hydrogen). Unsaturated fatty acids are usually described as monounsaturated or polyunsaturated, depending on the chemical structure involved.

Fats or oils that are described as 'saturated' or 'highly saturated' contain a high proportion of saturated fatty acids. 'Polyunsaturated' or 'high in polyunsaturates' means that the proportion of polyunsaturated fatty acids is high.

Saturated fats are the fats which are causing extreme concern on health grounds. Found in butter, cheese, milk fat, cream, beef, lamb, pork, bacon, lard, many margarines and cooking fats, saturated fats are not essential for health (as far as is known at the moment). They are unhealthy because they make the blood more sticky and are likely to get 'stuck' on arterial walls. They are thought to be a contributory factor to heart disease, particularly arteriosclerosis. Not essential to health, indeed damaging to health, they should be avoided where possible.

Monounsaturates, found for example in olive oil, are thought to have a neutral effect on the body (though current knowledge of nutrition is far from complete: monounsaturates may have good or bad effects which have not yet been discovered). Monounsaturates can occur with other fats – half of the fats found in beef are monounsaturates, though the rest are saturated. Half of the fats in mackerel oil are monounsaturated, and the rest are polyunsaturates. There appears to be some uncertainty as to the effects of monounsaturates on the body.

The same is not true of the *polyunsaturates*, which are acknowledged to have a beneficial effect. Certain essential polyunsaturates cannot be made in the human body and have to be supplied in our food. They protect against heart disease, making the blood less likely to clot. For a healthy diet, we must consume a certain amount of polyunsaturates, which can be found in corn oil, soya, sunflower and olive oil, some fish, unprocessed fish oils and margarines labelled 'high in polyunsaturates'. Heart-conscious America has adopted polyunsaturated margarine in a big way.

Hydrogenated vegetable fats have had hydrogen added to them, and thus have the same effects in the body as saturated fats. *Trans fatty acids* are also similar to saturated fats once they are in the body.

The food industry likes saturated fats because they are stable, thus ensuring a long shelf-life for a product. The beneficial fatty acids are usually unstable, going rancid after a short period of time. Processes such as hydrogenation cure this instability, but remove the beneficial effects of the food. The fats that make the most economic sense for the manufacturer are, unfortunately, unhealthy.

The NACNE report recommended a decrease of 25 per cent in the amount of fat that we consume, although the amount of polyunsaturates in the diet should be maintained. The message is: less fat overall; much less saturated fat; same amount of polyunsaturates.

Sugars   Sugars, like starches, are carbohydrates, which are converted into energy in the body and are sometimes called 'energy foods'. In *Shopping for Health* (1987), Janette Marshall distinguishes between 'refined carbohydrates' (not recommended) and 'unrefined carbohydrates' (recommended).

Unrefined carbohydrates are as near to their original state as possible, and go through a complicated process of digestion in the body before releasing their energy. Foods like wholemeal bread and pasta, brown rice, porridge, wholegrain flours and root vegetables, provide a sustained, slow-release type of energy: the fibre in them slows the process of digestion.

Refined carbohydrates, like table sugar and white flour, have been processed so much that they lose their dietary fibre, as well as some vitamins and minerals. Refined sugar is a concentrated source of calories: when sugar in processed food is replaced by artificial sweeteners with no calories, people can eat the same amount of food but lose weight. Sugar in processed food can be, and often is, a source of overweight.

Sugar also absorbs too quickly in the bloodstream, producing swings of blood sugar levels: it has poor nutritional quality, rots teeth and is bad from the overall health point of view. In 1982, 374,000 general anaesthetics were given to children under fifteen for the purpose of extracting teeth: a year later, 48 per cent of five-year-old children were estimated to have tooth decay.

These dental deficiencies are directly related to the amount of sugar we consume (on average about 2 lb a week). Some of this is added to tea, coffee and cereals: the rest is hidden in sweets, confectionery, soft drinks and snacks. The food industry likes sugar because it is a cheap, stable bulking agent: it is used extensively in biscuits, cakes, instant foods and even savoury products like tomato sauce, brown sauce and salad cream.

Current concern over artificial additives means that sugar can be advertised as a 'natural' product. It is also marketed extremely hard. In 1985, the Health Education Council spent about £750,000 on promoting healthy eating: in the same year, Rowntree Mackintosh, Mars and Cadbury spent £66.7 million on advertising their chocolate products. In 1988, chocolate advertising amounted to £81.7 million.

The sugar lobby launched a formidable counter-attack to the NACNE findings, culminating in a 1987 campaign based on the US Food and Drug Administration's Report on Sugars and Sweeteners. 'Sugar is just fine', 'Sugar no danger to health', the advertisements said. In fact this was not the case: the FDA found no evidence of sugar being 'uniquely responsible' for specific health problems, but they did not give it the clean bill of health that was implied. Neither did they condone current levels of sugar intake.

The NACNE report, and others, are unequivocal: we have to halve the amount of sugar we eat. This refers not just to the sugar that we know we are eating: it includes sugar disguised in other products, whether as sucrose (i.e., made from cane or beet sugar), fructose (i.e., made from fruit), lactose (i.e., milk sugar), maltose (malt) and glucose or dextrose (grapes).

Salt Comparisons of different populations around the world have shown that those nations with high salt intake tend to have high blood pressure, which is a major risk factor associated with heart disease and strokes. Comparisons within populations have not been able to show the same relationship, probably because sensitivity to salt varies between individuals.

People, and societies, who are free of high blood pressure tend not to be overweight, to exercise a lot, to eat low amounts of animal fat, have a low intake of sodium (sodium chloride = salt) and a high intake of potassium.

NACNE estimated that the average intake of salt in the UK was between 8 and 12 grams per day. The World Health Organization committee which considered salt in food (*Prevention of Coronary Heart Disease*, 1982) recommended an intake of 5 grams per day. This implies a reduction of salt intake by 25 to 50 per cent.

Alcohol　　Over the past 20 years there has been a steady increase in the alcohol intake of the British population. The price of alcohol relative to other foods has fallen: it is estimated that between 4 per cent and 9 per cent of the total energy intake is derived from alcohol in different regions of the country.

This level of consumption is associated with a wide range of physical disorders, including diseases of the liver, the blood, the nervous system, the muscles, the metabolism and increased susceptibility to infection. The illnesses are often incurred by people who would not regard themselves as alcoholics.

NACNE point out that guidelines for a better British diet have suggested that average intake, per head of population, should be no more than one pint of beer per day. Overall, national reductions of 30 per cent of alcohol intake should be aimed for.

Fibre and starch　　Fibre is obtained from unrefined foods – fruits, vegetables, beans, cereal grains. Lack of fibre causes constipation. Forty per cent of the British population complain of constipation, and associated complaints are common – piles, varicose veins, hiatus hernia and diverticulitis. The British are a constipated nation.

'Fibre' is contained in a number of vegetables and cereals, often as the rough outer shell of the plant. Cereals such as wheat, barley and oats consist of a starchy middle surrounded by a fibrous coat.

Fibre in the diet encourages the speed of food through the intestine, and softens stools, thus preventing constipation. Children who are not used to sufficient quantities of fibre in their diet will suffer the consequences later in life: constipation, haemorrhoids, diverticular disease.

Eating more fibre does not mean adding bran to junk food: it means eating more whole food, more wholemeal bread, wholemeal pasta, brown rice, chick peas, lentils, pulses. At the moment, we eat on average 0.75 oz of fibre a day in Britain: vegetarians eat twice as much, and Africans living away from Western influence twice as much again. Constipation is rare among these communities: diverticular disease is less common among Western vegetarians. The British attitude to food has been to block up the system with processed food and then try to remove the blockage with laxatives. NACNE recommends a 50 per cent increase in the amount of fibre we eat.

'Refining starch' means removing the outside of the food, processing it, and usually eating it in combination with processed sugars. This rots the teeth and constipates. Starches should be eaten as much as possible in their original condition. Jacket potatoes are a good example of how to eat a vegetable containing starch and fibre: crisps are an example of how not to do it.

Responses to NACNE

NACNE appears to have set in motion a process which is still continuing in Britain. On the one hand, organizations like the London Food Commission and Action and Information on Sugar are vigorously promoting and broadening the NACNE message. Other organizations, mainly those funded by industry, are dismissive of NACNE and regard it as out-of-date and cranky. The British Sugar Bureau, for example, says that NACNE 'was not an official report and is no longer being taken seriously'.

The government has responded slowly, arguing that food choice should be the responsibility of the individual rather than the subject of government legislation. This argument has two fallacies: first, it works only if products are clearly labelled as to their contents; and secondly, it works only if the citizen can afford the healthier diet.

Years after it was advised by its own Department of Health Committee on Medical Aspects of Food Policy (COMA) to improve public information on food, the government has delayed introducing a simple labelling scheme. By 1992 the EC is likely to impose a scheme.

The government's provisional labelling proposals are generally regarded as unsatisfactory: they have been criticized because full nutritional labelling is to remain voluntary; the language used in the labelling is arbitrarily difficult, when easier explanations and presentation could be adopted; information about added sugar and salt will not be allowed; and food sold in imperial units will have its labelling in metric units. The promised labelling of irradiated food does not inspire confidence in food campaigners – irradiation abuses have already been proved to occur.

Food practices are changing in Britain, particularly in high-income households who are aware of the issues and can afford the (currently more expensive) healthier food options. The London Food Commission have published a number of reports on the effects of poverty on food. *Tightening Belts* (Cole-Hamilton and Lang, 1986) found that diet-related health problems are most common among those with low incomes; children and women in such circumstances are at risk of under-nutrition; people from low-income households eat more fatty and sugary food, and less fruit, vegetable and high fibre food than people who are better-off; and food is a flexible item on household budgets, tending to get cut back when times are hard. A NACNE diet would cost about 35 per cent more than the typical low-income current expenditure on food.

These findings appear to be confirmed in a Health Education publication, *The Health Divide* (M. Whitehead, 1987). Poorer people in Britain are responding to the new nutritional advice, as far as their pockets will allow: consumption of brown and wholemeal bread has increased in all income groups over the last ten years. Sugar consumption is also dropping in the nation as a whole – that is, people are using less sugar at the table.

Unfortunately, the amount of sugar used in processed food has increased. Purchases of packet sugar have dropped 35 per cent since 1950, but the total sugar intake has remained at 2 lb per week. It is disappearing from our coffee cups and reappearing in our dinner. This particularly affects the poor. When they are short of money, they buy the cheapest foods available: and the cheaper foods are often the ones higher in fat and sugar.

The responsibility for a healthier national diet lies with the food manufacturers and the government, but currently appears to be mainly the prerogative of the voluntary sector (Lang and Cole-Hamilton, 1989).

The salmonella crisis

The Environment Digest (January 1989) gives a good summary of the UK's salmonella crisis. There are over 1,000 species of salmonella which cause food poisoning, and they live in poultry and livestock. According to the Food Hygiene Laboratory, nearly 80 per cent of raw chicken is contaminated with salmonella. In a fit human, salmonella usually causes diarrhoea and vomiting, although it can have serious, even fatal, complications.

UK cases of food poisoning from salmonella have doubled between 1981 and 1987 – to 20,000 per year – but cases of *Salmonella Enteritides* have increased sixfold over the same period (to 6,857 in 1987). The following year, however, there were 12,000 cases of *Enteritides*: 26 people died because of blood poisoning. Some observers believe that the number of cases, and of deaths, is substantially higher than this.

Enteritides is passed from the chicken to the egg, and is thought to have spread through the animal content of chickenfeed being contaminated. The Minister of Agriculture admitted that, in 1988, 21 out of 83 processing plants – the sources of the feed – were contaminated. None of the suppliers were prosecuted, production was never halted, no infected feed was destroyed.

Department of Health sources told the *Observer* that 'before 1981 we wanted more thorough health testing for the industry . . . but we were overruled by industry interests more concerned about costs'.

When the crisis finally went public in late 1988, 30 million eggs a day were being consumed in Britain. An estimated one in 7,000 eggs was contaminated, or some 4,000 eggs daily. One in ten people eating an infected egg will become ill, so some 400 people per day would suffer. This implies a figure of 146,000 cases of food poisoning per year.

See also ANIMALS; FOOD ADDITIVES; PESTICIDES; RADIATION

REFERENCES

Action and Information on Sugar / London Food Commission, *The Sugar Offensive*, n.d.

Cole-Hamilton, I. and T. Lang, *Tightening Belts*, London Food Commission, 1986.

Lang, T. and I. Cole-Hamilton, *Food provision for people with low incomes in the UK*, National Council for Voluntary Organizations, 1989.

Lang, T., S. Robb, T. Lobstein and I. Cole-Hamilton, *This Food Business*, Channel 4/New Statesman and Society, 1989.

A Discussion Paper on Proposals for Nutritional Guidelines for Health Education in Britain, NACNE, 1983.

Luba, A. and I. Cole-Hamilton, *Food Labelling*, London Food Commission, 1986.

Marshall, Janette, *Shopping for Health*, Penguin Books, 1987.

Sheppard, J., *The London Commission's Food Facts*, n.d.

Walker, Caroline and G. Cannon, *The Food Scandal*, Century Arrow, 1985.

Whitehead, M., *The Health Divide*, Health Education Council, 1987.

'Contaminated feed for sale', *New Scientist*, 21 January 1989.

Environment Digest, No. 20, January 1989.

Mason, D. and G. Vines, 'Eggs and the fragile food chain', *New Scientist*, 17 December 1988.

Vines, G., '"All Britons" face high risk of heart disease', *New Scientist*, 11 March 1989.

CONTACTS

Action on Sugar and Health
Health Education Association
London Food Commission
Soil Association
Vegan Association
Vegetarian Association

Department of Health and Social Security

Ministry of Agriculture, Fisheries and Food

(industry-funded bodies)
British Nutrition Foundation
British Sugar Bureau
Butter Information Council
Food and Drink Federation
Food Manufacturers' Federation

Forestry in the UK

Forestry policy in the UK is the result of decisions made after the First World War, which have become established practice and have only recently been questioned. British forestry policy has been criticized because of its choice of trees for planting, its apparent disregard of the environment and its short-term outlook. In its defence, it can be said that the national forestry industry is starting to learn from past mistakes: although that defence would not include the environmental despoliation currently being carried out by some private foresters.

The Forestry Commission

The Forestry Commission was founded in 1919, as a direct result of the First World War. The motive for its foundation was 'strategic' – a conscious act of forward planning against the possibility of another war. At the beginning of the century, our woodlands had shrunk to 5 per cent of the land area, and the UK was importing timber from all over the world. This was acceptable until the First World War, when imports were interrupted: Britain cut down 180,000 hectares of woodland to fill wartime requirements that were not being met from abroad. In order to protect supplies of timber in the event of future hostilities, it was decided to increase the amount of wood grown at home.

The Forestry Commission was given a dual role, as a profit-making national body, and as the country's leading authority on forestry. It was allowed to buy land, grow trees on it and sell the timber produced. It also gave advice and grants to private foresters wanting to start their own schemes: to some extent, too, it regulated their activities through the use of legislation or financial incentives.

In the post-war period, the Commission faced a daunting task. Private landowners had been showing little enthusiasm for forestry, as the growing cycle took 100 years or so to produce profits. Britain's woodlands had declined in area for a number of years, making the UK one of the world's least wooded nations, and the requirement now was to fill the UK's 'timber gap' as quickly as possible.

The Commission decided the solution was to change the types of trees grown in Britain. Oak trees may take 150 years to grow, and produce only 4 to 6 cubic metres of wood per hectare. Certain conifers, on the other hand, need only 50 years to mature, and can theoretically yield 18 cubic metres of wood per hectare. To meet the strategic objective of becoming more self-sufficient in wood, the UK decided to start growing conifers on a large scale.

Traditionally, there had been a large proportion of broadleaved trees in British woods. Now, however, the native oak, lime, elm, hornbeam and cherry were ignored in favour of 'exotic' (i.e. foreign) conifers like the Sitka spruce and Norway spruce, and the Lodgepole

Area of productive woodland, 1988

1. Forestry Commission (thousands of hectares)

	High forest		Coppice	Total
	Conifers	Broadleaves		
England	193	40	1	234
Wales	125	6	—	131
Scotland	519	4	—	523
Great Britain	837	50	1	888

2. Forestry Commission and private woodlands (thousands of hectares)

	High forest		Coppice	Total
	Conifers	Broadleaves		
England	393	429	38	860
Wales	175	60	2	237
Scotland	937	78	—	1,015
Great Britain	1,505	567	40	2,112

Source: The figures do not include 173,000 ha classed as 'unproductive'.
Forestry Commission, *Forestry Facts and Figures 1987–8*.

pine, as well as the native Scots pine. The rolling treescape of England began to be replaced by regimented rows of conifers, and moorland areas of Scotland, cleared of trees in the seventeenth century, became increasingly afforested.

In the last 60 years the area of forest plantations and woodland in the UK has doubled to nearly 2 million hectares. Half of this is owned by the Forestry Commission, which is now the biggest single landowner in Britain. Ninety-four per cent of the Commission's forests are conifer.

The arguments against conifers

The central argument against coniferization is the same as that made against modern agriculture: that the UK is paying large sums of money to people who are ruining the environment. The current system encourages foresters to dig up a landscape that has taken centuries to develop, and then replace it with something that may possibly turn a quick profit, without regard to the environmental consequences.

The target areas for afforestation are usually either the deciduous woodland of lowland Britain – which in large areas is being replaced by conifer plantations – or the moorland and mountainous areas which have not been cultivated for centuries. These, too, are being covered in a carpet of conifers.

The arguments against the introduction of conifer trees centre round the scale of planting – nearly three-quarters of the entire productive woodlands of the UK are now conifers – and the environmental changes which they bring about.

Threat to wildlife The ancient woods, mountains and moors support a wide variety of wildlife which has evolved over hundreds of years and frequently does not survive in the new conifer forest. When a conifer plantation is started, there is initially an increase in the number of small mammals, which attract predators such as short-eared owls and kestrels. As the trees grow, and the canopy becomes dense, the wildlife changes. Some birds can adapt, but the previously established plants, birds and animals tend to disappear.

Wildlife at risk, claim the conservationists, includes many of England's orchids, butterflies, and nightingales, pied flycatchers, wood warblers and hawfinches. In Scotland, mosses and liverworts are in danger, as well as golden eagles, peregrine falcons and golden plovers.

Dangers of monoculture It is ecologically a high-risk strategy to cover large areas of the country with one, or at best two, species of tree, especially when they are exotic rather than native species: there is a possibility of wholesale disaster in the form of disease or insect pest.

Problems have already arisen in Scotland with the pine beauty moth, which is native to the British Isles and has, up to recent years, lived in equilibrium on its food plant, the Scots pine. Now, however, it has invaded Lodgepole pine plantations, and increased greatly in numbers. Several hundred hectares of trees have been stripped of their needles and killed. Foresters have started spraying large areas with insecticide, a process which wipes out large numbers of other insects as well as the target moth. Twenty square miles were listed for spraying during 1985.

Another threat has been posed by the accidental introduction of the great spruce bark beetle into parts of England and Wales. Controls on the felling and transport of timber have been introduced to try to stop the spread of the beetle, which kills Sitka spruce. If the pest reaches the huge Sitka spruce plantations of southern Scotland, the consequences could be disastrous.

Effects of land use changes

Large-scale changes in land use lead to problems further down the ecological chain, particularly in regard to the acidification of water bodies. When land is drained and planted with conifers, ACID RAIN is more efficiently channelled into local streams and lakes, as the trees attract the pollution and divert it into the ground.

Lakes in Scotland are now being given tree-free zones around their perimeter in an attempt to stop the acidification process. The new planting policy is successful in the short term, but it is too early to say what the long-term effects of afforestation will be. The Acid Waters Review Group has pointed out that afforestation itself increases the acidity of soil in certain areas, exacerbating the effects of atmospheric pollution by filtering it out of the air and channelling it into the ground.

Access and aesthetics Conifers are not always well suited to the land on which they are planted, with wind damage being a restriction on production from high, exposed land. Because of the risk that the trees will blow over before reaching maturity, many plantations, especially in north and west Scotland, are never thinned, and remain dense and dark. Walkers find it impossible to get through the forests, and that part of the countryside effectively becomes removed from public access.

The initial objection to conifer forestry was on aesthetic grounds: in the 1930s, protest against afforestation in the Lake District led to an agreement concerning the first 'no-go' area for forestry in Britain, covering the core of what was later to become the Lake District National Park.

'Aesthetic' arguments carry little weight when the British country-side is being discussed. The theory is that 'hard' economics is the only criterion that should be used when discussing an environmental issue such as forestry. Perhaps the nadir of this approach occurred in 1966 and 1967, when the Forestry Commission poisoned 1,000 hectares of young Northampton oaks. It was a logical response to a Treasury directive to increase output: the land would be more productive if planted with conifers.

Environmentalists point out that there is a value to an open moorland, a broadleaved forest or a mountainside, which cannot be adequately costed using traditional economic methods. This is a difficult case to argue to economists who judge the value of a forest by the number of telegraph poles it will produce: until modern economics lifts its eyes from the profit and loss account and takes a longer-term view, the lack of agreement between the two sides of the argument will persist.

The failure of the economic case Having said that, the case for our continued pursuit of forestry is extremely shaky, even using conventional economics. In December 1986, the National Audit Office (NAO) published a report called *Review of Forestry Commission Objectives and Achievements* which was dismissive of British forestry's commercial viability.

The target financial rate of return for trading operations in the public sector has been set at 5 per cent – but forestry operations cannot achieve this figure in the UK, so the Forestry Commission rate of return has been set at 3 per cent. It meets this financial requirement with the help of subsidies for non-commercial activities (recreational use of forestry land, etc.).

However, says the NAO report, 'the Commission expects to achieve an average return of only 2.25 per cent on new investment; and for a large part of its current new planting programme which is on the poorest sites the Commission expects a return of only 1.25 per cent.' Forty per cent of total new planting over the next ten years is planned for the north of Scotland, at a rate of return of only 1.25 per cent.

The government-appointed auditors could see no reason why the Forestry Commission operates at profit levels significantly lower than those expected for other public services. They considered, and rejected, the arguments put forward.

- *The need for a strategic reserve of timber*. This requirement was removed in 1958: '. . . when the forest estate extended to 470,000 ha, little more than half its present size, the strategic objective was removed and replaced by commercial, social, and environmental objectives.'
- *Forestry creates jobs*. 'The costs of job creation in forestry are extremely high. Moreover new planting is a poor method of alleviating the immediate distress of unemployment, as its initial labour needs are small and the larger employment benefits do not arise for 40–50 years.'
- *Only 10 per cent of our timber demands are met from the home market. We need to become more self-sufficient in wood production*. 'In view of the relatively low financial returns which can presently be achieved over most of the Commission's land available for planting, resources currently devoted to planting might be more usefully employed elsewhere in the economy to produce goods whose sale abroad would generate sufficient funds to buy imported timber.'

The NAO concluded:

There appears to be no clear rationale for setting a target for the return on new forestry investment which is substantially lower than that required for other forms of public sector investment. This is particularly so as the non-financial considerations advanced to justify new planting do not appear to be persuasive.

The social case for forestry

There is a social case which can be made for increasing the area of Britain under forest. By comparison with the rest of Europe, the UK's forest estate is small.

Europe's forests

Country	Area nee(mill. ha)	Percentage of total area		
		Forestry	Agriculture	Urban/other
UK	24.1	10	78	13
Benelux	3.3	21	46	33
Denmark	4.2	12	67	21
France	54.6	27	57	16
FRG	24.4	30	58	12
Eire	6.9	6	68	26
Italy	30.1	27	63	10
Neths	3.4	10	72	18
Greece	12.9	45	30	25
Spain	49.9	25	41	34
Portugal	8.6	35	56	9

Source: Forestry Commission, *Forestry Facts and Figures 1987–8*

If the UK wanted a greater diversity of habitat and countryside, it would be logical to expand the area of our forests – but only if the expansion was based on a species mix rather than just on conifers, and if greater public access to the countryside, rather than less, was the result of the new policy. This appears reasonable as the public would underwrite the substantial costs involved.

The current (1985 figures) situation, however, when 0.87 per cent of all Forestry Commission and private planting is broadleaved trees, is not acceptable. Any expansion of Britain's forests should be tied to an agreed policy of greater environmental sensitivity.

Since 1967, the Forestry Commission has actually had a special responsibility to cater for public recreation and to enhance the beauty of the countryside. The latter led to the employment of landscape architects, who recommended softening the edges of conifer forests with hardwood and larches, and taking more care about how trees were felled: arguably a cosmetic policy but at least one that nodded in the direction of environmental awareness.

In terms of recreational facilities, however, the Forestry Commission has achieved results: there are now 646 forest walks and nature trails on Forestry Commission land, 624 picnic places, 32 camp sites, 17 visitor centres, 20 arboreta, 8 forest drives, and 191 forest cabins and holiday homes. The Commission should be praised for the establishment of these facilities, though some critics say that they are still in short supply, and that their intense usage is an indication of how popular a much expanded programme would be.

Rather than expanding forests in the uplands, many conservationists hold the view that new broadleaf woods should be established in the more fertile soil of the lowlands, in place of heavily-subsidized cereal crops. New developments in the EC, especially the imposition of crop quotas, may make this a more attractive proposition. In the meantime, the suggestion is being strongly resisted by lowland farmers, and by the owners of large private estates – the current beneficiaries of our strange forestry subsidies.

Private forestry schemes

The criticisms received by the Forestry Commission are small compared to the obloquy being heaped on the private forestry lobby. This does not apply to all private forestry owners, some of whom have a record of careful husbandry stretching back many years: it is aimed at the tax-loopholers who have been asset-stripping the countryside since the early 1980s.

The tax wangle was criticized by the Parliamentary Committee of Public Accounts, the National Audit Office, the Treasury, the Nature Conservancy Council, the Ramblers' Association, and the Royal Society for the Protection of Birds (among others). It is difficult to find an observer – other than those financially involved – who can justify the continuance of the loophole. One environmentalist has commented: 'There's no logic or reason for this scheme to go on. The only reason that it does is because the private forestry lobby has powerful friends in government.'

From a (conventional) economic point of view, the scheme produced strange distortions. Competition between the afforestation companies has pushed land prices up to £350 an acre in Scotland and £400 in parts of Wales – if the land is sold for forestry. Sold as grazing land, it will fetch only £50 to £150 per acre.

Tax-breaking trees

The popularity of private forestry is attributed to an accountant who apparently became known as 'the father of the modern forestry movement'. The success of the tax avoidance scheme depended on the ability of forestry owners to determine what type of tax they pay on their forests. A wealthy owner was allowed to buy a forest and choose to be taxed under Schedule D taxation, which allows all expenses in starting and running the forest to be set against tax. For owners paying income tax at the then top rate of 60 per cent, a substantial amount of money was removed from their tax bill.

Normally, full tax on the investment is levied when the trees are felled, and the final profit is made. This could be sidestepped by selling the forest when it is about ten years old. There was no requirement to pay back the planting grant of £100 an acre, ten years' tax avoidance has been achieved, and a profit has been made on the land sale – as land with young trees is worth more than land without. As a bonus, the sale is free of Capital Gains Tax.

The next owner, often a financial institution such as a pension fund, could buy the land and elect to be taxed under Schedule B. This allows a notional income tax, one-third of the annual rental of the land before it was afforested, to be paid – in return for complete exemption from tax when the day of profit finally arrives. The institution picks up a long-term investment, with land and timber prices increasing annually, that will yield some £15,000 an acre in timber when the trees are harvested. After that, the land can be sold again.

The scheme, being perfectly legal, was acceptable to wealthy individuals and investing institutions alike. The victims are the tax-payer – who lost, according to the National Audit Office, £10 million a year – and the environment. There is little tax efficiency in environmental protection.

The result is that large areas of Scotland are being covered with conifers for no reasons other than tax avoidance. Nearly 90 per cent of all afforestation in Britain takes place in Scotland, with the area under conifer afforestation increasing by 750 square miles in the last ten years.

The trade is serviced by four main companies whose aim, apparently, is to buy new land for planting. A company might manage 200,000 acres of existing plantations, which do not provide the high turnover and quick profits of 10,000 acres of new planting. The incentive is to cover more and more of Scotland with coniferous tax perks.

Environmentally, this takes a heavy toll. The most recent example of coniferization is in the Flow Country in Caithness and Sutherland – described by an independent group of experts as 'the largest and finest example of a landscape which is a thousand years old', and ranked as one of the world's outstanding ecosystems, equivalent in importance to the African Serengeti or the South American rainforests.

A report by the RSPB has outlined the environmental consequences of afforestation in the area, and the threat it poses to the bird population – 70 per cent of Britain's greenshanks, 22 per cent of dunlins, 11 per cent of golden plovers, as well as 11 species requiring special protection under the EC Directive on the Conservation of Wild Birds. The intrusion on the peatland would rip up part of an area of international standard because of its hydrology, vegetation and ornithology; and forestry in the Flow Country would only be achieved with great difficulty, because the land is so unsuitable for planting. In normal market conditions, the planting of this area would be completely untenable, but because of the tax subsidies available, afforestation would provide returns of between 18 and 33 per cent on the original investment.

In March 1988, the government announced the abolition of the tax-avoidance facility – but also announced that its target of planting 33,000 hectares of new forest each year was to remain unchanged. A new system of grants was introduced, which trebled the grant available for large-scale conifer plantations, and doubled the grant for broadleaves. In November, the government yielded to pressure from its political heartland, and told the Forestry Commission not to plant conifers in unimproved land in England over 800 ft above sea level. The instruction did not apply to Scotland and Wales, where most planting occurs.

The Forestry Commission's new role

In August 1985, an amendment to the Wildlife and Countryside Act laid a general duty on the Forestry Commission to achieve a balance between afforestation and environmental conservation. The government made a parliamentary statement in July 1985, committing itself to stemming the depletion of Britain's broadleaved woods, especially the ancient woodlands, which have shrunk rapidly since 1945. The Forestry Commission revised its grant policy to make broadleaved planting more financially attractive, and has produced a number of publications stressing its role in protecting the environment and in encouraging the growth of broadleaved woods.

On the other hand, government legislation has weakened the Forestry Commission's policing role in the establishment of new forests, and the continuing existence of tax subsidy has led to an acceleration of conifer planting. The Forestry Commission has slowed down its planting programme, but the slack has been taken up by private interests. Private planting has more than doubled in the last five years.

Conifer and broadleaved new planting, 1985–6

	Conifer	Broadleaf
Private	18,170 ha	849 ha
Forestry Commission	4,277 ha	56 ha

Source: Forestry Commission, *66th Annual Report*, 1985–6

In addition, the overall health of the British forests appears to be declining rapidly, with an overall decline exactly the same in character and scale as in Western Germany. The most likely central cause of this is ACID RAIN.

The Forestry Commission survey of tree health in the UK, published in December 1988, divided 1,800 surveyed trees into four classes, according to their crown density (i.e. how thick their foliage was). The survey system works by comparing each tree to an 'ideal' specimen, and estimating how much foliage is missing. The four classes are:

> Class 0: 0–10% reduction in crown density.
> Class 1: 11–25% reduction.
> Class 2: 26–60% reduction.
> Classes 3 + 4: 61–100% reduction.

Only 41 per cent of all broadleaves, and 33 per cent of conifers, were classified as Class 0 (i.e. had lost less than 10 per cent of their foliage compared to an 'ideal' tree). A quarter of the survey trees had lost more than 25 per cent of their foliage, and almost two-fifths had between 11 and 25 per cent loss of crown density.

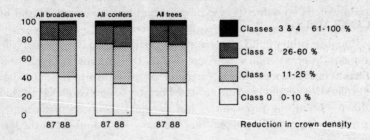

Comparison of 1987 and 1988 grid survey results. The presentation follows the format adopted by the ECE for these types of data.

Source: Forestry Commission Note 139, 1988

See also ACID RAIN; COUNTRYSIDE IN THE UK; DEFORESTATION

REFERENCES

Dudley, Nigel, *The Death of Trees*, Pluto Press, 1984.

Forestry Commission, *Forestry in England, Scotland and Wales*, 1985.

Forestry Commission, *66th Annual Report*, 1985–6.

Forestry Commission, *Forestry Facts and Figures 1985–6*.

Forestry Commission, *Forestry Facts and Figures 1987–8*.

Lowe, Philip, et al., *Countryside Conflicts*, Gower / Temple Smith, 1986.

Price, Colin, et al., 'The Environment in Forestry Policy', in Goldsmith and Hildyard, *Green Britain or Industrial Wasteland*, Polity Press, 1986.

Pye-Smith, Charlie and Chris Rose, *Crisis and Conservation*, Penguin Books, 1984.

National Audit Office, *Review of Forestry Commission Objectives and Achievements*, December 1986.

United Kingdom Acid Waters Review Group Second Report, *Acidity in United Kingdom Fresh Waters*, Department of Environment, December 1988.

Environment Digest, April and November 1988.

Forestry Commission, *Research Information Note 139*, Forest Health Surveys 1988. Preliminary Results, 1988.

'Forestry in the Flows of Caithness and Sutherland', *Birds* (RSPB magazine), June 1987.

McClusky, Jim, 'Shroud for the British Landscape', *Landscape Design*, December 1986.

Mills, Stephen, 'Forestry in Britain: Planting for Alternative Futures', *New Scientist*, 4 August 1983.

Tompkins, Steve, 'Birds, Conifers and Money', *Birds* (RSPB magazine), Autumn 1986.

CONTACTS

Council for the Protection of Rural England

Elms Across Europe

Friends of the Earth

Greenpeace

Men of the Trees

Soil Association

Country Landowners' Association

Forestry Commission

Genetic Engineering

'Genetic engineering' is a new science, largely developed over the last 20 years, that reaches into the territory of a number of other sciences. Broadly speaking, it refers to the practice of changing the properties of a living organism by adding, removing or copying genes (i.e. the internal parts of a cell that transmit particular characteristics from a parent to an offspring).

The purposes of genetic engineering are varied, from trying to cure disease, to furthering human knowledge, to making enormous amounts of money. The likely consequences of the research also cover a wide spectrum of possibilities.

Biotechnology

Discussion of genetic engineering can be confusing, as definitions of the science vary. Some observers argue that it is not, strictly speaking, a science at all, but rather a tool that can work for industry in a number of ways – rather like 'information science'. It has also been described as one of the practical applications of molecular biology (a tradition that started a century ago in chemistry, that of understanding life in terms of its underlying molecular structures).

The most commonly accepted definition places it as a strand of biotechnology, which is defined by the Biotechnology Directorate of the Science and Engineering Research Council (SERC) as: 'The application of biological organisms, systems, and processes to manufacturing and service industries' – a very broad (and somewhat incomprehensible) definition which appears to cover anything that grows, is processed and can be sold. 'Biotechnology' thus includes more traditional food-processing such as brewing, distilling and food manufacturing – although this definition appears to be being replaced by a 'new' biotechnology, which according to SERC incorporates certain developments. These can be summarized as:

Basic progress in understanding DNA (see below)

Development of techniques to screen, choose and grow useful micro-organisms

Development of techniques to manipulate, change, or mix together genetic material in a cell, in order to change the way it operates

Development of techniques for developing plant cells and tissues, to be used for growing crops

Developments in biochemical engineering.

How genetic engineering works

The basis of genetics is that parents pass on some of their distinguishing characteristics to their children ('parents' here can mean humans, animals, plants or any other living organism). Most living things are objects of unbelievable complexity: Richard Dawkins in *The Blind Watchmaker* (1986) points out that the human body is a truly colossal population of some 10 trillion cells, all descended from one ancestor, the fertilized egg in the mother's womb. This egg contains within its own cells the blueprint for making a human body: when these cells split, the blueprint is passed on to the resulting cells, which split and pass them further. A few dozen generations of splitting produce cell populations in the thousands of millions, all related to each other, and all working from the same internal blueprint.

The blueprint is called DNA (deoxyribonucleic acid), and is a chemical present in all living things. It was discovered as recently as 1944: in 1953, Watson and Crick achieved international fame by working out what it looked like – the famous, and complex, 'double helix'.

The DNA molecule is enormous by molecular standards – looking somewhat like two chains, wrapped round each other like strands in a rope. The 'links' in the chain are the basic units of information, and are called 'bases'. There are four bases in DNA, which work like letters in an alphabet: the arrangement of the bases along the chain forms a code, which when decoded is the 'blueprint' for the body it is constructing. Different parts of the blueprint are read to perform different bodily functions, but the parts work together because all the cells 'agree' as to the whole.

It is difficult to imagine the complexity of the message that is being conveyed. Bains (in *Genetic Engineering for Almost Everybody*, 1987) comments that the actual DNA molecule is a quarter of a millionth of a centimetre across, but even so, if all the DNA in a fertilized human egg could be put together in one long double helix, it would be two metres long. If this were magnified until it was as wide as a cassette tape, it would be over 2,800 km long and would take more than two years to play on a taperecorder.

DNA structure varies between organisms, but is always built around the four bases. Genetic engineering became theoretically possible when it was realized that certain parts of the chain controlled certain genetic functions – hair colour, size, number of fingers, etcetera. If parts of the chain could become detached, this would affect the genetic message being passed on.

Genetic engineering became practically possible in the early 1970s, when it was discovered that certain enzymes would split the chain in such a way that parts of a different chain, from a different organism, could be attached to it. The result? A new DNA molecule, one never seen before. This new DNA was called 'recombinant DNA', or rDNA for short.

History of genetic engineering

The possibility of creating hybrid plants, or, more explosively, hybrid animals, by altering their genetic structure, raised some serious ethical questions. In an unusual move, the scientific community imposed a worldwide ban on the use of recombinant DNA techniques in 1975, while it tried to sort out the philosophical and moral dilemmas. This ban was relaxed after a short period of time, and nowadays, according to Bains, thousands of laboratories with tens of thousands of employees around the world perform recombinant DNA research.

In 1979, a small research company called Genentech put its shares on the open market, listing future possible products such as insulin, interferon, various hormones and vaccines: the value of their shares doubled within a few hours of trading. Commercial genetic research had arrived.

Funds poured in and research mushroomed. The number of scientists working in biotechnology in British universities doubled between 1983 and 1987, and this figure would have been higher if the universities could have offered long-term jobs instead of short-term contracts. Many scientists left for richer pastures overseas.

Research tends to be in one of three areas: plant and animal research, medical products and enzymes. Medical research has already produced results: Genentech announced that they had produced human insulin in 1978, which after undergoing testing for a number of years was first offered for sale in 1985. This was no mean accomplishment: with 2 million diabetics in the English-speaking world, and an annual increase in numbers of 6 per cent by 1984, a secure supply of insulin was a significant medical discovery.

Other discoveries were less than entirely successful – interferon and sometostatin, the human growth hormone, have yet to fulfil all the expectations placed upon them. The introduction of genetic engineering was accompanied by some very optimistic statements about finding cures for most known ailments – statements later realized to be over-optimistic in view of the complexities and uncertainties of genetic research.

The possibilities are very alluring. General Electric have been developing a bacteria that would 'eat' oil – thus the numerous oilspills round the world (see MARINE POLLUTION) could be cleaned up without the current use of large amounts of detergent and the people to apply it.

Plant research has tended towards making plants more resistant to adverse weather or pests. A frost-resistant bacterium was developed, with the intention of protecting crops. In an interesting development, two research organizations tried to genetically manipulate crop plants to be resistant to the herbicide glyphosate (it is an effective weed-killer, but kills plants too). Plant research has aroused considerable controversy (see below).

The most controversial work, however, has been on animals. A cross between a goat and a sheep has been developed, and was patented in 1987. Transgenic chickens have been produced. Transgenic lambs have been born, carrying the human blood-clotting Factor IX.

Doubts about genetic engineering

There are parallels between the development of genetic engineering and the discovery of nuclear power. Both were occasions of monumental scientific breakthrough, in which mysteries of unbelievable complexity were unravelled through sheer human brilliance. Both opened up avenues of scientific research that were challenging and stimulating enough to attract battalions of extremely talented scientists, which created a scientific impetus behind the discipline.

Both also attracted multi-million-dollar corporations, who scented large profits and gave a business drive to the scientific push.

There is money to be made out of genetic engineering: Stanford University expects to earn $10 million a year by 1992 from the patents on the process for inserting foreign DNA into a bacterial cell. Genentech are attempting to patent a protein called t-PA, which is twice as effective as normal remedies for dissolving blood clots, and could therefore reach a $1 billion a year market catering for people at risk from heart attack. Insulin is an example of an engineered product that is already successful; doubtless there will be others that are just as successful.

On the other hand, there are arguments against genetic engineering. These rest, first, on the basis that it is not just the organism that is altered, but its offspring and the offspring after that. The problem with removing or adding genetic material is that scientists cannot guarantee what side-effects may occur; and once a mistake has been made, the organism cannot be recalled. It has the potential to develop and mutate uncontrollably, in a chain reaction whose consequences are completely unpredictable.

These arguments rest on the 'What if?' question. What will happen if oil-eating bacteria do not die as planned when they have eaten their oil slick, but mutate and look for another source of food? What will happen if pigs implanted with human genes develop viruses that could also damage human health? What will happen if frost-resistant crops become the dominant species, and the world's climate warms a few degrees (see GREENHOUSE EFFECT)?

These questions are dismissed as science-fiction fantasy by genetic scientists, but are of greater concern to ecologists who will have to deal with the wider implications of genetically-altered organisms: the first international conference on the release of genetically-engineered micro-organisms into the environment, at Cardiff in 1988, saw a number of statements from ecologists concerned that 'we know very little of the fate and absolutely nothing of the effects' of released micro-organisms (ENDS Report no. 159). This is of more than academic interest: there were four such releases of manipulated organisms in Britain in 1986–7. These passed without reaction from the environment movement: in the USA, such releases have been the subject of legal challenges by organizations such as Jeremy Rifkin's Foundation for Economic Trends.

The second argument rests on the responsibility of the scientists themselves. A number of techniques have been developed to prevent the release of unlicensed organisms, but these have been circumvented. In 1980, a scientist called Martin Cline, in spite of having had permission for the experiment refused by the American authorities, obtained permission in Israel to attempt to manipulate human marrow cells genetically.

In 1986, an American research organization, the Wistar Institute of Philadelphia, immunized 40 cattle at an Argentine research station with a live virus with a gene coding intended to immunize against rabies: this experiment took place without the knowledge of the Argentine authorities, in what was described by a scientist in ENDS Report no. 159 as 'an inept and incredibly stupid way'. The immunized cattle were milked by hand, their untreated milk was drunk by caretakers who were not vaccinated, and no warning was given on the farm that the experiment was under way.

Another case occurred in 1987, when a scientist injected elm trees with a genetically-altered bacterium, before applying for permission to do so.

These were three of a handful of incidents involving unauthorized release of organisms outside a laboratory – in each case conducted by scientists who were convinced of the rightness of their case, but without official approval. There are possibilities of a mistake with enormous consequences – as there are for military research into possible biological weapons being carried out by the governments of both the USSR and the USA.

The third area of worry about genetic engineering concerns animal research. Groups such as Compassion in World Farming are campaigning strongly against this practice, which they allege causes needless suffering, in the same way as factory farming or vivisection (see ANIMALS). One case they quote, that of a pig born with a human growth gene, resulted in the animal being lethargic, riddled with arthritis and apparently impotent.

Other groups, such as Rifkin's in the USA, are fighting against the American practice of patenting animals that have been genetically manipulated. In April 1987, the US Board of Patent Appeals decided that scientists from Washington University, who had genetically engineered oysters that were larger and tastier than normal, would be able to patent them. Since then, a type of genetically-altered mouse carrying human cancer genes has been patented in the US and is now on the market. At the moment, European law does not allow the patenting of animals, though industry is lobbying hard against this, and in 1989 an EC draft Directive evolved – 'Directive on the Legal Protection of Biotechnological Inventions', which, if passed, would change the situation; the Directive was the subject of heated debate in early 1989. In the UK, the Health and Safety Executive produced voluntary guidelines for research into transgenic animals. The voluntary guidelines would, it was announced, receive legislative backing later in the year.

The idea of owning the rights to an entire subspecies or breed was so startling that it threw up a coalition of environmentalists, farmers and religious groups to fight the decision. The general secretary of the National Council of Churches commented: 'The gift of life from God, in all its forms and species, should not be regarded solely as if it were a chemical product, subject to genetic alteration and patentable for economic benefits.'

This moral dimension could well be the greatest obstacle that genetic engineering has to face. In a way, it is to be hoped that this will be the only problem that the science encounters: if there is a large-scale scandal caused by an organism that 'goes wild', then it will not just be the manufacturers that will suffer: the entire globe could be at risk. In these circumstances, it would seem that a science not yet 21 years old should be treated with extreme caution.

See also ANIMALS; MARINE POLLUTION

REFERENCES

Bains, William, *Genetic Engineering for Almost Everybody*, Penguin Books, 1987.

Dawkins, Richard, *The Blind Watchmaker*, Longman, 1986.

'Altered Organisms Released in Australia', *New Scientist*, 18 June 1987.

Anderson, Ian, 'Activists Savage Outdoor Gene Test Plot', *New Scientist*, 4 June 1987.

Anderson, Ian, 'Rumpus over Rogue Release of Microbes', *New Scientist*, 27 August 1987.

Biotechnology Directorate, 'Monitoring the Biotechnology Labour Market', Science and Engineering Research Council, 1987.

Compassion in World Farming, *Agscene*, May 1988.

Connor, Steve, 'A Rebel with a Cause', *New Scientist*, 11 June 1987.

Connor, Steve, 'The Battle for Britain's Biotechnology', *New Scientist*, 11 August 1988.

Connor, Steve, 'A Licence on Life', *New Scientist*, 20 August 1987.

D'Silva, Joyce, 'Patenting of Animals – A Welfare Viewpoint', *Agscene*, Compassion in World Farming, June 1989.

Environment Digest No. 21, February 1989.

Environmental Data Services (ENDS) Report no. 159, April 1988.

Erlichman, James, 'Warning on Genetic Engineering', *Guardian*, 19 June 1987.

Murphy, Caroline, 'The "new genetics" and the welfare of animals', *New Scientist*, 10 December 1988.

CONTACTS

Agricultural Genetics Company
Celltech
Compassion in World Farming (CIWF)
Foundation for Economic Trends
Genentech
UK Genetics Forum
Natural Environment Research Council
Royal Society for the Prevention of Cruelty to Animals (RSPCA)
Science and Engineering Research Council

The Greenhouse Effect

The 'greenhouse effect' describes the build-up in the atmosphere of pollutant gases which block heat coming from the earth, sending the heat back to the earth's surface rather than allowing it to escape into space. The resulting increase in global temperature caused by this effect is currently small, but appears likely to accelerate over the next century. The consequences of this temperature increase could be extremely disturbing.

How the greenhouse effect works

The sun is the most important source of energy for the earth, sending a spectrum of radiation to the planet, as X-rays, ultraviolet and visible light, infra-red radiation, microwaves and radio waves. Much of this energy arrives as visible light (see RADIATION).

Carbon dioxide, which is present in small quantities in the earth's atmosphere, allows visible light to pass through it. The light waves are absorbed by the earth, which in turn emits radiation, but mostly of a longer wavelength – as infra-red radiation. Carbon dioxide (CO_2) absorbs infra-red radiation, or reflects it back to where it came from.

CO_2 thus works in the same way as glass in a greenhouse, allowing solar radiation to pass through it, but then holding back the longer wavelength radiation that attempts to return. The result is a warmer temperature in the greenhouse than outside it.

This is a natural process, and an essential system for maintaining the earth's temperature. Without carbon dioxide in the atmosphere, the earth's surface would cool very rapidly at night, much more rapidly than at present. On the other hand, increasing or reducing the amount of carbon dioxide in the atmosphere could increase or slow down the speed at which this greenhouse effect occurs. This appears to be happening at the moment: and the process is exacerbated by the presence in the atmosphere of other substances which act in the same way as CO_2.

Carbon dioxide build-up

Carbon dioxide forms a very small part of the earth's atmosphere, which consists roughly of 78 per cent nitrogen, 21 per cent oxygen, 0.9 per cent argon, and 0.03 per cent carbon dioxide. Although small in percentage terms, this is still an enormous amount, approximately 2,600 billion tonnes of CO_2.

The gas is emitted into the atmosphere partly by burning wood but primarily by burning fossil fuels (i.e., coal and oil). At the moment, about 5 billion tonnes of carbon a year are sent into the atmosphere as a result of this process, equivalent to 18 billion tonnes of carbon dioxide. A large proportion is absorbed by the oceans, but about 8 billion tonnes of CO_2 are not assimilated in this way, and remain in the air. This is a significant annual addition to the CO_2 already in the atmosphere.

Concentrations of carbon dioxide are usually measured by checking how much CO_2 there is in a million molecules of air. American measurements on Mauna Loa, Hawaii, indicate that CO_2 concentrations in the air have increased from 312 parts per million (ppm) in 1957 to 350 ppm in 1988: an increase of 38 ppm, or 12 per cent, in under three decades.

Analyses of ice cores suggest that CO_2 concentrations for the last several thousand years have been reasonably close to the preindustrial value of 280 ppm. If this is true, it implies an increase of carbon dioxide concentrations in the air of 25 per cent over the last 100 years.

Global warming

If the greenhouse theory is correct, then a build-up of carbon dioxide in the air would be accompanied by an increase in temperature around the world. This also appears to be happening. Current scientific consensus was outlined at the Villach Conference, 1985, organized by the United Nations Environment Programme, the World Meteorological Organization, and the International Council of Scientific Unions. After the conference, an agreed statement was issued, which said:

• based on analysis of observations, there had been an estimated increase of 0.3 to 0.7 degrees C in global mean temperature over the last 100 years;

• this increase was consistent with the observed increase in CO_2 and other greenhouse gases, though the scientific proof of this was not firmly established;

• carbon dioxide was not the only gas contributing to the greenhouse effect: other gases building up in the troposphere include nitrous oxide, methane, chlorofluorocarbons and tropospheric (i.e., low-level) ozone;

• the cumulative effect of the build-up of these gases, if current rates continue, would be equivalent to a doubling of CO_2 from pre-industrial levels, possibly as early as the 2030s;

• if atmospheric carbon dioxide levels double, it is assumed that the mean surface temperature of the globe would increase by between 1.5 and 4.5 degrees C.

Fears about global warming

Although a global temperature rise of some 3 degrees C does not seem an excessive amount, it has caused consternation among scientists and environmentalists: in a period spanning half a human generation, the globe would experience an overall warming greater than has occurred throughout the history of humanity. In the eleventh to thirteenth centuries, the world was less than 1 degree C warmer than today, there were vineyards in southern Britain, Greenland was green (and colonized by Vikings), and Switzerland suffered attacks by locusts. A temperature increase three times greater than this – some models indicate there will be a 4 degrees C, or even 6 degrees C, increase – would have very radical consequences. The shaded spike on the graph (opposite) shows the marked contrast between projected temperature increases and the experience of the last thousand years.

A temperature increase of such a scale is so alien to human experience that it is very difficult to forecast the outcome. A number of scenarios have been outlined, however, none of which are particularly comforting:

Serious climatic changes The popular misconception that the greenhouse effect would be beneficial ('open-air cafés in Scunthorpe') is wrong. Large areas of the world will experience climatic shocks: some

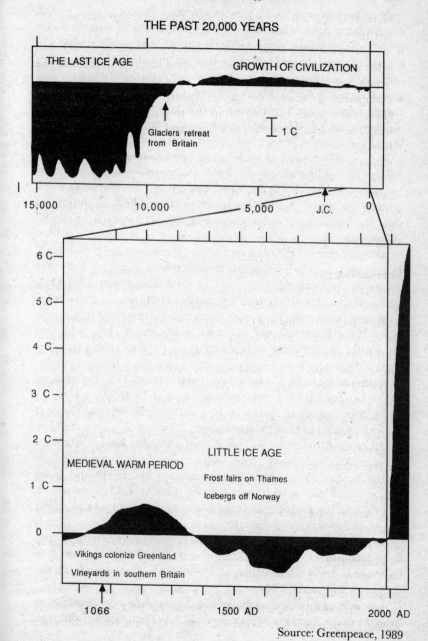

THE PAST 20,000 YEARS

THE LAST ICE AGE

GROWTH OF CIVILIZATION

Glaciers retreat
from Britain

1 C

15,000   10,000   5,000   J.C.   0

6 C

5 C

4 C

3 C

2 C

1 C

0

MEDIEVAL WARM PERIOD

LITTLE ICE AGE

Frost fairs on Thames

Icebergs off Norway

Vikings colonize Greenland

Vineyards in southern Britain

1066   1500 AD   2000 AD

Source: Greenpeace, 1989

regions may lose up to 30 per cent of their annual rainfall – with concomitant problems relating to agriculture, food supply, forest health, soil moisture, drinking-water supply, and public health. (In Britain the Institute of Hydrology believes global warming could result in a 40 per cent drop in water collecting in our reservoirs, leading to widespread water shortages.) Other areas may gain 60 per cent in annual rainfall – with problems caused by storm damage, agricultural loss, flash flooding, and implications for public health. Third World countries, dependent on one crop, face economic disaster.

Sea level rise　The temperature of the oceans would increase, leading to some melting of Arctic ice, which could result in a rise in sea levels around the world. Surface ocean temperatures have already risen since the beginning of the century by between 0.3 and 0.9 degrees C, an increase that correlates to the warming of the land. Sea-level measurements over the same period suggest an average global rise of 15 centimetres (nearly all of this attributable to the expansion of the oceans as they warm). What will happen if atmospheric CO_2 levels double is a matter for argument: estimates of the resulting rise in sea level vary between an increase of 30 and 150 centimetres by the year 2050. If the latter increase occurred, many major cities would be inundated: the projected rises would occur 100 times faster than has occurred globally before.

When the sea rises, coastal areas are eroded or flooded. Populations could be defended by sea defences, but at huge cost. The US government estimates that, if current trends continue, it will have to spend $3 billion to protect its coastline.

Other countries more at risk do not have this kind of financial solution at their disposal. A one-metre sea-level rise would flood over 10 per cent of Bangladesh. Other countries like Egypt and India would suffer on a widespread basis. Half the Commonwealth countries in the Pacific – all small island nations – are at risk. Some would disappear.

As it is the fertile, food-growing delta areas which are most at risk, large food-growing regions would be lost. Drinking water would be poisoned because of salination. Starvation on a huge scale threatens.

Climate refugees　Forced by starvation, agricultural loss, flooding, or drought, large numbers of people would be moving within countries and between them. The United Nations is already considering what to do with the world's 'climate refugees': they will be the most visible symbol of the global disruption that has caused their upheaval.

The greenhouse effect now

All the above is concerned with possible future effects of climate change – and, as such, they are hypothetical. What of the greenhouse effect now?

One of the leading climatic scientists in the USA, Dr James Hansen of NASA, told a Congressional hearing in June 1988: 'It is time to stop waffling so much and say that the evidence is pretty strong that the greenhouse effect is here.' Fred Pearce, in *Turning Up The Heat* (1989) lists the reasons why Hansen's comment was timely:

- that week, the US Agricultural Department had listed half the counties in the country as suffering from drought;
- half the grain crop was lost;
- almost 2,000 barges sat useless on the Mississippi River: water levels were ten metres below normal. There was too little water to keep the barges afloat on a river with the third-largest drainage basin in the world;
- Hansen had a computer model showing that the first five months of 1988 had set the world on target for the warmest year since records began 130 years earlier (his model was right – the British Meteorological Office announced in February 1989 that the previous year was the hottest on record);
- Hansen also knew that 1987 was the previous record-holder for world temperature, with the third-, fourth- and fifth-hottest years being in the 1980s also – 1980, 1981 and 1983.

In their book, *The Greenhouse Effect* (1989), Stewart Boyle and John Ardill give some international contexts for events that occurred in 1988:

- three-quarters of Bangladesh was inundated by a huge flood, with a quarter of its population being made homeless. Three thousand died in the monsoon floods, and 5,000 died in a tropical cyclone;
- in the Anhui Province of China, 70,000 wells ran dry but elsewhere in the country more than 1,400 died in floods and storms;
- one in four Jamaicans became homeless and the island's economy was in tatters in the wake of Hurricane Gilbert;

- Hurricane Joan flattened 15,000 square kilometres of forest in Nicaragua, and devastated the town of Bluefields;
- in the drought-stricken heart of Africa, 200 millimetres of rain fell on Khartoum in less than 24 hours. More than a million were made homeless. Gabon had its first floods in 20 years. Desert Africa was on the verge of the worst locust plague on record;
- for the first time in a decade, India is buying grain on the world market.

It may be argued that these were isolated incidents – coincidence. This could well be true. In May 1989, however, the environmental computer network GreenNet carried a round-up of climatic catastrophes:

- in the USA, April 1989 was the third-driest since 1895. Extreme or severe drought was occurring in most of California, Nevada, Arizona, Utah, Wyoming, Kansas and Iowa. Additionally, portions of north-east Oregon, central Washington, Idaho, western Montana, North Dakota, central Minnesota, Nebraska, northern Missouri, western Illinois and south-east Texas contained areas of severe or extreme drought. The author of this report, Nicholas A. Sundt, of the US Office of Technological Assessment, commented that 30 per cent of the US was under drought conditions. At the same time in 1988, the figure had been 20 per cent;
- the US wheat stockpile, badly hit by the drought of 1988, was expected to be one of the smallest since World War II. The '88 drought hit grain-producing areas in Canada, the USA, Australia, Argentina and the Soviet Union. The world food reserves shrank to a 57-day supply, according to the Worldwatch Institute. The commodities market was getting very jumpy, because of the combination of low reserves, uncertain weather forecasts, and major uncertainties about national and international grain requirements. 'Less-developed' countries requiring substantial grain imports which would be hard hit by increased prices included Angola, Bangladesh, Ethiopia, Haiti, Jamaica, Laos, Lebanon, Mozambique, Nicaragua, Peru, Sierra Leone, Somalia, Sri Lanka, Sudan and Vietnam;
- portions of Uruguay and Argentina had been dry for nearly twelve months – cutting wheat production by 20 per cent and corn production by a third;

- the 1988 US drought was matched by similar conditions in Canada. In 1989, also, Canada was experiencing severe drought conditions in some areas;
- large parts of the Soviet Union experienced the warmest winter for 40 years.

These climatic disturbances are not proof that the greenhouse effect has arrived – but they are the types of disorders that would be expected when climatic change begins to occur. If 1988 or 1989 were not the years when the greenhouse effect arrived, they would not be too far removed in time – with the size of the global temperature expected, the arrival of the greenhouse effect should be anticipated for some time in the 1990s, if it is not here now.

The greenhouse gases

It is not just carbon dioxide that contributes to the greenhouse effect: there are four other pollutants that are credited with contributing to global warming. Estimates vary, but the typical analysis of different contributions is usually taken from Hansen (*Journal of Geophysical Research*, August 1988):

*Relative contribution of greenhouse gases
to global warming in the 1980s*

Carbon Dioxide	50%
Methane	18%
Chlorofluorocarbons	14%
Tropospheric ozone, etc	12%
Nitrous oxide	6%

Water vapour is also a significant greenhouse gas but is not usually quantified because of its large-scale natural occurrences.

Carbon dioxide CO_2 is released into the air by burning coal, oil or gas, with coal-burning being by far the largest contributor. About 13 per cent of the gas emitted from coal-burning power stations, for instance, is CO_2. Equipment exists to remove CO_2 from these emissions. If all power stations in the USA used this equipment, CO_2 emissions would be cut by 10 per cent. If the whole world used the technology, emissions would drop by 30 per cent.

This could be achieved at a cost, in 1980 prices, of $15 per tonne of CO_2 removed – but there would be an enormous problem of disposal of liquid carbon dioxide afterwards, which would have to be piped to 3,000 metres below sea level before being dumped. Electricity prices would have to increase by 50 to 70 per cent to pay the costs of this.

A more attractive solution would be to redesign power stations, and make better use of energy in factories, homes and on the roads. If these were planned in an effort to conserve energy, rather than using energy as a disposable throwaway product, fossil fuel demand could be reduced by up to 50 per cent – the most intelligent way of reducing carbon dioxide emissions (see ENERGY: CONSERVATION). This presupposes a change of philosophy in planners, politicians, and energy suppliers.

Chlorofluorocarbons (CFCs) CFCs' contribution to the greenhouse effect could be the second largest (after CO_2) in the next 50 years, although not currently. Restriction in production of CFCs seems likely in the future, as this is the best way of preventing their build-up in the atmosphere (see OZONE LAYER).

Ozone The problems with this gas occur in two areas: in the troposphere, near the earth's surface, and in the stratosphere, higher up. The higher concentrations form the OZONE LAYER, which shields the earth from harmful ultraviolet rays. Depletion of ozone at this height would result in greater entry of ultraviolet light to earth, increasing the energy reaching the earth's surface, and assisting the greenhouse effect. Prevention of this occurrence would entail reduction of CFC emission.

Build-up of ozone in the troposphere is the result of emissions of nitrogen oxides and hydrocarbons (see ACID RAIN), primarily from power stations, vehicles and the use of solvents. There is evidence that tropospheric ozone is increasing over North America and Europe: it has been calculated that a doubling in this concentration throughout the entire troposphere would lead to a one degree C increase in surface air temperature.

The technology for minimizing nitrogen oxide and hydrocarbon emissions from motor vehicles is already well-established, and has been fitted to a third of the world's car fleet, though not to Britain's (see AUTOMOBILE POLLUTION). Technology for reductions of nitrogen oxides from power stations is already being introduced into Japan, though not yet to the rest of the world (see ACID RAIN).

Protection of the ozone layer, and reduction of low-level ozone build-up, could both be achieved using current knowledge. International political will, however, is also essential.

Nitrous oxide Tropospheric nitrous oxide (N_2O) has increased over the last few years. Caused by extensive use of nitrogen fertilizer, by combustion of wood and fossil fuels, and partly by the chemical industry, emissions of N_2O are likely to increase less rapidly as a result of fuel consumption trends and limits on the amount of land available for cultivation. On the other hand, N_2O can stay in the atmosphere for about 170 years, so concentrations of the gas are expected to increase by a significant proportion during the next few decades. Figures of 20 to 50 per cent have been suggested: how to achieve N_2O reductions in the atmosphere is not yet a subject of complete scientific agreement.

Methane Released in the production of coal and natural gas, by burning vegetation and as a result of intensive cattle farming, methane concentrations began to increase 300 years ago but have accelerated over the last 20 years, increasing in the atmosphere by 1 to 2 per cent per year. There is considerable uncertainty over the reasons for this increase.

The systems of production for these gases described above are all human-based. All of the gases except CFCs are also created naturally, but the mechanisms for their formation are not described here. The argument put forward by the Villach conference is that artificial production of these gases is disturbing the atmospheric equilibrium, and that:

> While some warming of climate now seems inevitable due to past actions, the rate and degree of future warming could be profoundly affected by government policies on energy conservation, use of fossil fuels, and the emission of some greenhouse gases.

Scientific uncertainties and Doomsday scenarios
The Villach comment about inevitable warming because of past actions touches on the centre of the greenhouse problem: world

climate depends on a number of variables which will, as likely as not, combine in unpredictable ways. The relationship between the oceans and the global carbon cycle is central to this.

The Biogeochemical Ocean Flux Study (BOFS) report (1989) gives one of the best descriptions of this relationship. More heat is stored in the top five metres of the oceans than in all the earth's atmosphere (around 25 per cent of the heat input to Britain is first absorbed by the surface waters of the North Atlantic, before being released to warm the air). The oceans are also the major natural factor determining the carbon dioxide content of the atmosphere – with carbon inputs from human activity being small in comparison to natural ocean–atmosphere exchanges. There is nearly 50 times more carbon in the oceans than in the atmosphere, and around 20 times more than on land (in plants, animals and soil). The relationship between the oceans and the air is critical to the carbon dioxide content of the atmosphere – the seas can either slow down or speed up the rate of temperature change caused by human activity.

The ocean's role in absorbing atmospheric carbon is inadequately understood, but it appears to be related to temperature. As sea water cools in polar regions, the solubility of CO_2 increases, and the gas is absorbed into the sea. When this water wells up in near-equatorial regions, CO_2 is released into the atmosphere. BOFS estimates that there is an annual uptake by the oceans of 105 billion tonnes of carbon, with an annual release of 102 billion tonnes. These figures are admitted to be back-of-an-envelope guesstimates based on the fact that nearly half of the humanly produced CO_2 in the atmosphere seems to disappear.

The oceans appear to act as a storage facility for both heat and carbon dioxide, taking them in to release them later on. For this reason, most scientists believe that we are already committed to an amount of global warming – because of atmospheric pollution absorbed by the oceans, but due to be returned.

The uncertainties are enormous – based around cloud formation and reflectivity, hydrological cycles, the contribution of deforestation, and the interaction of pollutants. Some scenarios are frightening, however. Geologists are very concerned by the amount of methane – billions of tonnes – trapped beneath the tundra as 'clathrates'. If substantial Arctic warming were to take place, the clathrates could release huge quantities of methane into the atmosphere. Methane is 20 to 30 times more effective as a greenhouse gas than carbon dioxide: once the clathrates start emitting the gas, a positive feedback would develop ('positive feedbacks' can be explained by describing the process of rolling a boulder down a hill: one push, and it gains its own momentum). The methane would lead to global warming, which would lead to more methane emission, *ad infinitum*. This, one of the worst of climatologists' nightmares, is called the 'runaway greenhouse effect'. Fears such as these are prompting international moves to halt global warming.

How to stop the greenhouse effect

No one has yet developed the solution to the greenhouse effect – the sources of pollution are widespread, ranging from transport to electricity to gas to oil to agriculture to deforestation; and the solution to global warming lies not in the hands of one country, but of all. Savings in carbon emissions in one part of the world are useless if negated in another.

The greenhouse effect is largely the product of the industrialized nations, however, as they are the world's largest energy users (see ENERGY), CFC producers and consumers, car manufacturers and users, and enthusiasts for nitrogen fertilizers. The solution to the greenhouse effect needs a radical rethink of the entire Western industrialized lifestyle – and of the financial interrelationships between North and South.

The solutions to the greenhouse effect will be difficult, expensive, and involve some sacrifice. Third World countries will expect those responsible for the greenhouse effect to carry the burden of repairing it.

Nuclear power and the greenhouse effect

The key to the solution of the greenhouse effect is not in cleaning up greenhouse emissions: this is not possible on the scale that is necessary. The solution is not to emit the pollutant in the first place. CO_2 emissions are prevented by rigorous conservation of energy; tropospheric ozone, by energy conservation and a switch away from the internal combustion engine; methane and nitrous oxide, by getting rid of nitrogen fertilizers, moving away from dairy farming, and examining all agricultural crops for their methane output. The age of the technological fix has disappeared: the important thing is to avoid the creation of the pollutant in the first place.

Nuclear power is thus an irrelevance in solving the greenhouse effect. Coal-fired power stations contribute some 10 per cent of the greenhouse problem, so replacing all of them with nuclear power stations would remove only one-tenth of the greenhouse effect. If this were to be done, and energy use to go on as normal, one nuclear power station would need to be built every one to two days for the next 38 years to meet the demand for nuclear power (according to a study by Keepin and Kats). There would be enormous nuclear proliferation at a time of great international instability: the cost (£80 billion a year) would drain the economies of many Third World countries, and sterilize other initiatives for solving the greenhouse effect – and the risk of serious nuclear accidents would multiply. Other greenhouse pollutants would continue to be produced, and global warming would continue.

See also ACID RAIN; AUTOMOBILE POLLUTION; ENERGY; OZONE LAYER

REFERENCES

Association for the Conservation of Energy, *Solutions to Global Warming*, 1989.

Biogeochemical Ocean Flux Study (BOFS), *Oceans and the Global Carbon Cycle*, NERC Marine Services Directorate, May 1989.

Boyle, S. and J. Ardill, *The Greenhouse Effect*, New English Library, 1989.

Breuer, G., *Air in Danger*, Cambridge University Press, 1980.

Pearce, Fred, *Turning Up the Heat*, Bodley Head, 1989.

Royal Commission on Environmental Pollution, *Tenth Report*, 1980.

UK Photochemical Oxidants Review Group, *Ozone in the United Kingdom*, 1987.

UNEP/GEMS, *The Greenhouse Gases*, 1987.

World Resources Institute, IIED, *World Resources 1986*, Basic Books, 1986.

'Global Warming Chills Europe', *New Scientist*, 22 January 1987.

GreenNet, May 1989: Climate Institute, 'British Met. Office reports 1988 warmest year' and 'Drought poses threat to world agriculture', *Climate Alert*, Vol. 2, No.1, Spring 1989.

Shabecoff, P., 'EPA proposes rules to curb warming', *New York Times*, 14 March 1989.

Sundt, N. A., 'Drought Update', 24 May 1989.

Gribbin, J., 'The longer range forecast', *Guardian*, 15 August 1986.

Keepin, Bill and Gregory Kats, 'Greenhouse warming: comparative analysis of nuclear and efficiency abatement strategies', in *Energy Policy*, Vol. 16, no. 6, Butterworths, December 1988.

Pearce, F., 'How to Stop the Greenhouse Effect', *New Scientist*, 18 September 1986.

Schneider, S. H., 'The Greenhouse Effect: Science and Policy', *Science*, 10 February 1989.

Tucker, Anthony, 'Spectre of the "Greenhouse Effect" Fades', *Guardian*, 6 January 1987.

CONTACTS

Association for the Conservation of Energy

Climate Action Network

The Commonwealth Secretariat

Council for the Protection of Rural England (CPRE)

Council for the Protection of Rural Scotland

Council for the Protection of Rural Wales

EC

Friends of the Earth (FoE)

Greenpeace

IIED

Institute of Terrestrial Ecology (ITE)

Natural Environment Research Council (NERC)

Nature Conservancy Council (NCC)

Transport 2000

UKCEED

UK Department of Energy

UK Department of the Environment

UNECE

UNEP

World Resources Institute

World Wide Fund for Nature

Marine Pollution

Seven-tenths of the Earth is covered by water, in a continuous ecosystem broken only by intermittent land masses. The oceans perform an important role in moderating the earth's climate: they are also the source of an enormous range of plant and animal life. *The Gaia Atlas of Planet Management* (edited by Norman Myers, 1985) gives an excellent description of both these functions.

The major currents of the oceans deliver huge masses of water over long distances, providing a continuous interchange between warm equatorial water and cold polar areas (see ANTARCTICA); the enormous quantities of water in the seas absorb extremes of climatic change, providing a powerful buffer for what would otherwise be drastic fluctuations in our weather; and the oceans' capacity to absorb gases in enormous quantities has (until recently) been one of the successful regulators of carbon dioxide in the air (see GREENHOUSE EFFECT).

The oceans are extremely fertile in the number of life forms they support. At the most basic level, phytoplankton (Greek for 'drifting plants') flourish in a thin layer of water stretching to 100 metres in depth, exploiting the energy from the sun and nutrients in the water to expand and multiply. They form the food supply for zooplankton – animal grazers, frequently single-celled creatures, but ranging in size up to flatworms, small jellyfish and shrimps.

These two types of plankton are so abundant that, according to the *Gaia Atlas*, they are estimated to generate, respectively, 16 billion and 1.6 billion tonnes of carbon (the basic material of living tissue) each year. They form the food source for a variety of larger creatures, which in turn have an annual productivity of around 160 million tonnes. Plankton-eating species, particularly the herring family, supply humans with about two-fifths of their fish.

Areas of greatest plankton abundance are found where the seas are rich in nutrients (i.e. useful food). The ocean environment is as varied as its terrestrial equivalent, with ranges of mountains, semi-desert areas and places of extreme fertility. The most productive places are along the coasts of the land masses: these receive a number of nutrients washed from the land to the sea, which feed a range of life forms in the warmer, shallower waters around the coast.

Less than 1 per cent of the seas are occupied by coastal ecosystems (the vast bulk of ocean being the less productive open seas, or the slightly more productive continental shelf). The four main types of coastal ecosystem are: estuaries; tidal wetlands of temperate zones (i.e. saltmarshes); their equivalents in tropical zones (i.e. mangroves); and coral reefs. All are facing particular problems in relation to human activity, connected with development (see WETLANDS) or pollution. Pollutants can be transported into the marine environment along rivers (see WATER: UK RIVERS, ESTUARIES, AND GROUNDWATERS) or can arrive via the air (see ACID RAIN). Substantial quantities of pollution are deposited deliberately in the seas via pipelines or from ships.

The various types of marine pollution can be roughly classified as: oil, sewage, persistent pollutants and radioactive materials.

Oil

Oil pollution of the oceans is a newsworthy event in the UK. Various episodes have highlighted the effects of oilspills on our wildlife:

- the sinking of the *Torrey Canyon* in 1967, whose leakage of 50,000 tonnes of Kuwaiti oil killed seabirds in oil slicks from Cornwall to Guernsey;

- the wrecking of the supertanker *Amoco Cadiz* in 1978. More than 200,000 tonnes of crude oil killed 30,000 seabirds, as well as 230,000 tonnes of fish and shellfish, along 100 miles of Brittany's coastline (the $85.2 million awarded by a US court in January 1988 was barely enough to cover clean-up costs; the French government is appealing for compensation of $1.6 billion); the case was still unsettled by mid-1989;

- the grounding of the *Kowloon Bridge* on the west coast of Ireland in November 1986: the ship oozed from her 1,200 tonnes of bunker oil – stickier and more environmentally damaging than crude – for more than two months, again killing thousands of birds and polluting over 70 miles of Irish coast;

- the grounding of the *Exxon Valdez* in March 1989. Some 250,000 barrels (about 10 million gallons) of oil were spilled in Prince William Sound, Alaska, when the ship, piloted illegally by the third mate, struck two charted reefs and ran aground. Because of inadequate environmental protection measures by the oil industry, the oil slick was not contained and in six days covered an area of 100 square miles. By the end of April, the 3,000-square-mile slick had coated some 300 miles of shoreline. The spill, the largest recorded in the USA, occurred in what a University of Alaska biologist described as 'one of the most productive marine environments in the world', at a time when young sea creatures were hatching, and other animals were laying eggs. The waters are home to one of the world's ten largest populations of the rare sea otter, more than 200 bird species, whales, seals, porpoises and sea-lions.

Yet, surprisingly enough, oilspills from wrecked ships are not the major cause of oil pollution at sea. The United Nations Environment Programme (UNEP), in *The State of the World Environment 1987*, reckons that 500,000 tonnes of the 1.6 million annually discharged into the sea by shipping is released accidentally: the remainder is non-accidental in origin and results from regular discharge by ships of contaminated ballast water and water used for flushing out tanks.

Sanger (in *Ordering the Oceans*, 1986), even more surprisingly, points to a 1975 study by the US National Academy of Sciences: they estimated that 6 million tonnes of oil per year was entering the oceans. More than half of this comes from land-based sources – from coastal facilities like oil refineries, from oilwell blow-outs and leakages, and fallout from the atmosphere, but mostly coming via run-off from rivers and city drains. More oil enters the oceans from automobile exhausts, and from oil-changes in city garages that are then dumped down the drain, than from any other source.

More recent figures (*World Resources 1987*) estimated total marine oil pollution at 3.5 million tonnes, with 48 per cent coming from land. Again, municipal and industrial wastes represent the single largest source.

Sewage

UNEP has pointed out that the discharge of untreated or partially treated domestic waste water into the sea has caused considerable pollution in areas close to major sewage outlets. The seas near Athens, Barcelona, Venice, Marseilles, New York, San Francisco and Sydney are given as examples. The dangers from this type of pollution are limited to areas within a few kilometres from the point of discharge, but they have caused health problems and economic losses.

World Resources 1987 points out that municipal effluents are one of the principal sources of chronic pollution in the marine environment. The harbours and coastal waters of nearly every major port city in the Third World are polluted with raw sewage and industrial discharges, and the situation is getting worse. Even in relatively developed regions, sewage is pumped into the sea untreated: in the Mediterranean, an estimated 90 per cent of the sewage generated around the coast is still dumped raw into the water.

Many of the waters around the UK are polluted with raw sewage. In 1976, the EC published its directive on bathing waters, telling members to designate as 'Eurobeaches' those bathing areas traditionally used by a large number of bathers. These beaches would have to comply with certain bacteria standards to protect public health.

Somewhat cynically, the UK in 1980 designated only 27 beaches, out of about 600 at which bathing regularly takes place – fewer than Luxembourg, which does not even have a coastline. Resorts such as Blackpool, Brighton, Hastings, Eastbourne and Skegness were not classified as bathing beaches. The reason for this appeared to be the high cost of cleaning the bathing waters to the required standard.

In July 1986, the UK bowed to public pressure and the threat of an action from the European court, and announced a £280 million clean-up programme for Britain's beaches. This appeared to be a change of heart – but, as Greenpeace pointed out, no extra cash was being released to pay for this programme: the government had simply added up cash allocated to sewage treatment plans for the next five years.

The UK's complacency on sewage in bathing waters is based on a 1959 report which concluded: 'Unless water is so fouled as to be aesthetically revolting there is little evidence to suggest that bathing in sea contaminated with sewage constitutes a risk to public health.' New evidence, however, suggests otherwise. *New Scientist* (21 May 1987) reported evidence that sea-bathers in Britain risk infection because dangerous viruses and bacteria discharged into the sea in raw sewage stay alive longer than had previously been thought. Bathers face stomach, skin, ear and eye infections. The modern British practice of piping raw sewage 4 kilometres out to sea may do no more than spread the pathogens along the coast.

The EC Directive says that Eurobeaches must have no more than 10,000 coliform bacteria (i.e. bacteria that live in the intestines) in 95 per cent of 100 millilitre samples of seawater, and that there should be no more than 2,000 faecal coliforms. Fred Pearce describes in *Watershed* (1982) how the US Environmental Protection Agency interviewed 30,000 people after they had visited beaches at several resorts. It found 'appreciable swimming-related rates of gastroenteritis' associated with bacteria densities lower than those in the EC Directive. In 1987, Greenpeace commissioned a study of 2,000 people from two resorts, one with clean water, the other with sewage pollution. Those who swam in polluted water showed more incidence of gastrointestinal disorders.

The health risks associated with sewage-polluted water are exacerbated by the practice of connecting industrial effluents to the sewerage system (see next section). Bathers wishing to check the cleanliness of UK resorts could refer to the *Golden List of Beaches in England and Wales*, published by the Coastal Anti-Pollution League (1985). The University of Surrey has also published an analysis of water quality on 27 resorts along the Kent/Essex Coast, the Fylde Coast, the Cornish Coast and the Yorkshire Coast (*The Public Health Implications of Sewage Pollution of Bathing Water*, 1987).

Many countries now use secondary sewage treatment before discharging effluent into the sea. In Canada, the US and Japan, secondary treatment is carried out in 75 per cent of treatment plants; in Sweden, tertiary treatment is carried out in 80 per cent of plants. In the UK, however, the Royal Commission on Environmental Pollution pointed out in 1984 that 'At present, there are many sewage outfalls near well frequented beaches with no prior treatment of the sewage', and that 'The evidence we have received has shown that many bathing waters and beaches on the coast of the United Kingdom suffer from an undesirable form of contamination by sewage'.

The situation is unlikely to have improved since then: 22 per cent of sewage treatment works were unable to meet their own discharge standards in 1986, because of financial restraints (see WATER: UK RIVERS, ESTUARIES AND GROUNDWATERS). In August 1988, the *Observer* pointed out that there are more than 400 sewage outfalls in the UK adjacent to coastal waters, of which 227 dump untreated sewage into the ocean. In EC terms, UK coastal waters compare very badly.

Percentage of sea waters tested in each country that conforms to the EC Directive for coliform bacteria as of 1986	
Netherlands	93.7
Ireland	85.8
France	85.7
Italy	81.5
Denmark	76.6
Luxembourg	74.5
Belgium	50.0
UK	44.1

Note: West German figures unavailable, although all sea waters passed
EC standards
Source: *Observer*, 7 August 1988

Finally, even treatment of sewage can cause marine pollution when the waste products are dumped at sea. After the liquid and solid sewage is treated, a sludge remains which can contain up to 60 per cent of the original contaminants. The UK is the only nation to continue dumping this sludge in the North Sea – some 9.4 million tonnes a year, at 13 sites round the coast, with the majority being dumped in the Thames Estuary, Firth of Clyde and Liverpool Bay. Dumping increases the input of nutrients such as nitrogen and phosphorus into the marine environment, increasing the risk of eutrophication (see below). Incidences of fish disease in the US have been associated with sewage sludge dumping.

Persistent pollutants
The two best-known persistent pollutants in the marine environment are the pesticide DDT and the polychlorinated biphenyls (see PESTI-CIDES; PCBs). Organochlorine pesticides generally are persistent in the environment: they are part of a number of synthetic organic (i.e. artificially made, containing carbon) compounds called 'xenobiotics', which break down extremely slowly and so circulate in ecosystems for many years. Xenobiotics build up in the food chain (they are eaten by

small fish, which are eaten by larger fish, etcetera, with the quantity of xenobiotic becoming larger as it is absorbed by larger animals or people) and thus represent an increasing threat to people who unwittingly eat polluted fish.

Another group of persistent pollutants are the heavy metals, such as mercury, cadmium and lead, which are released in enormous quantities from industry.

Metal pollution first came to prominence in the Minamata Bay episode in Japan. Since the 1930s, the Chisso chemical plant had been discharging methyl mercury into the bay which local villagers used as a source of shellfish. This mercury was known to be toxic, but it was heavily diluted in the waters of the bay, and was believed to be dispersed.

In the 1950s, the villagers began to exhibit what came to be known as 'Minamata disease'. John Elkington describes the symptoms of methyl mercury poisoning in *The Poisoned Womb* (1985): severe mental retardation, seizures, loss of co-ordination, partial or total loss of vision or hearing. It also affects embryos in the womb, so that apparently healthy mothers were giving birth to severely affected children. All in all, 1,385 villagers suffered mercury poisoning and 649 died (*World Resources 1987*).

The company was forced to pay $80 million in indemnities, with more to come. The Global Environment Monitoring Service (GEMS), set up after the United Nations Conference on the Environment in 1972, commented:

A million or two in environmental research and monitoring, when fish were first found floating dead in Minamata Bay, when cats went mad and when people began to develop symptoms of a strange disease, would have been cheaper and infinitely more responsible. But the cruel truth is that almost to the end lack of scientific evidence could stand as a secure defence for inaction.

The environment movement argues that this defence is still being used to justify continued pollution. Elkington points out that coastal industries discharge into the Mediterranean some 5,000 tonnes of zinc, 1,400 tonnes of lead, 950 tonnes of chromium, and 10 tonnes of mercury each year. Various rivers flowing into the Mediterranean are estimated to add a further 100 tonnes of mercury, with atmospheric pollution contributing four times this amount.

Generally, when mercury levels in edible fish exceed one part per million (1 milligram per kilogram), in Europe and North America, people are banned from eating it. This has frequently occurred in the North Sea over the past few decades, and sporadic bans have been applied.

Radioactivity

Radiation pollutes the world's oceans from four separate sources: atmospheric fallout, dumping of radioactive waste, discharges from nuclear installations and discharges from nuclear-powered vessels. The latter is usually accidental.

The marine – and terrestrial – environment suffer continuing fallout of radiation from the airborne testing of nuclear weapons in the 1950s and 1960s (see NUCLEAR WEAPONS: ENVIRONMENTAL EFFECTS). The dumping of radioactive waste in the sea, carried out by the UK, Belgium, The Netherlands and Switzerland between 1967 and 1982 in the Atlantic Ocean off the coast of Spain, was halted by a decision of the London Dumping Convention in 1983 – much against the wishes of the UK (see NUCLEAR ENERGY: NUCLEAR WASTE).

The major source of marine radiation pollution in the UK is the reprocessing plant at Sellafield (formerly Windscale). The plant does not inspire confidence: in a number of documented instances, from its deliberate release of plutonium into the North Sea in 1952–3 as an 'experiment' (*Observer*, 23 February 1986), to its official warning on safety grounds by the Health and Safety Executive in December 1986, Sellafield appears to have been dogged by inefficiency and an unacceptable standard of environmental pollution.

Greenpeace points out that at least 250 kg of plutonium, theoretically enough to kill 250 million people, have been discharged into the Irish Sea, making it the most radioactive sea in the world (the maximum permissible lung dose of plutonium 239 – discharged from Sellafield – is a quarter of a millionth of a gram; two-millionths of a gram produces 100 per cent cancer mortality in beagles).

Greenpeace also comments that for 30 years or so the 'management policy' for radioactive waste in the UK has been to discharge low-level waste through two two-mile pipelines directly into the Irish Sea at the rate of 2.2 million gallons a day. Until 1984 the amount of radioactivity released to the marine environment by the plant was 96 per cent of the total output of the whole UK nuclear industry, and cumulatively equalled all other aquatic discharges in the world.

The Sellafield management claims that radioactive pollution can be brought down to acceptable levels: this is not the solution sought by the Irish, Manx and Norwegian governments, who want the plant to close down. This was also the opinion of *New Scientist*, which, in a 27 February 1986 editorial titled 'Shut This Open Sewer', commented:

Even by the standards that the nuclear industry sets itself (leaving aside completely the standards that its critics might set) the catalogue of leaks, accidents, contaminations and pollutions for which the Sellafield plant has been responsible over the past three decades amply merits complete closure.

Radioactive leaks from nuclear-powered vessels and craft carrying nuclear weapons are responsible for a small amount of radioactive contamination (see NUCLEAR WEAPONS: ENVIRONMENTAL EFFECTS). Though small in scale, these episodes could have significant local effects, which would increase in the event of a large-scale nuclear accident.

Other marine pollutants

There are other marine pollutants, including:

Plastics, which are not easily broken down by natural processes, and thus tend to accumulate in the oceans. Birds and mammals often eat plastic, mistaking it for food: *World Resources 1987* estimates that up to 1 million seabirds and 100,000 cetaceans (i.e. whales, dolphins, porpoises, etcetera) die every year because of plastic pollution. Polyethylene and polypropylene packaging pellets have been found in densities as high as 1,000–4,000 per square kilometre on the surface of the North Atlantic, South Atlantic and Pacific Oceans – and studies of birds in the Pacific have found plastic debris in the stomachs of 90 per cent of chicks observed.

Nitrates, see WATER: UK WATER SUPPLY.

Atmospheric deposition of sulphur and nitrogen, see ACID RAIN.

Effects of marine pollution

Although the oceans are vast, the ecosystems nearest the land masses are the most productive in terms of aquatic life. They are also the nearest to the land-based pollution sources, are shallow, and therefore are vulnerable to pollution. This has had unfortunate consequences in a number of areas. Some of these are cited as examples.

The North Sea

The North Sea is a relatively shallow, enclosed basin with a volume of about 47,000 cubic kilometres. The water circulates in an anticlockwise direction. Water discharged from estuaries on the East Coast of Britain spreads throughout the central North Sea, while water from the Continental estuaries tends to stay in the eastern part of the sea. One consequence of the movement of water, driven partly by the predominantly westerly winds, is that the outflow from British rivers follows the general circulation into the North Sea, crossing the North Sea towards the German Bight. In contrast, water from Continental rivers remains trapped along the coast and passes into the German Bight and the Wadden Sea. As a result, contaminants concentrate in the eastern coastal zone of the southern North Sea. So while Britain exports its pollution, Continental pollution remains largely in Continental waters. (*New Scientist*, 19 November 1987)

Britain's export of pollution in this way to the Continent echoes its policies on atmospheric pollution (see ACID RAIN), and are an indication of the reason why the other North Sea states – Belgium, Denmark, France, The Netherlands, Norway, Sweden and West Germany – are keen on international action to clean up the area. At a meeting of the International Conference on the Protection of the North Sea in November 1987, the states agreed to:

- end the dumping of harmful wastes into the North Sea by end 1989;
- improve controls over input of dangerous substances from rivers;
- ensure an end to incineration of waste at sea by end 1994, with a 65 per cent reduction in toxic waste burn by end 1990;
- reduce the input of organic nutrients (nitrogen and phosphorus);
- ensure that the best available technology is used to reduce pollution from radioactive discharges;
- prohibit the dumping of garbage from ships.

Britain alone insisted on continuing to dump sewage sludge.

The agreement was a substantial improvement on previous meetings – three years before, no action had been agreed – and reflected in part the intense pressure that the UK had been receiving on the issue, both diplomatically and from groups such as Greenpeace.

Direct Inputs into the North Sea, maximum tonnes per annum					
	Cadmium	Mercury	Copper	Lead	Zinc
Germany	0.6	1.8	1.7	0.4	9.2
Netherlands	2.5	0.3	29.3	25.7	78.4
Norway	0.9	0.6	63.9	4.9	77
Denmark	0	0.1	2.9	9.1	9.1
UK	15.8	2.6	214.8	132.6	986.1

Source: *Quality Status of the North Sea*, Department of the Environment, September 1987

Problems in the North Sea continue, however: in 1988 a 'killer algae', *Chrysochromulina polylepsis*, started growing in waters off the Swedish coast, and multiplied into a massive algal bloom. This jelled into a floating mass many kilometres wide, which at one time was doubling in size every 20 hours. As the 'killer algae' spread, it suffocated fish over large areas of sea, and other marine life such as mussels, starfish and crabs.

In Sweden, at least 80 tons of fish were lost: Norwegian fish farm losses included 500 tons of dead salmon. The algae cost the Norwegian fishing industry $200 million in its first two weeks, and long-term effects on the industry are expected to be serious. To multiply like this, algae need high concentrations of nitrogen and phosphorus and warm water. The former are supplied by pollution: the latter may be a consequence of global warming (see GREENHOUSE EFFECT), though there is as yet no scientific agreement on this.

In the summer of 1988, thousands of seals died in a viral epidemic that started on the coasts of Scandinavia and Germany, and spread across the North and Baltic Seas. About a third of the area's 16,000 harbour seals were estimated as having died. Around the UK, some 3,000 common seals died (the estimated number may increase over time) out of a population of 25,000. Some grey seals were also affected, and an estimated 17,000 seals died in total around Europe, but the full impact of the disaster can only be assessed in later breeding seasons. In November 1988, the virus was reported as having affected porpoises too.

The virus was finally established as a member of the morbillivirus group – which includes canine distemper, human measles, rinderpest and goat plague. It was not, however, canine distemper as originally reported, so the illness was not spread by dogs. There was in 1988 much discussion as to whether pollution had harmed the immune systems of the seals, making them more susceptible to disease – but no conclusive evidence for or against this theory was presented. Green-peace scientists found very high levels of mercury and concentrated mixtures of PCBs in five grey seals and a pilot whale examined in the Irish Sea.

The Mediterranean WWF *News* (January–February 1988) gives some depressing statistics about the Mediterranean. It has 18 coastal states and a population around the basin of 100 million. About 100 million tourists (35 per cent of the world total) holiday there every year. An estimated 90 per cent of sewage generated around the Mediterranean's coast is dumped raw into its waters.

The Med has 60 large oil refineries operating on its coastline, whose products are extremely damaging to the marine environment. Some 320,000 tons of phosphorus are dumped into the sea every year: tourism development is threatening the Mediterranean monk seal (population down to 350 in the area) and the Mediterranean logger-head turtle (being driven to extinction). The beaches are washed by 300 million tons of dirty water, billions of cubic metres of polluted air clog the atmosphere, and coastal fishing communities blame declining fish catches – caused by pollution of breeding grounds and industrialized fishing practices – on seals and dolphins (see **Over-fishing**, below).

In October 1987, the *International Herald Tribune* reported a killer algae growth in the Adriatic, off the Italian coast. Piles of rotting fish washed up on to Italy's north-eastern coast, with local scientists noting the disappearance of most fish life up to four miles off the shore, in some places stretching up to 15 miles. Life had disappeared in a marine area of 400 square miles.

The Po, Italy's biggest river, is the source of two-thirds of the pollution threatening the Adriatic. It carries raw sewage from Milan and Turin, the effluent from thousands of factories, pesticides and huge amounts of fertilizer residues. Scientists working for Kronos 1991, a national environment group, analysed the Po water and calculated that every year it dumps into the Adriatic at least 60,000 tons of nitrates, 13,000 tons of ammoniacs, 7,000 tons of phosphates, 5,400 tons of detergents, 9,500 tons of crude oil, 1,554 tons of lead, 950 tons of zinc, 850 tons of chrome, 243 tons of arsenic and 65 tons of mercury. Italy's government was unable to confirm or deny this analysis: the last official survey of the Po was in 1976.

On the positive side, the United Nations Environment Programme has sponsored a multi-billion dollar scheme committing coastal states to protect the sea. Mr Aldo Manos told a press conference in July 1988 that when the Mediterranean Action Plan was launched in 1975, 65 per cent of Mediterranean beaches were considered clean: now the figure was 80 per cent. Pollution from the four major rivers – the Rhône, Po, Nile and Ebro – remained a problem, but the Italian government's decision to set aside $3.5 billion to clean up the Po signalled growing determination to deal with the problem.

The environment movement does not yet share this optimism. A contemporary report from the World Wide Fund for Nature deprecated the 'declining state' of the Mediterranean's environment.

Coastal waters in the USA   In October 1987, *International Business Week* carried pollution of the oceans as its cover story. The feature reported numerous pollution incidents, with dead dolphins being washed ashore in New Jersey: millions of dead fish washing up on Long Island Sound: algae blooms running along the Atlantic shore: pollution threatening the $6 billion US commercial and recreational fishing business, with 33 per cent of US shellfish beds closed in 1987. Bass fishing was banned in 1986 in New York's waters because the fish were contaminated with PCBs: oysters in the polluted Chesapeake Bay were dying of a mystery disease called MSX (Maryland, Virginia, Pennsylvania and the District of Columbia have now agreed to reduce the amount of nitrogen and phosphorus flowing into the bay by 40 per cent by upgrading sewer plants and managing agricultural runoff).

Overfishing

When fish stocks collapse, it is sometimes difficult to identify the cause exactly. Overfishing is a frequent reason. As Wolfgang Friedmann commented in *The Future of the Oceans* in 1971, in the century from 1850 to 1950 the world fish catch increased tenfold, at an average rate of about 25 per cent each decade. Since 1938, the world fish catch had more than tripled. In 1968, when Friedmann was researching his book, the world fish catch was estimated at 64 million tonnes.

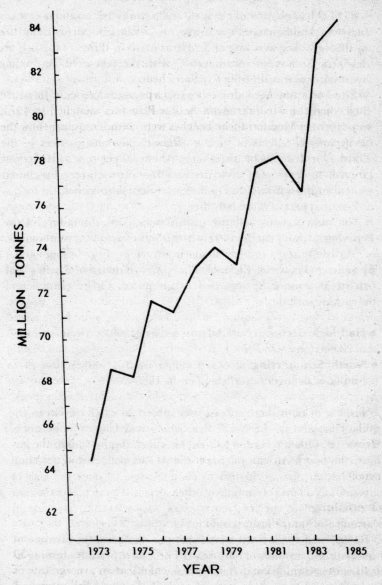

World fishery production, 1973–1985

Source: *The State of the World Environment*, 1987

UNEP has pointed out that the 1985 world fish production was a massive 84 million tonnes, with average annual fish catches from 1980 to 1985 growing at a rate of 3.2 per cent. Two-thirds of the fish are destined for human consumption, with the rest used for feeding livestock or manufacturing fertilizers.

The Food and Agriculture Organization estimates that the world catch ought not to exceed 100 million tonnes a year if the risk of substantial depletion of fish stocks is to be avoided. Apart from the environmental effects of such a collapse, the consequences in the Third World would be distressing. About 60 per cent of the population of the developing world derives 40 per cent or more of its annual protein supplies from fish. For many developing countries, the food is an essential part of their daily diet.

The most famous collapse of fish stocks was the failure of the Peruvian anchovy catch in 1971–2: this was caused by a combination of overfishing and a sudden change in sea temperature brought about by a current known as 'El Nino'. The episode is used as a warning that fish stocks cannot be regarded as unlimited. Other examples of overfishing include:

- **Haddock** catches in NW Atlantic fell from 250,000 tonnes in 1965 to 20,000 tonnes in 1974.
- **North Sea herring** stocks declined from 4 million tonnes to 1 million because of overfishing in the 1960s.

Fishing of both these species was subject to catch quotas in the mid-1970s, and in the North Sea fishing was banned until stocks recovered. Other recorded fish declines include the California sardine, the South African pilchard, the Alaska pollack and the chub mackerel. As the world fish catch increases, so does the risk of substantial collapse of supplies of other species. The virtual extinction of certain whale species (see WHALES AND WHALING) is a useful warning of what the future could bring.

In 1987 and 1988, Norwegian fishermen witnessed the invasion of hundreds of thousands of harp seals. These were literally starving to death and becoming entangled in fishing nets in their attempts to get food. The phenomenon was eventually attributed to the collapse of stocks of capelin (a kind of sardine) which had been overfished. A similar type of incident occurred in Scotland, 1988, when the sand eel fishery collapsed. There were large-scale deaths in the local bird populations.

See also CHEMICAL WASTES; NUCLEAR ENERGY: NUCLEAR WASTE; NUCLEAR WEAPONS: ENVIRONMENTAL EFFECTS; PCBS; PESTICIDES; WATER; WETLANDS; WHALES AND WHALING

REFERENCES

Elkington, John, *The Poisoned Womb*, Penguin Books, 1985.

Friedmann, Wolfgang, *The Future of the Oceans*, Dennis Dobson, 1971.

Myers, Norman (ed.), *The Gaia Atlas of Planet Management*, Pan Books, 1985.

Pearce, Fred, *Watershed*, Junction Books, 1982.

Quality Status of the North Sea, Department of the Environment, 1987.

Royal Commission on Environmental Pollution, Tenth Report, HMSO, 1984.

Sanger, Clyde, *Ordering the Oceans*, Zed Press, 1986.

United Nations Environment Programme, *The State of the World Environment 1987*, UNEP, 1987.

World Resources Institute, IIED, *World Resources 1986*, Basic Books, 1986.

World Resources Institute, IIED, *World Resources 1987*, Basic Books, 1987.

'British scientists link seal deaths to cattle pest', Lightowlers, Philip, *New Scientist*, 22 October 1988.

'Cleanup of Beaches May be a Waste of Money', *New Scientist*, 21 May 1987.

Coastal Anti-Pollution League Ltd, 'The Golden List of Beaches in England and Wales', 1985.

Environment Digest, August to October 1988, April 1989

Feger, Helene, 'Sunshine, Sand, and an Ocean Full of Filth', *Observer*, 7 August 1988.

Greenpeace, 'Radioactive Waste Discharges from the BNFL Processing Plant, Sellafield, UK', May 1987.

Greenpeace, 'Save the Sewage – Toxic Pollution Briefing', 1988.

'The Mediterranean: a Sea to Save', *WWF News*, January–February 1988.

Milne, Roger, 'Pollution and Politics in the North Sea', *New Scientist*, 19 November 1987.

'North Sea Conference Sees Progress', *Bulletin of UK CEED*, October–December 1987.

'Officials blast handling of huge Alaskan tanker spill', UPI, March 1989.

Pearce, Fred, 'Seal virus spreads to porpoises', *New Scientist*, 5 November 1988.

The Robens Institute, *The Public Health Implications of Sewage Pollution of Bathing Water*, University of Surrey, Greenpeace Environmental Trust, 1987.

'Shut This Open Sewer', *New Scientist*, 27 February 1986.

'Troubled Waters', *International Business Week*, 12 October 1987.

'UN Billion-dollar Plan Cleans up
  Mediterranean', *Guardian*, 27 July
  1988.

CONTACTS

Coastal Anti-Pollution League
Dolphin Watch
Friends of the Earth
Greenpeace
Marine Conservation Society
North Sea Forum
Royal Society for the Protection of
  Birds (RSPB)

Sea Shepherd
United Nations Environment
  Programme (UNEP)
United Nations Food and
  Agriculture Organization (FAO)
World Wide Fund for Nature
  (WWF)

Military Spending, Worldwide

World expenditure on arms and armies has increased dramatically since the Second World War, both in the 'developed' and the 'developing' countries. Military spending is an environmental issue because of the impact of weapons testing on the atmosphere and the oceans (see NUCLEAR WEAPONS: ARMS RACE), the toxic effect of the weapons on people, animals and vegetation, and the rapid depletion of natural resources to produce equipment that does not return anything to the environment.

It is also an environmental issue because of the idea of 'opportunity costs'. Every usage of time or resources requires the sacrifice of the alternative uses to which these could have been put. Spending money on tanks means that there is less to spend on such things as reversing desertification, feeding people or cleaning up polluted water supplies.

In global terms, the rapidly increasing military expenditure has distorted Research and Development priorities, diverted the path of investment and industrialization, and increased unemployment by concentrating finance in a capital-intensive sector (this in spite of the fact that approximately 100 million people, depending on how the calculations are made, can be said to work in military jobs: if the money had been used in more labour-intensive industries, millions more could have been employed).

For the industrialized countries, devoting too large a proportion of Gross National Product to defence appears to hinder economic efficiency. For a Third World country, expenditure on armaments means that precious foreign currency has to be found. More peasants have to be pushed off the land for cash crops, more tropical rain forests have to be cut down, more wetlands have to be drained. The drive towards military hardware creates the devastation that it is supposed to be protecting against. Those affected lose two ways: they lose the environment that they have grown up with, and the armaments purchased with their land are used to keep them subdued and prevent insurrection.

In his book *World Armaments and World Hunger* (1986), Willy Brandt quotes an African proverb: 'Human rights begin with breakfast.' The rights to clean water, air and food are the most basic rights of all. These rights are jeopardized in economies distorted by arms trading: and the stimulus for this accelerating spiral of weaponry originated in the financial institutions and governments of the developed world.

The size of the problem

In 1980, the Brandt Commission estimated that world military spending approached $450 billion a year. Seven years later, the Brundtland Commission stated that the global military spend had increased to $900 billion by 1985 – around $2.5 billion a day, or £1 million a minute.

Ruth Leger Segard, in *World Military and Social Expenditures* (1986) comments that world military expenditures have increased twelve-fold compared with 50 years ago.

The permanent military bureaucracy now outnumbers all other public employees and administers the largest share of government revenues. With a global procurement budget exceeding $250 billion annually, the military component of government also has a powerful constituency in the economy, an arms industry which has become a multinational industrial giant . . . In the world of multi-billion-dollar corporations, the military sector as buyer, employer, and producer has become the biggest business of all.

Two countries, the USA and the USSR, lead the field. With less than 11 per cent of the world's population, they had in 1985 23 per cent of the world's armed forces, 60 per cent of the military expenditures, more than 80 per cent of the weapons research, and 97 per cent of the world's nuclear warheads and bombs.

Some 80 per cent of worldwide military expenditure comes from the developed countries, according to the UN Department for Disarmament Affairs. Of the developing countries, major oil exporters account for 7 per cent of global expenditure, the other developing countries some 10 per cent. Over 80 per cent of all military expenditure is on conventional weapons and armed forces: even for the five nuclear-weapon states, conventional arms make up the bulk of military costs.

The military sector

- According to a 1983 United Nations study, well over 70 million people were engaged at that time, directly or indirectly, in military activities worldwide. The figure includes some 25 million persons in the world's regular armed forces. If those in paramilitary forces or reserves had been added, the total might have been twice as high.
- Approximately 4 million civilians were employed in defence establishments worldwide: over 3 million scientists and engineers were engaged in military Research and Development (R and D), with the scientists alone numbering over 500,000: over 5 million workers were directly engaged in the production of weapons and military equipment.
- Military expenditures represent an average of around 20 per cent of governmental expenditures. According to some estimates, in developed countries military spending is about equal to government spending on education or health: in developing countries it equals three times the public expenditure on health and is a third more than the public expenditure on education.
- By 1985, global expenditure on military R and D was estimated to be approximately one-quarter of the total R and D worldwide.
- Military spending has high opportunity costs over the long run in terms of investment, employment, productivity and growth. For most of the period since the Second World War, the economic performance of those developed countries that spend less on defence in relation to Gross National Product has been better in terms of real rates of growth, investment, and productivity.

Source: UN Dept. for Disarmament Affairs, *The Relationship Between Disarmament and Development*, 1987

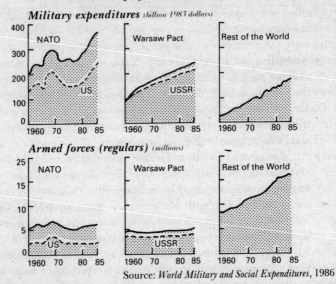

Military expenditures *(billion 1983 dollars)*

NATO | US

Warsaw Pact | USSR

Rest of the World

Armed forces (regulars) *(millions)*

NATO | US

Warsaw Pact | USSR

Rest of the World

Source: *World Military and Social Expenditures*, 1986

The drive to sell arms

The cost of rapid upgrading of armaments is enormous, but can be reduced if the weapons are exported as well as being used at home. The example of the Mirage III jetfighter is often used to illustrate this point. Its manufacturer, Dassault, built the plane essentially for the French air force, which wanted 200. By selling 350 of them abroad, Dassault reduced the cost of the aircraft to the French government by 25 per cent.

The rivalry between the USA and USSR has intensified the quest for more sophisticated weapons, a policy which is subsidized by a powerful export drive. Both countries are also prepared to use Third World battlegrounds to fight their own ideological wars. John Clark, in *For Richer, For Poorer* (1986), points out that superpower rivalry has exacerbated many of the conflicts since the Second World War – an estimated half of them have involved outside intervention from East or West, either in the form of direct help or a willingness to supply arms.

Since 1945 there have been some 120 wars, mostly fought in the Third World, with around 18.5 million fatalities. The increasing militarization of the Third World has had unfortunate consequences for human rights. In 1960 there were approximately 22 military-controlled governments: by 1985 there were 58, almost half of which were in Africa. Control is exerted by the use of 'internal' military hardware – water cannon, stun batons, torture equipment. One of the major suppliers of this equipment is Britain.

According to John Clark, Third World military imports trebled between 1962 and 1981. The Brundtland Commission point out that military spending in developing countries has increased fivefold since the early 1960s. Varying estimates as to the effect of this on Third World debt have been published, but it seems that between 15 and 25 per cent of total accumulated Third World debt can be put down to the arms bill.

A large part of this is the responsibility of western financial institutions and governments. In the early 1970s, quantities of money were deposited at western banks from the newly rich oil-exporting nations. The banks provided the interest on these petrodollars by lending money to other nations – the world's poorest countries – at a higher rate of interest. Among other items, the countries bought arms. While commodity prices remained high, the debtor nations were in a position to repay loans: in the slump of the 1980s, however, this no longer remained the case (see NORTH–SOUTH RELATIONSHIP).

The International Monetary Fund provides short-term loans to tide over defaulting nations, but stipulates loan conditions requiring cuts in food subsidies, health and education, and wages: no such requirements apply to military spending, however, as the IMF does not interfere with 'national security'. Governments imposing this type of social reorganization in a volatile political climate are forced to rely on their armed forces to stay in power.

The effects of arms expenditure

Over-investment in the military sector does not contribute to a strong national economy. Two of the leading developed economies – Japan and West Germany – have benefited from the restraints placed on their military commitments after the Second World War. Their powerful economies are not carrying the weight of a vast military research programme.

There are implications other than the effect on the economy. John Clark describes a survey of 141 countries, carried out by health statisticians, which concluded that there was a correlation between military spending and infant mortality. The report concludes that

The UK

In the UK, the Ministry of Defence announced in August 1987 that Britain had moved into second place in the league of international arms dealers, behind the USA but ahead of the Soviet Union and France. The exports – according to the MoD, £5.3 billion – were regarded as crucial to the British economy.

At the same time, however, concern was being expressed in Britain about the size of the country's military Research and Development (R and D) programme: out of a total expenditure of £4.5 billion, more than half was being spent on defence. This type of R and D does not produce 'spin-off' benefits. *New Scientist* commented on 14 May 1987:

> What does Britain get out of such a huge budget devoted to defence R and D? The Ministry of Defence can point to a handful of successes, such as the thermal-imaging camera developed at the Royal Signals and Radar Establishment, but that's about it.

All of Britain's competitors in Europe – even France, which has its own nuclear weapon system – spend more on civil R and D than on military. Britain's anomalous position stems from the fact that its defence budget has increased by 29 per cent since 1979, while other programmes, including investment in universities and civil R and D, were cut back.

Internal dependencies are set up which become difficult to break. According to Defence Secretary George Younger, his £8 billion procurement budget accounts for half the output of the British aerospace industry, and 20 per cent of the output of the electronics industry. A large number of jobs are thus directly or indirectly supported by the defence budget.

UK defence expenditure, according to MoD figures, is heavily biased towards the south-east (54 per cent of the total) and south-west (11 per cent) of the country. The defence budget contributes some £4 billion a year to the prosperity of the south of England – and, as this is the heartland of the Conservative Party, also contributes to the electoral popularity of the government. Once this type of input gets locked into place it becomes increasingly difficult to remove it.

2 million infant deaths a year may be attributed to military spending, before a shot is fired.

Clark compares the 1982 budgets of six countries, looking at their military spending, the percentage spent on social factors (education, health, housing, social security and welfare combined) and the infant mortality rate per thousand births.

Three comparisons (1982 figures)

Country	% spent on military	% spent on social	Infant mortality rate (per 1,000 births)
Sri Lanka	1.4	23.5	37
Pakistan	33.5	10.1	119
Costa Rica	2.9	69.5	20
El Salvador	11.9	29.0	70
Kenya	13.2	28.0	81
Uganda	19.8	26.6	108

Source: Oxfam, 1986

The effects of a large military programme appear to be self-evident: if a country allocates a substantial proportion of its income to buying arms and paying soldiers, then it has less to spend on protecting the health of its citizens, developing agriculture or protecting the environment.

Opportunity costs

A number of commentators have detailed the investments sacrificed to military spending:

Willy Brandt

- The world military expenditure of half a day would be enough to finance the entire World Health Organization programme to eradicate malaria;
- the cost of a modern tank could improve storage facilities for 100,000 tonnes of rice, so that annual wastage of 4,000 tonnes or more could be avoided – a day's ration for 8 million people;
- the price of a fighter plane would equip 40,000 village pharmacies;

- the price of a nuclear submarine is equivalent to the education budgets of 23 developing countries with 160 million children of school age.

John Clark

- One hour's global military expenditure is the same amount as that spent over 20 years by the World Health Organization in its successful campaign to eliminate smallpox;
- for the price of a single Hawk fighter plane, it would be possible to supply 1.5 million people with clean, safe water.

Ruth Leger Sivard

- For the cost of less than half an hour's world military outlay, the United Nation's Food and Agriculture Organization destroyed a plague of locusts in Africa, saving enough grain to feed 1.2 million people for a year;
- in the USSR more than twice as much money goes to defence than to education and health combined;
- in the US 170 times as much public research money goes for transport into space as for mass transit on earth;
- three governments in five spend more to guard their citizens against military attack than against the enemies of public health.

Jonathon Porritt

- 54 per cent of UK government-sponsored R and D is spent on arms and defence, compared with 37 per cent in France, 10 per cent in West Germany and 4 per cent in Japan;
- a considerable proportion of the resources extracted from the earth are used to make weapons: the military use of oil amounts to more than 5 per cent of the global total; more aluminium, copper, nickel and platinum are used for military purposes than are used for *all* purposes in Africa, Asia and Latin America combined. We are literally consuming the planet in order to make it safe.

Brundtland Commission

- An Action Plan for Tropical Forests would cost $1.3 billion a year over the course of five years – this annual sum is the equivalent of half a day of military expenditure worldwide;

- implementing the UN Action Plan for Desertification would cost $4.5 billion a year during the last two decades of this century – the equivalent of less than two days of military spending;
- one of the greatest environmental hazards in the Third World is lack of clean water for household use, contributing to 80 per cent of disease: the UN Water and Sanitation Decade, although given only a fraction of support needed, would have cost $30 billion a year during the 1970s – the approximate equivalent of ten days of military spending;
- to supply contraceptive materials to all women already motivated to use family planning would cost an additional $1 billion a year on top of the $2 billion spent today – this additional $1 billion is the equivalent of ten hours of military spending.

See also NORTH–SOUTH RELATIONSHIP; NUCLEAR WEAPONS

REFERENCES

Brandt, Willy, *World Armament and World Hunger*, Gollancz, 1986.

Brandt Commission, *North–South, a Programme for Survival*, Pan Books, 1980.

Brundtland Commission, *Our Common Future*, OUP, 1987.

Clark, John, *For Richer, For Poorer*, Oxfam, 1986.

Porritt, Jonathon, *Seeing Green*, Basil Blackwell, 1984.

Sivard, Ruth Leger, *World Military and Social Expenditures*, World Priorities, 1986.

UN Dept. for Disarmament Affairs, *The Relationship between Disarmament and Development*, 1987.

World Bank, *World Development Report 1986*, Oxford University Press, 1986.

Campaign Against Arms Trade, *Newsletters*, 1987.

'Defence and the Great Divide', *Guardian*, 23 April 1987.

New Scientist, 14 May 1987.

CONTACTS

Bertrand Russell Foundation
Campaign Against Arms Trade
Christian Aid
Department for Disarmament Affairs, United Nations

Oxfam
Third World First
War on Want
World Development Movement

North–South Relationship

The North–South relationship describes the financial and political interlock between the world's rich and poor nations. The term 'North–South' is more politically neutral than using descriptions such as 'developing' or 'less-developed' countries. 'Third World' is also used to differentiate countries with a world view different to that of Washington (the First World) and Moscow (the Second).

The relationship between most of the Third World and the First is uneven, with the bulk of population in the South, and a disproportionate amount of energy, consumption of natural resources and wealth accumulating in the North.

The Brundtland Report identifies 26 per cent of the world's population as the 'Developed Countries', and points out that they consume:

85% of the world's paper
79% of its steel
86% of other metals
80% of commercial energy.

In *How the Other Half Dies* (1976), Susan George quotes the president of the World Bank: 'the people of the United States . . . with 6 per cent of the world's population, consume about 35 per cent of the world's total resources'. The quarter of the world living in developed countries eats fully half the world's food. Its animals eat a quarter of all the world's grain. Meanwhile, hundreds of millions of people – figures quoted vary between 350 million and 800 million – are chronically undernourished. According to UNICEF, a quarter of a million young children in the developing world die *every week* from frequent infection and prolonged undernutrition.

The developed countries run the world according to their own priorities. International trade discriminates against the Third World; transnational companies operate policies in the South that are unacceptable or illegal in the North; multilateral development agencies attempt to impose solutions to Third World problems that are more closely tailored to First, rather than Third World, requirements. And although conditions in the Third World have improved during the twentieth century, the situation has deteriorated rapidly over the last ten years.

This uneven relationship poses a risk to the survival of the planet: the continuance of the South's economic disadvantage is perpetuating some of the world's worst environmental crises. A number of these problems have global causes and can be solved only by international action. This becomes impossible when key countries function at such a basic level of existence that environmental protection is a luxury.

Global problems

An example of one of these crises is the GREENHOUSE EFFECT which is causing global warming. Slowing down the greenhouse effect involves an internationally-based reduction in pollutant emissions and, importantly, the protection of the world's forests. Both these measures are impossible in certain Third World countries, which are both chopping down tropical rainforests and boosting their industrial consumption of fossil fuels in order to pay off their international debt.

Other short-term solutions, forced on countries by economic imperative, lead to environmental destruction described in other entries (see DESERTIFICATION; BHOPAL; WATER; CHEMICAL WASTES; MARINE POLLUTION; SPECIES EXTINCTION; WETLANDS). In many cases, governments have survived by buying large quantities of weapons and using them to repress their citizens (see MILITARY SPENDING, WORLDWIDE). Money spent in this way is lost to environmental protection. The arms race is one of two central impediments blocking action to protect the world environment, says the United Nations Environment Programme in *The State of the World Environment 1987*. The other is the international debt crisis.

The debt crisis

When the charter for the United Nations was drawn up in 1945, there were 51 member states: now there are 159. As nations decolonialized, split or gained independence in other ways, a need arose for cash. Modernization depended on imported technology and external expertise, which had to be paid for in dollars.

The private banks, traditionally, had not loaned large sums to the Third World since the 1930s – because of the financial crisis then, 70 per cent of all Latin American bonds had defaulted, and the US banking system contracted by a third as the banks collapsed. Lending resumed in the 1960s, however, and took off in the 1970s.

The reason was the oil price rise of 1973. The oil states had substantial amounts of surplus cash, which was deposited in Western banks. First World countries were unsuitable for profitable investment, as they were engulfed by recession. Third World nations, however, were desperate for cash. The banks loaned the oil money – 'petrodollars' – to the Third World, and made enormous profits on an apparently risk-free basis. Countries, unlike companies, couldn't go bust; provided that the loan repayments were made on time, the banks' capital was 'working', and their balance sheets looked healthy.

During the 1970s, the debtor countries were encouraged to borrow enormous amounts of money – sums so large that they couldn't be repaid from export earnings, but only by borrowing more cash. Bankers and governments between them set up a system that was unstable, viable only as long as further loans were possible.

For the Third World countries, these loans were attractive, because inflation exceeded the long-term interest rates, and they were in effect borrowing money at negative interest. The loan scheme was also welcomed by the banks, who were so delighted by the enormous income generated that they severely overcommitted themselves, lending in some cases twice as much capital as they actually possessed.

The big banks' exposure to the big debtors: US and UK banks' outstandings in Mexico, Brazil, Argentina, and Venezuela as a proportion of capital (%)

UK		USA	
National Westminster	73%	Citicorp	112%
Barclays	62%	BankAmerica	121%
Lloyds	165%	Chase Manhattan	126%
Midland	205%	Manufacturers Hanover	150%
		J. P. Morgan	83%
		Chemical	119%
		Bankers Trust	95%
		First Chicago	87%

Source: H. Lever and C. Huhne, *Debt and Danger*, 1985

Two events brought on the inevitable crash. The second oil price rise, in 1979, caused a world recession, thus restricting the flow of funds for loans; and in the early 1980s, the USA moved from being a nation in credit ($140 billion in foreign assets in 1981) to being the world's largest debtor ($2,000 billion in public debt in 1986: this massive turnaround was produced by 'Reaganomics' – low-tax, big-spend economic policy, driven by colossal expenditure on defence).

To service its own debt, the USA had to offer very high rates of interest, which inflated interest rates on the world market. The Third World found that the easy loans of the 1970s carried unimagined penalties in the 1980s. Average interest rates in 1975 were 7 per cent: by 1981 they had leapt to 18 per cent. Interest rates are a factor over which the Third World has no control. US domestic policies can cause starvation in many parts of the world.

In 1982, Mexico realized that it could no longer pay the interest on its outstanding debt ($80 billion). This was a bombshell for the private banks. The nine largest US banks had 44 per cent of their capital tied up in loans in Mexico: if the country defaulted, there would be worldwide financial panic, with depositors trying to withdraw their funds, banks collapsing as a result, and incalculable consequences for the international financial system.

Reverse Aid

At the last minute, the International Monetary Fund stepped in and (by forcing private banks to lend another $5 billion) put together a loan for $8 billion which solved the crisis. Banks worldwide, however, had got the message that overcommitment to the Third World was dangerous – and they started the process of disentangling themselves.

For the Third World, this rapid disengagement was disastrous. Private finance became difficult to get, and there were enormous loans outstanding which had to be serviced. By 1987 this had reached more than one trillion dollars ($1,000,000,000,000), with most large debtors, apart from the Philippines and Poland, being in Latin America.

Debtor countries now found much of their income had to be diverted into paying interest on loans. In 1983, according to Hayter and Watson (*Aid: Rhetoric and Reality*, 1985) 50 per cent of Argentina's export earnings were due to be paid as debt interest, with similar figures for other countries:

Projected ratio of interest payments to exports in 1983 (%)			
Argentina	50	Algeria	14
Brazil	46	Indonesia	21
Chile	50	Korea (South)	18
Mexico	46	Philippines	48
Venezuela	29	Nigeria	11
Latin America and Caribbean	42		
Total other Less Developed Countries	11		

Note: These figures do not include repayment of capital.
Source: T. Hayter and C. Watson, *Aid: Rhetoric and Reality*, 1985

Repayment of the debts was an impossibility, although the Third World (under severe pressure from the First) continued to play by the rules and attempted to service the loans. The result of these repayments, however, was that enormous sums of money flowed from the South to the North. As Lever and Huhne comment:

The flows of finance between the advanced and developing worlds, which have in the past done so much to promote economic stability, employment and the progress of living standards, are now characterized by a perverse and dangerous anomaly. Until 1982 it was understood that there had to be, for a prolonged period, a one-way flow of resources from the advanced countries to the Third World to promote its development . . . Since the debt crisis which broke in 1982, those flows have been reversed for each important group of countries in the Third World. IMF estimates imply that in 1985 there was a resource flow from the fifteen largest Third World borrowers to their more prosperous creditors worth $37 billion, or one quarter of their entire earnings from the sales of their exports of goods and services.

The public perception in the First World is that we are subsidizing the Third: in fact, the opposite is true. A phenomenon known as 'Reverse Aid' is taking place, in which the Third World subsidizes the First. The debt burden has proved so great that many Third World nations have finally admitted that it cannot be met, and have asked for assistance from the international community.

1988 was the fifth successive year in which Reverse Aid flowed from the Third World to the First – some $43 billion, bringing the total since 1983 to $143 billion. The 15 most heavily indebted countries paid $31 billion (these included Brazil, Argentina, Mexico, and Venezuela) and their citizens suffered yet another fall in incomes per head.

Consequences of the debt crisis

When a country finds itself unable to repay its debts, it applies to the International Monetary Fund (IMF) for a loan. Without IMF approval, no other sources of credit can be obtained by nations with dubious credit ratings, so the range of options is extremely limited.

The IMF is a multilateral agency, that is, it is run by a number of different countries. Its independence, however, is open to question. Fifty-nine per cent of controlling votes are held by the industrialized countries (with the US holding 19 per cent of votes, and the UK 7 per cent). IMF policy tends to favour US preferences, which in the 1980s were for retrenchment and cutbacks on social spending.

The IMF, in releasing cash, makes a series of conditions that the debtor country has to accede to. These conditions, called 'adjustment programmes', or, more realistically, 'austerity programmes', involve the debtor removing food subsidies, cutting wages, reducing expenditure on social services such as health, education and public transport, raising taxes and privatizing national assets. The purpose of the programme is to concentrate all the country's efforts on exporting: the perceived way to resolve the national debt is through selling to other countries.

IMF policies have unfortunate consequences: in the First World, they have been associated with misery and unemployment, but in the Third, they mean starvation and death. Third World wages were barely adequate before the austerity programmes began: but standards of living dropped rapidly in the 1980s.

- *A Fate Worse than Debt* (Susan George, 1988) describes how real wages in Kenya declined by 20 per cent between 1981 and 1983, and by 1988 were lower than they had been in 1964. The real minimum wage (which most poor earners lived on) was 42 per cent lower in 1984 than it had been in 1975. Kenya found that, in 1977, 24 per cent of its children under the age of five were stunted: in 1982, the figure had increased to 28 per cent.

In 1980 a Peruvian earning the minimum wage had to work 17

minutes to earn enough for a kilo of rice: in 1984, two hours and five minutes were necessary – seven times as long.

In Argentina, according to official sources, there are 685,000 children in greater Buenos Aires alone who don't eat enough to stay alive, plus another 385,000 in the province of Buenos Aires.

- *For Richer, For Poorer*, an Oxfam book produced in 1986, reported a rising infant mortality rate in Ghana, with the percentage of malnourished children in the country at a staggering 53 per cent. From other countries, it noted:

  Brazil: an increase in low birthweight babies and an increasing proportion of infant deaths resulting from malnutrition.

  Sri Lanka: marked increase in wasting among children since the mid-1970s.

  Costa Rica: a doubling of the number of children treated for malnutrition in the previous three years.

  Zambia and Chile: a 30–40 per cent drop in household incomes since 1980.

  Zimbabwe: a 20 per cent cut in social services spending.

- UNICEF noted in *The State of the World's Children 1988* that the wellbeing of the young has been measurably deteriorating in at least 30 nations of the developing world. In many African countries, malnutrition is known to have increased. Child death rates had also increased in some countries, though more detailed research is needed.

Susan George's *A Fate Worse than Debt* gives a number of examples of the impact of IMF policies. Among these is the arrival of the 'IMF riot', which follows price increases for basic foods. These occurred in Egypt, 1977; in Morocco, 1984 (flour, oil, sugar and milk increased in price on average 133 per cent in previous four years – 100 people killed in riot); and in the Dominican Republic, 1984 (186 people killed).

People do not die just in riots, however. George quotes the work of two sociologists, Sell and Kunitz, who have correlated the effect of national Third World debt on average life expectancy of the population. '"Each additional $10 a year in interest payments [per capita] reflected 0.39 of a year less in life expectancy improvements over the decade [1970–80]." Their formula works out to an average 387 days of life forgone by every inhabitant of the seventy-three countries under study.'

Perhaps the most chilling quote in George's book comes from a Third World financier: '. . . the former governor of the Peruvian Central Bank, Manuel Moreyra, had to admit that "the social costs of the [IMF adjustment] policy are tragic. It means the death of some 500,000 children . . .".'

UNICEF makes the point that the death of millions of children is not the only consequence of these policies.

It cannot be stressed too often that the young children cannot 'ride out' such periods of austerity. Ninety per cent of the growth of a human brain and much of the growth of the human body is completed in the first five years of life. A child who has to go without adequate food or health care in those years will not grow to his or her physical or mental potential. There is no second chance.

. . . So it is that the greatest burden of recession is being passed on to the weakest and most vulnerable members of the world community.

Not even on economic grounds can such a process be justified. Sacrificing the growth of today's children for the growth of tomorrow's economy makes neither economic nor human sense.

Yet that is what present 'adjustment policies', with notable exceptions in some countries, have amounted to. And what it means to millions of small children, when all the financial euphemisms of recession and adjustment are stripped away, is that the once-in-a-lifetime chance for normal growth must be forgone.

Allowing this to happen is a disgrace to the present and a threat to the future. It is the antithesis of civilisation. It is a process which shames and diminishes us all.

Source: *The State of the World's Children 1988*, p. 26

Failure of IMF economic policy

The IMF's policy of export-driven recovery is not only harshly repressive: it is also unsuccessful in its aim of stimulating recovery.

There are now more than 40 countries under IMF surveillance, plus others, like Brazil and Nigeria, following IMF policy while refusing formal supervision. All have been told to export their way out of the crisis: but there is a significant overlap in most of the goods they trade. The result of a massive export drive by the Third World was that supplies of basic commodities increased, and prices plummeted.

In July 1986, the price of cotton fell by 50 per cent overnight. Tin prices collapsed by over 80 per cent in 1985. The International Fund for Agricultural Development reported in its 1986 Annual Report that 'Commodity prices, already seriously depressed, fell in real terms by an estimated 17% in 1986, and many stood at 40-year lows.'

For countries which already had shaky economies, and were diverting investment funds and export profits to repay financiers in the First World, the collapse in commodity prices was the last straw. As the *Guardian* pointed out (16 July 1987), the 1986 drop in commodity prices cost the African economies $19 billion: their manufacturing costs rose by 14 per cent: and the cost to their debt repayments was $12.3 billion.

The First World operates import-protection or price-protection policies to maintain the profitability of its key products (certain types of agricultural produce, processed food and manufactured goods). Third World commodity prices, however, are left to the mercy of the market. Low commodity costs are actually very convenient to the First World: as Susan George comments, the price of manufactured goods in the North has consistently outrun the price of raw materials from the South throughout the entire post-war period.

First World manufacturing – and its high standard of living – depends on low cost raw materials from the South. This was originally achieved through colonialization, but in modern times is accomplished by buyers' cartels and transnational price fixing. The IMF-sponsored collapse of commodity prices is a coincidental, but not unwelcome development for First World manufacturers. Depression of commodity prices is an additional subsidy from South to North.

The World Bank has published figures showing the real growth of commodity prices between 1950 and 1984. They show an annual average percentage change which is negative for the identified period:

Real growth of commodity prices, 1950–84 (average annual percentage change)

Commodity	1950–59	1960–69	1970–79	1950–84
Total agriculture	−2.92	0.00	0.01	−1.03
Beverages	−2.08	−1.26	7.46	−1.13
Cereals	−3.84	2.72	−1.31	−1.30
Fats and oils	−3.73	−0.73	−0.81	−1.29
Raw materials	−2.51	0.50	−1.72	−1.08
Metals and minerals	0.08	6.12	−4.06	−0.09

Source: *World Development Report*, 1986

Or, as Susan George puts it:

Today commodity prices are going, going, gone. The IMF, which does keep good track of these matters, measures the purchasing power of a basket of thirty primary commodities, excluding gold and oil, in terms of the manufactured goods they can buy. Starting from 100 in 1957, the IMF index has risen above that index only twice, in 1973 and 1974. Ever since, though there have been peaks and valleys, the trend has been downwards. By 1985 the index had plummeted to the lowest level ever – a dismal 66.

The consequences for countries depending on commodity exports are appalling. Thailand, for example, following the IMF's rules, increased its rubber exports by 31 per cent between 1984 and 1985. The result of all this effort, however, was an 8 per cent drop in its rubber revenues as the price of rubber collapsed.

When Zambia suspended its IMF-approved policies in 1987, it had improved its agricultural production by over 10 per cent, and increased its manufactures and exports. This was accomplished at a cost of massive unemployment, with 15 per cent of the civil service being laid off; a doubling of the price of maize to consumers; and a tripling of the cost of imports, with the devaluation of the zwacha. At the end of all this, its international debt had *risen* by 50 per cent, to $5 billion.

The International Monetary Fund lends the money and makes the rules. The problem is, from the Third World's point of view, that the game can't be won under current conditions, no matter how it is played.

Exploitation of the Third World

Commodity price manipulation is a traditional form of Third World exploitation: Reverse Aid is a new, but very remunerative system. There are other, more obvious forms of exploitation, often perpetrated by transnational companies.

The transnational companies (TNCs) wield enormous power in the Third World. John Clark in *For Richer, For Poorer* (1986) identifies a rare insight into commodity trading in Nestlé's 1976 report 'Nestlé in Developing Countries'. The report stated 'the volume of our purchases of coffee and cocoa is so vast that it influences the market for these commodities'. According to information published elsewhere, in 1974 Nestlé paid the Ivory Coast just a quarter of the average world price for coffee and Ghana half the going rate for cocoa. Clark continues:

The companies involved in commodity trade, shipping, wholesaling and retailing, take the major share of the final selling price for Third World produce. It is estimated that only 11.5% of the retail price of bananas – a commodity which, after all, requires little processing – gets back to the producer countries. With tea it is not more than 30%.

The major companies probably have greater influence over world trade than governments. They control, after all, 40% of the entire world's trade and up to 90% of commodity trade. The top 30 companies on average each had a bigger trade than the exports of the poorest 50 countries put together.

Third World First has collated information concerning the relative power of transnationals and Third World countries:

- exporting countries receive on average only 15 per cent of the final price of commodities; 85 per cent goes in profit to transnational corporations and to cover transport costs;
- four major corporations control 60–80 per cent of cocoa sales;
- Unilever, the world's largest agribusiness transnational, has an annual turnover greater than the GNP of 25 African states;
- in the 1960s, Brazil tried to export processed coffee. The US government, under pressure from the instant coffee companies, threatened to cut off aid;
- in Africa, tea production has increased six-fold since 1960. Africa's per capita food production is steadily declining.

The last point relates to the transnationals' power to control good agricultural areas, and grow crops for export to the wealthier North – at the expense of people's stomachs in the South. It will also reflect the advice given to the Third World by the international community to concentrate on export crops and, if necessary, import foodstuffs for the indigenous population.

Exploitation of the Third World takes different forms, and frequently results in destruction of people's health or their environment. Examples include buying large sections of the Amazon jungle and running it for a handful of years as a cattle ranch until the soil is destroyed (see DEFORESTATION); selling pesticides in Third World countries even when they have been banned on health grounds in the First World (see PESTICIDES); following industrial practices that would not have been possible in the First World (see BHOPAL); dumping toxic waste (see CHEMICAL WASTES); or hard-selling processed baby milk to people whose babies would be healthier with mothers' milk alone.

The UK's record in the Third World

The UK government has no central policy on the environment in the Third World. A number of different departments have an influence – the Foreign Office, the Overseas Development Administration, the Department of Trade and Industry, and (to a small extent) the Department of the Environment.

Development issues receive very low priority. They tend to be discussed in terms of human crisis – like the Ethiopian disaster – so policy is reactive rather than forward-looking. UK–Third World policy can be split into two areas – trade and overseas aid. Trade and aid policies favoured by the North are wrecking the environment of the South.

The limiting factor of the government's policy towards the Third World is the large reduction in overseas aid that has occurred since 1979. On the other hand, there has been some progress in the last two or three years, in terms of staffing at the ODA and in governmental attitudes internationally. The government is making the right noises: it needs now to back them up with cash.

One benchmark of assessing a government's attitude towards the Third World is the amount of money it is willing to give in aid. Friends of the Earth estimates that 1 per cent of Western GNP (Gross National Product) is needed to make a significant impact on the problems of the Third World: the United Nations target figure is 0.7 per cent of GNP. When the Conservative government came to power in 1979, the UK was allocating 0.44 per cent of GNP as aid. The figure by 1987 was 0.33 per cent.

UK Aid Programme, 1978–87		
	Gross aid	% of GNP
1978–79	£764 million	0.44
1979–80	£834 million	0.40
1980–81	£968 million	0.41
1981–82	£1,016 million	0.39
1982–83	£1,033 million	0.36
1983–84	£1,100 million	0.36
1984–85	£1,165 million	0.35
1985–86	£1,193 million	0.33
1986–87	£1,266 million	0.33

Source: *Hansard*, 25 March 1987

The percentage of GNP devoted to aid has fallen consistently through the term of the present administration. Opposition MPs pointed out in December 1986 that this represents an approximate 15 per cent real reduction in the overseas aid budget since 1979.

Internationally, UK aid provisions are towards the bottom of the league. In 1985, in terms of aid as a percentage of GNP, Britain ranked ninth out of the 14 donor countries of the Council of Europe (tenth to fourteenth were Italy, Switzerland, Ireland, Luxembourg and Spain).

There are two types of aid, multilateral and bilateral. Multilateral aid, in which the UK sets up a fund with a number of other countries, usually does not have a 'trade-with-the-UK' stipulation attached. It is used to fund organizations like the World Bank and other development agencies. Current government policy favours zero real growth in the overall budgets of multilateral development agencies to which we contribute.

Bilateral aid, in which Britain gives money to one country, generally has trade conditions as part of the deal. In 1985–6, bilateral aid formed 58 per cent of the total aid package: around three-quarters of bilateral aid is tied to trade. This means that slightly under half of our total aid has strings attached.

This type of aid frequently produces results that are not environmentally defensible. The intention of the financing is to stimulate trade with the UK in certain products or services, and the money is earmarked for specific purposes. The project, though protecting British jobs and profits, often turns out to be unsuitable for the local environment.

Aid figures are often distorted by the addition of projects that one would not normally classify as 'aid'. *For Richer, For Poorer* gives these recent examples of British government aid grants, some of which appear to be 'normal' aid, and others which look rather unusual. All are included in the aid budget:

- £190 million on emergency relief for Africa from 1984–6;
- £65 million providing Westland helicopters for India;
- £2.2 million to help extend primary health-care services for poor people in Orissa State, India;
- £7 million to build a new hospital in the Falkland Islands;
- £18 million to pay for a new repair yard to replace the naval dockyard in Gibraltar.

Mrs Thatcher appears to have little personal commitment to overseas aid. When Timothy Raison left the post as Minister for Overseas Development in 1986, he said that the only time the Prime Minister mentioned aid to him was when she sacked him.

See also BHOPAL; CHEMICAL WASTES; DEFORESTATION; DESERTIFICATION; MARINE POLLUTION; MILITARY SPENDING, WORLDWIDE; POPULATION; SPECIES EXTINCTION; WETLANDS

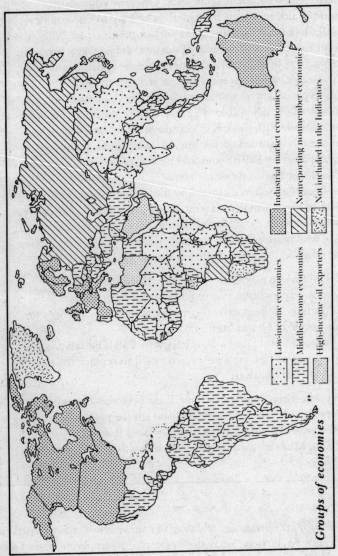

Groups of economies

The map shows what group a country has been placed in on the basis of
its GNP per capita and, in some instances, its distinguishing economic
characteristics. Only countries with a population of more than 1 million
have been included.

Low-income economies

Middle-income economies

High-income oil exporters

Industrial market economies

Nonreporting nonmember economies

Not included in the Indicators

REFERENCES

Chetley, Andy, *The Baby Killer Scandal*, War on Want, 1979.

Clark, John, *For Richer, For Poorer*, Oxfam, 1986.

George, Susan, *How the Other Half Dies*, Penguin Books, 1976.

George, Susan, *A Fate Worse than Debt*, Penguin Books, 1988.

Grant, James P., *The State of the World's Children 1988*, UNICEF, OUP, 1988.

Hayter, Teresa and Catharine Watson, *Aid: Rhetoric and Reality*, Pluto Press, 1985.

International Fund for Agricultural Development, *Annual Report 1986*, Rome, Italy, 1986.

Lever, Harold and Christopher Huhne, *Debt and Danger: the World Financial Crisis*, Penguin Books, 1987.

United Nations Environment Programme, *The State of the World Environment 1987*, UNEP, April 1987.

World Commission on Environment and Development (the Brundtland Commission), *Our Common Future*, OUP, 1987.

World Bank, *World Development Report 1986*, OUP, 1986.

World Bank, *World Development Report 1987*, OUP, 1987.

Hansard, 12 January 1987 and 25 March 1987.

Huhne, Christopher, 'Third World pays back $43bn to its rich creditors', *Guardian*, 19 December 1988.

Lone, Salim, 'Debt Sinks the Hope of Africa', *Guardian*, 18 July 1987.

'Money Makes the World Go Round', *New Internationalist*, February 1987.

Third World First Factsheets.

CONTACTS

Christian Aid
Ethical Investment Research Investigation Service
Friends of the Earth
One World
Oxfam
Red Cross/Red Crescent
Third World First

UNCTAD
UNICEF
United Nations Environment Programme (UNEP)
United Nations Food and Agriculture Organization (FAO)
War on Want
World Development Movement

Nuclear Energy

HISTORY

Nuclear energy and nuclear weapons are two of the most controversial environmental issues of the late twentieth century. Born together during intensive scientific research in the 1930s and the Second World War, it was the more aggressive twin that appeared first, in explosions at Hiroshima and Nagasaki in 1945. Nuclear energy played a Cinderella role for the next decade, and began to be developed for civil uses only during the late 1950s.

Since then, it has expanded rapidly: never fulfilling its promise in terms of amount of electricity forecast or the price at which this was to be done, but nevertheless achieving an impressive rate of development. According to the Brundtland Commission, some 15 per cent of all the world's electricity is now produced from nuclear origins, although nine-tenths of this is the result of only ten countries' operations.

There is little in common between proponents of nuclear power, who claim that the technology is clean, safe and cheap; and opponents, who say it is environmentally destructive, dangerous and expensive. The situation is complicated by the intense secrecy that surrounds the nuclear industry, making it difficult to establish realistic costings, or to separate the civil nuclear industry from its military stablemate.

How nuclear power works

Oil- and coal-burning power stations heat water to produce steam, which drives a turbine and thus generates electricity. Nuclear power stations generate electricity in exactly the same way.

Walter Patterson's book *Nuclear Power* (1983) gives a very clear picture of how nuclear power works. The technology depends on the inherent instability of uranium, a substance in which the protons and neutrons in the nucleus of the atom are bound together less tightly than in other elements. If this nucleus is hit by a stray neutron from another atom, it will split into two parts, at the same time releasing two or three neutrons of its own. This 'splitting' is called nuclear fission.

If two of these neutrons in turn hit other uranium nuclei, then four to six neutrons will be released: and the process accelerates. If there is enough fissionable material in close proximity, the result is a chain of events in which nuclei split and their neutrons then split other nuclei. This is called a chain reaction.

Do this with maximum speed, and the result is an atomic explosion; control and regulate the reaction, however, and the result is merely enormous quantities of heat. This boils water to power the electricity generators: and the result is called nuclear energy.

The beginnings of nuclear power

The first nuclear reactor was constructed at Chicago in 1942, when a pile of graphite bricks (the term 'nuclear pile' was derived from this) containing balls of uranium and uranium oxide generated 200 watts of heat. The potential for nuclear energy has been available since that day, but research concentrated on the scramble to produce atomic weapons and then the hydrogen bomb. Uranium supplies were diverted to bomb-testing programmes (see below).

The first British pile, at Windscale, began operating in October 1950, the second in 1951. These were built for military purposes, producing fuel for Britain's first atomic bomb, which was exploded in 1952. Demand for military plutonium (which is manufactured from uranium) increased rapidly, with the result that four reactors were built at Calder Hall, next to Windscale, and four at Chapelcross in Dumfriesshire.

The Calder Hall reactor was opened by the Queen in October 1956, in a blaze of publicity heralding the arrival of 'the world's first nuclear power station' (heat from the reactor was used to generate electricity for the national grid).

The Queen's speech contained the sentence: 'It may well prove to have been among the greatest of our contributions to human welfare that we led the way in demonstrating the peaceful uses of this new source of power.' In fact, as Durie and Edwards point out in *Fuelling the Nuclear Arms Race* (1982), Calder Hall's main contribution was to provide plutonium for Britain's nuclear weapons – an estimated 25 per cent of the plutonium needed for Britain's nuclear stockpile by the mid-1960s.

Atoms for peace

Reactor development in the USA in the late 1940s and early 1950s was also motivated by military priorities. The move towards civil nuclear use began when President Eisenhower launched his 'Atoms For Peace' campaign in 1953, in an effort to divert nuclear research away from its purely aggressive role.

The USA offered to donate fissile material to an international body so that peaceful uses of atomic power could be developed, provided that other nuclear powers (the USSR) made a similar donation. The offer foundered under diplomatic negotiations, but did lead to the formation of the International Atomic Energy Agency (IAEA) in 1957, as a UN agency, with the task to 'seek to accelerate and enlarge the contribution of atomic energy to peace, health, and prosperity throughout the world'. The IAEA's role was to help the development of civil nuclear power.

Norman Moss's *The Politics of Uranium* (1981) describes how Britain became the first country to embark on a civil nuclear power programme (coal and oil were both more expensive in the UK than in the USA). The UK Atomic Energy Authority (UKAEA) was formed in 1954: in recognition of the twin needs of civil and military nuclear development, the Authority was not placed under parliamentary control, but was given semi-autonomous status under ministerial supervision. At the time of the UKAEA's formation, according to the government, nine-tenths of atomic work in the UK had been concerned with the production of nuclear weapons.

This was changing, however. A White Paper in 1955 announced a plan to build nine nuclear power stations with a total capacity of 2,000 megawatts (roughly the electricity requirement of 2 to 3 million Western Europeans today). This target was tripled a year later, in response to the Suez crisis. France, Germany, the USSR and the USA followed the British lead. The initial UK reactor in this programme – which was also used covertly to provide plutonium for UK and US military stockpiles in the 1960s and 1970s – came on line in 1962.

It was a time of extraordinary optimism in the nuclear industry. The Chairman of the UKAEA made a speech to science writers in

1954 in which he said the day might come, thanks to nuclear power, in which 'our children will enjoy electricity in their homes too cheap to meter'. Plans were discussed for miniature atomic reactors to be installed in homes as boilers, research began on an atomic-powered aircraft (later abandoned as unsafe), there was even talk of nuclear-powered vacuum cleaners.

The US government gave grants to 26 countries to help them build research reactors. As nuclear enthusiasm spread, a number of countries invested in the technology. The next 15 years saw a rapid expansion in the number of research reactors commissioned, although the trend peaked in the 1960s.

Research reactors commissioned worldwide

1940–49	11 commissioned
	1 shut down
1950–59	143 commissioned
	11 shut down
1960–69	267 commissioned
	39 shut down
1970–79	81 commissioned
	92 shut down
1980–86	30 commissioned
	46 shut down

Source: International Atomic Energy Agency, *Nuclear Research Reactors in the World*, 1987

Current national programmes

Of more than 150 countries in the world, 26 have nuclear power. Of this figure, 18 countries have fewer than ten reactors.

(Austria and the Philippines each have a nuclear plant, which they decided not to operate after the Chernobyl disaster.)

Outside Eastern Europe, South Korea, Taiwan, Spain, Switzerland and Belgium have a significant proportion of their electricity

Civil nuclear electricity production, 1986: less than ten reactors

	Existing reactors	Reactors under construction	% national electricity produced by nuclear power
Argentina	2	1	11.3
Belgium	8	–	67.0
Brazil	1	–	0.1
Bulgaria	4	2	30.0
Czechoslovakia	7	9	21.0
GDR	5	6	11.6
Finland	4	–	38.4
Hungary	3	1	25.8
India	6	4	2.7
Italy	3	3	4.5
The Netherlands	2	–	6.2
Pakistan	1	1	1.8
S. Africa	2	–	6.8
S. Korea	7	2	43.6
Spain	8	2	29.4
Switzerland	5	–	39.2
Taiwan	6	–	43.8
Yugoslavia	1	–	5.4
China	0	1	
Cuba	0	2	
Mexico	0	2	
Poland	0	2	
Rumania	0	3	

Source: UKAEA, *The Nuclear Share of Electricity Production*, 1986

produced by nuclear power, with a combined total of 28 reactors. These five countries have only four more reactors under construction, however: their experience of nuclear energy has not led to a massive reordering programme. Development of nuclear power is proceeding, albeit more slowly, only in France, the UK, and some of the centrally planned economies: and this has slowed down as the effects of Chernobyl are assimilated. In September 1988, construction of a nuclear power station near Minsk, USSR, was halted as a result of public fears. Nine months earlier public outcry had prevented the completion of another plant, at Krasnodar in the Northern Caucasus.

The large bulk of nuclear power, four-fifths of production worldwide, is generated in eight countries.

Large-scale producers of nuclear electricity

	Existing reactors	Reactors under construction	% of national electricity produced by nuclear power	% of world nuclear electricity output
USSR	50	32	10	9.7
Canada	18	5	14.7	4.4
USA	99	21	16.6	27.0
UK	38	4	18.4	3.4
Japan	35	10	24.7	11.0
FRG	21	4	29.4	7.4
Sweden	12	–	50.3	4.4
France	49	14	69.8	15.9

Source: UKAEA, *The Nuclear Share of Electricity Production*, 1986

Opponents of nuclear power argue that, if nuclear energy was truly cheaper and more efficient than other sources, it would have been picked up with more enthusiasm by the world at large. As it is, four of the major nuclear proponents appear to have additional reasons for their preference: the USA, USSR, UK and France have large nuclear weapons programmes and research budgets, which would cross-subsidize the development of atomic power. The fifth country, Canada, has developed and is marketing its own nuclear reactor (the CANDU). It also has substantial reserves of uranium.

Of the remaining three, FRG and Japan are anomalous, as they are under post-Second World War obligations not to develop nuclear weapon capacity, and were dependent on the USA during the 1950s for financial and technological assistance. Psychologically and economically, they would have been sympathetic customers for the Atoms for Peace ideal. (Opposition parties in West Germany now favour a phase-out of nuclear power.)

The last country, Sweden, is to close down its entire nuclear electricity operation after an adverse result from a referendum. All nuclear power stations will be closed by 2010. Opposition opinion in the UK is moving in the same direction.

At the end of 1986, there were 394 reactors producing electricity worldwide, with 137 under construction. Around the world, the pace of nuclear development has slowed rapidly. There appear to be three main reasons for this: first, the cost of nuclear power (see below); secondly, environmental degradation caused by the technology (see below); and thirdly, the threat of large-scale environmental destruction, as exemplified by the disasters in the 1970s and 1980s (see CHERNOBYL, THREE MILE ISLAND). Since 1974, the IAEA projections for nuclear capacity installed worldwide by the year 2000 have dropped nearly 90%.

Keepin and Kats summarize the global disillusionment with nuclear power. Austria has decided not to bring its only plant on-line; Greece has abandoned plans to build its first plant; Yugoslavia has postponed construction pending safety evaluation; Finland has postponed new orders, and in Italy all major parties have turned against the country's nuclear programme. In 1986, Brazil cancelled five out of eight planned reactors and then suspended work on the two currently under construction. Mexico cancelled plans for its third and fourth reactors, suspended construction of the second, and may not be able to complete the first. China has postponed its nuclear programme indefinitely. Egypt, Kuwait and Saudi Arabia have shelved their nuclear programmes.

Even nuclear enthusiasts are having second thoughts. Japan's nuclear capacity forecasts for the year 2000 were scaled downward 31 per cent in 1984, and in the USSR, Mr Gorbachev has stated of nuclear power: 'It is not secure when the development of atomic engineering is justified by unacceptable risks . . .'

DIFFICULTIES AND COSTS

The pure physics of nuclear power are almost unbelievably exciting, but, from an engineering point of view, nuclear energy is exceptionally difficult to provide while maintaining cost efficiency and guaranteed safety. It demands strict quality control, constant supervision, and guaranteed reliability from all the components under stress. Looming over all this is the knowledge that one mistake could have catastrophic consequences.

The British nuclear power programme has encountered problems typical of the industry worldwide. Electricity from the first station to be commissioned, Berkeley in Somerset in 1962, cost three times that of the best coal-fired stations in the UK. The difference between planned and actual costs has continually dogged the nuclear industry, both in plant construction and provision of electricity.

The Calder Hall and Chapelcross reactors were the last in the UK to be produced on time and within budget, and these were military reactors built as prototypes. Construction overruns for the first generation of power stations (the Magnox) averaged two and a half years. Inadequate plant meant that planned electricity output was not achieved, making the nuclear stations more uneconomical. Department of Energy estimates in 1986 reckoned that electricity from coal plants was produced more cheaply than from the Magnox reactors.

The Central Electricity Generating Board accepted this as true in its 1988/9 evidence to the Hinckley C nuclear inquiry; CEGB chairman Lord Marshall even admitted on BBC television (*Brass Tacks*, October 1987) that, for Magnox stations, the economic benefit has always been 'jam tomorrow'.

The next generation of reactors (Advanced Gas-Cooled Reactors – AGRs) achieved an average ten-year construction overrun, function at 60 per cent efficiency, cost twice their projected price and frequently break down. This has a knock-on effect to the present day: in spite of falling energy prices worldwide, the Central Electricity Generating Board (CEGB) refused to lower the price of its electricity in 1987: it had to cover a large bill caused by inefficiency and breakdowns at the AGRs. The *Guardian* commented on 30 and 31 July 1987:

> The AGR stations, which are still being brought into operation – in one case fifteen years behind schedule – have turned into an engineering and financial nightmare for the CEGB ... The CEGB's financial director, Mr John Uttley, said that the price of failures and delays in the latest generation of advanced gas-cooled reactors was expected to be £100 million in the current financial year.

The Electricity Consumers' Council estimated in a 1988 report that delays in the AGR construction programme had cost £200 million over the previous three years.

In December 1988, the CEGB formally admitted that, at expected rates of return in the private sector, nuclear power is uneconomic in comparison to fossil-fuelled electricity generation. For three decades, however, the economic disadvantage of nuclear power had been disguised. Claims by the nuclear industry as to the price advantage of nuclear power over fossil fuels were the result of heavily massaged figures, cross-subsidization from military research budgets, and the use of unorthodox accountancy methods. The latter includes historic cost accounting (which does not take into account the cost of inflation) and current cost accounting (which does) – for different generations of nuclear power stations in order to 'get the figures right'. The House of Commons Select Committee on Energy (1981) expressed severe reservations about the CEGB's accounting procedures:

> The historic cost method used by the Board to justify past investments distorts the effect of inflation on capital costs, rendering the resulting figures highly misleading as a guide to past investments decisions and entirely useless for appraising future ones.

Seven years later, *New Scientist* commented in an editorial (10 December 1988):

> The bald fact is that after more than 30 years' development of civil nuclear power in Britain, the CEGB still cannot put its hand on its heart and say that fission is an economic proposition. The Magnox reactors failed this crucial litmus test, the design's successor, the advanced gas-cooled reactor, did worse. Now the much vaunted PWR looks doomed to occupy a 'jam tomorrow' niche.

Relative costs of generating systems

Colin Sweet's book *The Price of Nuclear Power* (1983) provides a perceptive analysis of the mechanisms used to present nuclear power in its most advantageous economic light. Sweet also makes the statement, which appears to be valid, that proponents of nuclear power tend to point to the *next* generation of power stations as that which will produce the cheap electricity – economic nuclear power is always around the next corner.

The British electricity supply industry, until 1988, insisted that electricity from nuclear power is cheaper than from alternative sources, which is why it wanted to start a programme of Pressurized

Water Reactors (see Glossary on p. 304). The difference between the two sides can best be summed up by a statement at an OECD symposium in 1982:*

Across OECD countries the cost of a nuclear plant may vary by nearly a factor of two ... depending on applicable safety standards and other cost factors, thus making nuclear power either the cheapest or the most expensive option relative to fossil fuels.

Thus both sides in the nuclear debate may be right: nuclear power can be the cheapest, or the most expensive, form of electricity production, depending on one's perception as to how much safety should be built into the plant, how much nuclear waste costs to manage, and how the predicted costs of decommissioning are calculated.

In the USA, nuclear plants are privately owned: the economics of nuclear power are decided by market forces, and hefty compensation claims await if things go wrong. Christopher Flavin in *Reforming the Electric Power Industry* (1986) points out that no new nuclear plant has been ordered in the USA since 1978, and 111 planned nuclear plants were cancelled between 1972 and 1984. The cancellations were primarily for economic reasons in the period 1973–79 (57 planned plants scrapped): the Three Mile Island disaster of 1979 did not begin the reactor cancellation programme, as is commonly thought, but reinforced it. All orders placed since 1973 have now been cancelled.

In 1970 the OECD projected that its members (24 leading Western industrial nations) would have 568,000 megawatts of nuclear capacity by 1985. The actual total was only about 180,000 megawatts. Plans for nuclear power construction levelled off worldwide in the mid-1970s, and the expected capacity has dropped more than 100,000 megawatts since 1978.

In the UK, the prospect of privatization has concentrated industry's mind on whether it would like to take over the running of nuclear power stations. The Confederation of British Industry commissioned a research paper from Oxford Economic Research Associates: this concluded that private industry would not want to run a nuclear programme, because of the high cost involved and the relative cheapness of coal stations:

* OECD, *Costs of Coal Pollution Abatement*, 1983.

The investment problem post privatization arises in part because of the government's commitment to the nuclear programme. Coal and gas turbine investments would be undertaken by the private sector on a stand-alone basis, provided an appropriate regulatory structure is put in place. The nuclear programme is unlikely to be undertaken by private companies acting in a competitive market, and this has forced the government to consider various methods by which privatization can be 'doctored' to ensure its continuation.*

In November 1987, the comparative prices quoted for nuclear and coal-powered electricity were 2.82p per kilowatt-hour for electricity from the newest planned nuclear station (Hinckley) and 3.03p per kilowatt-hour from a new completed coal-powered station (Drax). These were 'average lifetime costs' calculated by the CEGB, so they would presumably try to estimate coal prices for some time in the future. The CBI has pointed out that the CEGB frequently overestimates the price of coal in projections such as this – thus making the coal option seem more expensive.

In 1989, nuclear power enjoyed a short-lived comeback as the solution to the GREENHOUSE EFFECT. Closer examination, however, revealed that:

- nuclear power would not solve the greenhouse effect, as fossil fuel combustion in power stations provides only some 10 per cent of greenhouse forcing;
- it is seven times more expensive to replace this sector with nuclear power than with energy conservation (Keepin and Kats, 1988);
- energy conservation could be achieving results in months, whereas nuclear power would require at least a decade;
- the inordinate cost of nuclear power would remove resources from initiatives to reduce other greenhouse gases. Investment in nuclear power, at the expense of other, more efficient initiatives, would result in a net increase of carbon dioxide emissions.

The long-term case for nuclear energy looks even less arguable when the evolving costs of renewable energy are considered. The CEGB projected an optimistic cost for nuclear electricity of 2.9p per kilowatt-hour at the Sizewell Inquiry. Wind-power in the USA can currently deliver at 2p per kilowatt-hour (see ENERGY: RENEWABLE

*Oxford Economic Research Associates, *The Privatisation of the Electricity Supply Industry*, 1988.

ENERGY). In addition to this, nuclear power shows huge variations in construction costs. Keepin and Kats point to the different costs per kilowatt installed:

France	:	$1,000 (claimed: difficult to verify)
UK	:	$2,000
Brazil	:	$2,874
USA	:	$3,200
Philippines:		$3,387
Egypt	:	$4,000 (projected)
Argentina	:	$6,000 (estimated)

The cost of constructing a (1,000 megawatt) nuclear power station in France would be $1 billion. The US station would be three times as expensive, the Argentine six times as costly.

France claims these low-cost figures as a result of a large-scale, production-line nuclear programme that benefited from economies of scale. The French nuclear programme has been cited as one of the most successful civil nuclear developments in the world. The cost of construction, however, has left Electricité de France in debt to the tune of 200 billion francs (about £20,000 million), making it the sixth or seventh biggest debtor in the world, its debt surpassed only by national debts of countries such as Mexico and Argentina. Confidence in the nuclear industry has led the French to place most of their energy eggs in one basket: it remains to be seen whether this confidence is well-founded.

OPERATIONAL SAFETY

Nuclear power stations show the same range of operational history as other large industrial plant, varying from the successful to the incompetent to the disastrous. In Britain, the Central Electricity Generating Board points to the low level of radiation discharge from its power stations as an indication of operational efficiency.

This middle section of the nuclear fuel cycle, coming between nuclear fuel production and nuclear waste management, appears to be the cleanest (although there are exceptions such as Trawsfynydd nuclear power station, reported by Friends of the Earth to be discharging unacceptable levels of cobalt-60, caesium-134 and caesium-137). This assessment is changing as more is learnt of the effects of low-level radiation and its connection with leukaemia clusters (see

RADIATION): but, as far as the public is concerned, 'normal' discharges to the environment outside Britain's nuclear power stations have not, to date, provoked great controversy. Most argument has concentrated around facilities such as Sellafield and sites for dumping nuclear waste.

There is, however, anxiety about the possibility of a large-scale nuclear accident. The use of nuclear fuel in a reactor can have devastating consequences if things go wrong.

The first British reactors – the Magnox – do not have secondary containment domes, and many nuclear power stations are situated near large population centres. After Chernobyl, everybody living within a 30-kilometre radius (18.6 miles) of the reactor was evacuated – 130,000 in all. In the UK, this evacuation would probably be much more difficult, because of the large numbers of people affected.

Populations living within 19 miles of UK nuclear power stations

Station	Population	Reactor type
Berkeley	879,000	Magnox
Bradwell	682,000	Magnox
Dungeness	237,000	Magnox/AGR
Hinckley Point	454,000	Magnox/AGR
Hunterston	440,000	Magnox/AGR
Oldbury	984,000	Magnox
Sizewell	141,000	Magnox
Trawsfynydd	67,000	Magnox
Wylfa	59,000	Magnox
Hartlepool	987,000	AGR
Heysham	540,000	AGR
Torness	43,000	AGR
Calder Hall	130,000	Magnox
Chapelcross	160,000	Magnox
Dounreay	16,000	Prototype fast breeder reactor
Winfrith Heath	407,000	Steam generating Heavy Water

Source: *New Statesman*, 16 May 1986

Assuming a conservative radiation zone covering 100 miles, and an evacuation zone of 18.6 miles, Britain's nuclear power stations could contaminate large areas of the UK in the event of accident.

A large-scale nuclear accident is regarded by the nuclear safety authorities as highly unlikely in the UK. The Health and Safety Executive have published figures estimating the chances of a major civil nuclear accident as 1 in 1 million: if there were 20 nuclear reactors, then the chance of such an accident would be in the order of 1 in 50,000. These figures contrast oddly with figures issued by international bodies after the Chernobyl disaster. The US Nuclear Regulatory Commission suggests that Western Europe might expect a major accident once every seven years (see CHERNOBYL).

The possibility of this occurrence does not appear to be reflected in the UK's nuclear emergency plans, which appear to be markedly different to those of several other countries. Before the Three Mile Island incident, US regulations required off-site emergency plans covering a two to three mile radius round the reactor. After the disaster, the regulations were redrawn: the new zone is ten miles (16 kilometres) in radius.

- West Germany has a 6–10-km evacuation zone
- The Netherlands, 10-km warning zone
- Switzerland, 18-km warning zone
- France has a 10-km warning zone and a 5-km evacuation zone
- At Chernobyl, a 30-km evacuation zone was declared
- The UK has an evacuation zone of 2–3 km

The rationale behind the UK safety limit is that the likelihood of a serious incident is infinitesimal. The environmental movement says that a serious nuclear accident could happen in Britain: the nuclear industry says that it is extremely unlikely.

The insurance companies appear to agree with the environmentalists, on the basis of their actuarial assessment. Insurance costs against the consequences of a large-scale nuclear accident would be prohibitive. For that reason, liability of the plant operator is limited to £20 million per incident, to be topped up by the tax-payer if necessary to £230 million. This figure would not provide adequate compensation in the event of a major accident, and provides a hidden subsidy to the economic case for nuclear power.

NUCLEAR ENERGY AND NUCLEAR WEAPONS

There has always been an inextricable link between nuclear energy and nuclear weapons. Developed as a result of the same research drive (see above), it was the military use of the technology that became established first. There is still a substantial crossover between the two fields. Three areas – uranium enrichment, the manufacture of plutonium, reprocessing and waste disposal – form the bridge between civil and military nuclear power.

Uranium enrichment

Natural uranium contains 0.7 per cent uranium-235, with the rest being uranium-238. The majority of nuclear reactors needs more uranium-235 in the fuel than this, so the uranium is 'enriched' – an expensive, time-consuming operation, in the early stages involving vast machinery in which atoms of uranium-238 are painstakingly split off from the fuel in order to increase the proportion of uranium-235.

Reactor fuel commonly needs a uranium-235 content of 3 to 3.5 per cent: to get this, some four-fifths of the mass of uranium-238 has to be removed. This is routinely done to provide fuel for most of the world's power stations. If, however, the process is continued and more uranium-238 is taken out of the fuel, eventually the new substance will be mainly uranium-235 – and suitable for making an atomic bomb.

Because of the mechanical processes involved, most of the difficult work of enrichment goes into the early stages, to achieve a uranium-235 content of 3.5 per cent. When this has been done, a scientist is three-quarters of the way to getting a substance that is 90 per cent uranium-235.

As Norman Moss says in *The Politics of Uranium*: 'The difference between 3.5% enriched uranium and 90% enriched uranium is the difference between something that can provide heat and light to a city, and something that can blow it off the face of the earth.' For this reason, countries with nuclear weapons tend to look very carefully when a non-nuclear weapons country wants to develop an enrichment plant. In March 1987, the *Observer* revealed that Pakistan had built a secret uranium enrichment plant, and thus had the capacity to produce weapons-grade uranium.

Up to now, keeping track of these plants has been difficult but not impossible, as they are very large: the development of laser enrichment technology may change this, as such plants can be built in small factory-size units, without any external distinguishing signs.

Plutonium

Uranium-235 is a 'fissile' material – i.e. it will split in the right circumstances and promote a nuclear chain reaction. There is another substance that will react in a similar way, and is thus suitable for making atomic bombs – plutonium.

Plutonium was first manufactured in a laboratory in 1941, by bombarding uranium with neutrons. In certain conditions a uranium atom will capture a neutron; the neutron then splits, creating a new element, neptunium. This atom in turn can capture another neutron, and form plutonium – fissionable, radioactive, with a half-life of 24,400 years.

At the time of the discovery, uranium was in short supply, and plutonium was developed as another possible way of making nuclear weapons. By 1945, enough plutonium was amassed to make two atomic bombs, and enough uranium-235 to make one. In June 1945, the first plutonium bomb was tested in New Mexico. The bomb used at Hiroshima on 6 August was uranium-235. The second plutonium bomb was dropped at Nagasaki, three days later.

At the time of plutonium's discovery, it was difficult to get hold of uranium-235. Plutonium, however, could be recovered from the waste fuels of nuclear reactors: as uranium is 'burnt' in a reactor, and around 1 per cent of the unused uranium is turned into plutonium. This can be extracted from the spent fuel, and mixed with ordinary uranium to make 'mixed oxide' fuel, suitable for use in power stations. Alternatively, the extracted plutonium can be used for nuclear weapons. The procedure for chemically separating plutonium and unburnt uranium from spent nuclear fuel is called 'reprocessing'.

Reprocessing plants and waste disposal

At the end of the nuclear fuel cycle a choice is made: whether to store the spent nuclear fuel as it is, or reprocess it. Fuel from military reactors is frequently reprocessed, to provide plutonium for nuclear weapons. The justification for reprocessing fuel from civil reactors is to provide plutonium for 'fast breeder' reactors (which, theoretically, use plutonium to produce electricity and more plutonium: in spite of

40 years' research and – literally – billions of pounds, the technology remains unviable and under most forecasts may not be practicable for another 40 years, if then).

In the past, reprocessed fuel from British reactors has been used for military purposes, although this was officially denied until recently. On 20 March 1986, Walter Marshall, the head of the Central Electricity Generating Board, conceded that plutonium from Britain's civil stockpile had been transferred to military use, although this was not current practice. Plutonium swaps with the USA have, according to American sources, also led to British civil nuclear fuel being earmarked for military use.

The military dimensions of a reprocessing facility may explain why the UK government is so keen to keep the reprocessing plant at Sellafield open and to develop the new THORP (Thermal Oxide Reprocessing Plant) plant at the same site, to reprocess fuel from Britain's newer Advanced Gas-cooled Reactors (AGRs). In waste terms, reprocessing is an illogical process.

---

	4 cubic metres of spent nuclear fuel
	becomes
	2.5 cubic metres of high-level waste,
plus	40 cubic metres of intermediate waste,
plus	600 cubic metres of low-level waste
	after reprocessing.

All these new quantities of waste have to be stored somewhere. In the absence of reprocessing, only 4 cubic metres of high-level waste would have to be stored.

In Western Europe, there are two commercial-scale reprocessing plants: at Sellafield in the UK, and at Cap la Hague in France. The spread of reprocessing technology would increase the number of states capable of making nuclear weapons: at the moment, there are also pilot or military plants at Dounreay (UK), Marcoull (France), Mol (Belgium), and Karlsruhe (West Germany). Japan has a pilot plant and is building a full-scale plant. Argentina and India already have the technology, although not well-developed.

There has been no reprocessing of civil nuclear fuel in the USA since 1971. The Carter administration banned further reprocessing in 1977 because of the dangers of nuclear proliferation.

Nuclear reactors as military targets

All large power stations in the East and the West are already targeted in the event of war (whether nuclear or non-nuclear). The consequences of an exploding reactor could be seen in the wide-ranging destruction at Chernobyl: a country with a large number of nuclear power stations potentially has a host of such disasters on its hands if hostilities should break out.

Modern non-nuclear weapons are capable of breaking through nuclear power station containment domes: in many cases, this would not be necessary, as collapsing the water intake, eliminating the control room or severing the primary cooling circuit could achieve the desired result. The spent fuel cooling ponds adjacent to all reactors have no real structural protection against external military attack. The threat from terrorists should not be underestimated: terrorist bombers have struck at nuclear installations in France, Spain, South Africa, Switzerland, the United States and Argentina.

Given the spread of nuclear power stations, it seems probable that a civil nuclear station will sooner or later be at the centre of a terrorist attack. The consequences of large-scale bombing of nuclear stations in the event of full-scale war would be horrific. As the Royal Commission on the Environment commented in 1976: 'If nuclear power could have been developed earlier, and had been in widespread use at the time of the last war, it is likely that some areas of Central Europe would still be uninhabitable because of ground contamination.'

NUCLEAR WASTE

Nuclear waste exists in various forms – gas, liquid and solid – and strengths ranging from mildly to extremely radioactive. At present, no long-term solution for waste disposal has been developed. The question is becoming more pressing every year as the scale of the problem increases. The substances can be extremely dangerous: an accident in the Ural Mountains in 1957 (only recently officially acknowledged by the USSR, but believed to have killed hundreds of people) was allegedly caused by inadequately-contained nuclear waste.

The UK Department of the Environment usually classifies these materials in four different types.

Low-level waste   Dilute gases and liquids which can be discharged directly into the environment: paper, clothing, etc., which may be buried in shallow trenches; and very dilute industrial waste which may be disposed of with ordinary refuse.

Intermediate-level and short-lived waste   Waste of a higher activity, but not containing a high proportion of alpha-emitters (see RADIATION) such as plutonium, which has a long half-life. Solid and semi-solid items such as sludges, resins and contaminated equipment, in the past dumped at sea, but now stored at power stations or Sellafield.

Intermediate long-lived waste   Radioactive debris heavily contaminated with alpha-emitters such as plutonium. The vast majority of this consists of fuel cladding (i.e., the 'jacket' that surrounds nuclear fuel rods), a by-product of nuclear reprocessing (see below). Planned disposal for this would be in a deep depository, maybe an old mine.

High-level waste   Intensely radioactive, results from spent reactor fuel: either intact fuel rods or quantities of liquid after reprocessing. Generates large quantities of heat and needs to be continuously cooled.

In Britain, nuclear waste originates from four main sources:*

• the commercial nuclear fuel cycle;
• the military nuclear weapons programme and related activities;
• nuclear use in hospitals and medical research laboratories;
• the industrial use of radioisotopes.

Disposal systems
In the early days of nuclear power, disposal of nuclear waste was rather primitive. Both in the UK (Windscale – now known as Sellafield) and the USA (Hanford), radioactive substances were deliberately discharged into the environment for experimental purposes (*Environment Now*, July 1988).

'Dispersal' was regarded as an acceptable system – diluted wastes

---

* R. Chudleigh and W. Cannell, *Radioactive Waste: the Gravedigger's Dilemma*, 1984.

were discharged into the environment in quantities assumed not to cause damage to human health. This procedure came under intense criticism, as it enabled highly radioactive material to be discharged, on the grounds that it was combined with large quantities of low radioactive matter. Under this system, an estimated quarter to one-third of a tonne of highly radioactive plutonium was pumped into the Irish Sea from Sellafield.

Another early technique was 'sea-dumping' – in which the radioactive material was wrapped in concrete or steel containers and dropped over the side of a ship. Between 1949 and 1979, the UK dumped 67,337 tonnes of material in this way (70 per cent of which was concrete or steel 'packaging'). In the four years to 1983, the UK was responsible for 90 per cent of all nuclear dumping at sea.

The option became unpopular internationally, as countries which had decided against nuclear power were being exposed to marine pollution from other countries' nuclear wastes. The London Dumping Convention recommended a suspension of all radioactive dumping in 1983. The UK, although announcing its intention of ignoring the ban, was forced into compliance when the National Union of Seamen refused to take part in any more sea dumps.

As these two systems of disposal became the subject of international criticism, the UK was forced back to its third option – containment (in which the wastes are placed in containers and stored). This is a long-term programme – shorter-lived intermediate wastes will be radioactive for 200 to 300 years, and the longer-lived wastes contain materials that will be radioactive for thousands of years. As one environmentalist commented: 'If Julius Caesar had had nuclear power, we would still be looking after his nuclear waste.'

High-level nuclear waste is currently stored as a concentrated liquid in stainless steel tanks, surrounded by concrete and cooled in water. If the technology is adequately developed, it is planned to cast the liquid into glass blocks, and store it deep underground. In terms of volume, there is not a huge amount of high-level waste in Britain – about 2,000 cubic metres – but it needs particularly careful handling. In the USA, 12,000 tonnes of commercial high-level waste are already in storage. This is expected to quadruple in the next 15 years, and will need to be kept out of contact with the human environment for 10,000 years – longer than recorded history.

In the UK, the search for low-level waste storage facilities has to date been unsuccessful. One of four sites – Elstow, Killingholme, Bradwell and Fulbeck – was to become a waste dump, but the idea provoked intense local antipathy. The plans were abandoned as a political gesture six weeks before the 1987 general election.

In the absence of a programme for dealing with nuclear wastes, they continue to accumulate: 25,000 cubic metres of low-level waste a year, and 3,000 cubic metres of intermediate waste. Estimates of the amount of low-level waste needing disposal were revised upwards by 30 per cent in September 1987, because of the need to provide safe disposal for contaminated topsoil from Sellafield. The UK government has stated that there were 42,000 cubic metres of intermediate waste in storage in Britain on 1 January 1986, 59,400 cubic metres in February 1989.

The volume of British waste expected by the end of the century has risen from 350,000 to 500,000 cubic metres. In the interim, waste is to be stored at Harwell, at power stations, and at the existing waste disposal site at Drigg, in Cumbria – a site that is expected to be full by the mid-1990s, and has been described by *New Scientist* (7 May 1987) as 'an abomination . . . little better than a municipal waste tip'. In 1989, Sellafield and Dounreay were identified as the two likely sites for waste storage. The reasons behind this choice appear to be based on political rather than scientific arguments.

Internationally, there have been public scandals about the disposal of nuclear waste – specifically in West Germany. In 1988, West German police were investigating the illegal transportation between West Germany and Belgium of 2,438 barrels of low-level radioactive waste. Evidence of bribe-giving worth £7 million was produced: the sum represents over 10 per cent of the turnover of Nukem, the parent company of Transnuklear, the accused transporting operator. Transnuklear later lost its operational licence and was disbanded.

In January 1988, the possibility emerged that Nukem had been shipping weapons-grade material overseas, in contravention of the Nuclear Non-Proliferation Treaty. Similar allegations were made against a Belgian firm, Belgonucleaire.

Reactors as nuclear waste

Governments are frequently criticized for adopting nuclear power before adequate systems of nuclear waste disposal had been developed. Another problem is beginning to appear: what to do with nuclear reactors when they have finished their useful working life. Intensely radioactive, they need to be stored and safeguarded in the same way as other nuclear detritus.

As Cynthia Pollock comments in *State of the World 1986*, the technology for decommissioning (i.e. closing down and dismantling) a nuclear reactor is in its infancy: the largest reactor to be decommissioned to date being the 22-megawatt Elk River plant in Minnesota – a three-year project costing $6.5 million at 1974 prices. Radioactivity builds up in proportion to plant size and operating life – a 1,000-megawatt plant operating over 30 years will be a much more difficult and expensive proposition to decommission than a small reactor with a short working life. Today's reactors can produce 50 times more power, and will have operated over seven times as long as Elk River.

In Britain, the advanced gas-cooled reactor at Windscale has been undergoing decommissioning since 1981. The 33-megawatt unit will, if all goes to plan, have disappeared by 1996 (although its radioactive waste will remain): by 1987, the programme was two years behind schedule. Windscale, which contributed electricity to the national grid for 18 years, is a lot smaller than even the first generation of Magnox reactors (250-megawatts). Set beside the planned Sizewell B station (1,200-megawatts), it is tiny.

The Central Electricity Generating Board has nine Magnox stations which will be due for decommissioning in the next 25 years. According to Chudleigh and Cannell's *The Gravedigger's Dilemma*, the CEGB-estimated costs of decommissioning per station are between £150 million and £270 million. This should be treated as guesswork until practical experience provides accurate figures. In the United States, various estimates have been put forward for the costs of reactor decommissioning, ranging from $50 million to $3 billion per reactor. Most estimates favour the lower end of the ranges between £200 and £700 million: the Electricity Consumers' Council has described the costs of reactor decommissioning as 'massive'. In January 1989, the US government released an estimate of the cost of cleaning up radioactive and chemical pollution at its nuclear weapons and other research and industrial plant – a massive $46 billion over 20 years to deal with contamination. $1.8 billion was required in 1989 just to meet the Energy Department's own safety and environmental regulations.

Problems of decommissioning have been exacerbated by the ban on sea dumping, as the radioactive debris from retired power stations was originally destined for the oceans. Preferred decommissioning technique currently favours stripping the reactor and leaving the empty building for 50 to 100 years while radioactivity levels drop, before breaking it up. This has the disadvantage of leaving large radioactive structures in place for nearly a century, but is preferred because of cheaper dismantling costs and less radiation exposure for workers. Security and maintenance will need to be provided, if this system is adopted, until the power station is razed to the ground.

URANIUM MINING

Environmental damage from nuclear power is caused in three phases: first, in digging up uranium from the ground; secondly, in operating nuclear stations and their offshoots; and thirdly, in finding a place to get rid of used nuclear fuel and the large quantities of radioactive waste that accumulate. The entire sequence is called 'the nuclear fuel cycle'.

Digging up uranium

There are significant uranium reserves in the USA, Canada, France, Australia, South Africa, Namibia and elsewhere, although 85 per cent of uranium mined outside Eastern Europe comes from North America, southern Africa and Australia.

In *Nuclear Power*, Walter Patterson describes how uranium ore is dug up from surface or underground mines, and then fed into large crushing mills which grind it to the consistency of fine sand. Chemical treatment then produces a substance called 'yellowcake' which contains 85 per cent uranium. The yellowcake is accompanied by about one hundred times its weight of residual sand – waste material known as 'tailings', which accumulates in vast quantities.

Uranium extraction involves risks to health at all of its stages. In the mines, the radioactive ore produces a 'daughter' (i.e., derived) product called radon (see RADIATION), a radioactive gas which in turn produces intensely radioactive daughter products. Inhalation can cause lung cancer.

The US Public Health Service estimated at the end of the 1960s that of 6,000 men who worked in American uranium mines in the 1950s, 600 to 1,100 would die of lung cancer as a result of occupational radiation exposure. The USA represents the most civilized end of the uranium extraction business: in the harsher conditions of the Namibian uranium mine run by Rio Tinto Zinc, there was inadequate official documentation, according to *The Rossing File* (1980), of the black workers' occupational exposure to radiation. Casualties in these circumstances are likely to be much higher it can merely be surmised that thousands of uranium miners have died or will die from radiation-induced cancers.

Uranium tailings represent a more widespread threat to human health. Originally discarded without thought as just industrial waste, there are tens of millions of tons (estimates vary between 25 and 100 million tons) of radioactive tailings dumped in the USA alone, much of this piled on riverbanks in the south-west. Walter Patterson points out that in the 1960s, the sandy tailings were used as landfill beneath the foundations of buildings in many communities, notably Grand Junction, Colorado.

The radon gas emanating from these building structures . . . now exposes the local inhabitants – including children – to the same radon-daughter products which have already been responsible for thousands of lung-cancer deaths of miners from Joachimstal to Grand Junction.

Dr Rosalie Bertell (in *No Immediate Danger*, 1985) also makes the point that these tailings have been dug out of the ground, blasted, milled, dumped and blown hither and thither by the winds. Radioactive products that otherwise would have remained buried in the ground have been set free and are now residing on the surface of the planet: these products, however, are included as 'natural background radiation', as they do not obviously come from nuclear-weapons testing or nuclear power stations.

Radiation Doses, Effects, Risks (1985), published by the United Nations Environment Programme, notes that if current trends continue, there will be 500 million tonnes of tailings by the end of the century. 'These wastes remain radioactive for millions of years', comments the UNEP book, '. . . thus providing potentially the greatest long-term contribution to human exposure from nuclear power.'

A NUCLEAR GLOSSARY*

Becquerel, rem, rad, curie, (milli)sievert see RADIATION

Caesium-134 see CHERNOBYL

Carbon-14 see CHERNOBYL

Chain reaction A self-sustaining reaction, occurs in nuclear fission when the number of neutrons released in the reaction equals or exceeds the number of neutrons absorbed in, and escaping from, the reactor.

Control rod A rod containing material that absorbs neutrons; used to control or halt nuclear fission in a reactor.

Core The central part of a nuclear reactor that contains the fuel and produces the heat.

Critical Term used to describe a nuclear reactor that is sustaining a chain reaction. 'Going critical' is the phrase used to describe a nuclear reactor starting up – like starting a car.

Fission The splitting apart of a heavy atomic nucleus into two or more parts when a neutron strikes the nucleus. The splitting releases a large amount of energy.

Fission products Radioactive nuclei and elements formed by the fission of heavy elements.

Fuel rod A tube containing fuel for a nuclear reactor.

Half-life The time required for half of a given substance to decay. (see RADIATION)

Iodine-131 see CHERNOBYL

Meltdown The melting of fuel in a nuclear reactor after the loss of coolant. If a significant portion of the fuel should melt, the molten fuel could melt through the reactor vessel and release large quantities of radioactive material into the containment building.

Moderator Substance used to slow down neutrons in a reaction to a speed at which they are more likely to cause fission. Common moderators are graphite, water and heavy water.

Neutron An uncharged particle of the nucleus of every atom heavier than ordinary hydrogen; neutrons sustain the fission chain reaction in nuclear reactors.

* Adapted from *LINKS* no. 26, 1986. Other useful sources: UKAEA, *Glossary of Atomic Terms* 1984; Stephenson, Michael, and Weal, John, *Nuclear Dictionary*, Longman, 1985.

Plutonium see NUCLEAR ENERGY, p. 295.

Pressure vessel The tank containing the reactor core: also called the reactor vessel.

Pressurized Water Reactor (PWR) A nuclear reactor system in which reactor coolant water is kept under high pressure to keep it from boiling into steam.

Radioactivity The spontaneous decay of an unstable atom. During the decay process, ionizing radiation is given off.

Reactor (nuclear) A device in which a nuclear fission reaction can be started, maintained and controlled.

Reprocessing see NUCLEAR ENERGY, p. 295.

Strontium-90 see CHERNOBYL

Tailings see NUCLEAR ENERGY, p. 302.

Uranium see RADIATION

Uranium dioxide A chemical compound containing uranium and oxygen that is used as a fuel in nuclear reactors.

Uranium enrichment see NUCLEAR ENERGY, p. 294.

Venting The intentional release of gaseous materials into the environment.

See also CHERNOBYL; NUCLEAR ENERGY; RADIATION; THREE MILE ISLAND

REFERENCES

Bertell, Rosalie, *No Immediate Danger*, Women's Press, 1985.

Campaign Against the Namibian Uranium Contracts, *The Rossing File*, 1980.

Chudleigh, R. and W. Cannell, *Radioactive Waste: the Gravedigger's Dilemma*, FoE, 1984.

Durie, S. and R. Edwards, *Fuelling the Nuclear Arms Race*, Pluto Press, 1982.

Electricity Consumers' Council, *Privatising, a Chance for Change*, 1988.

Flavin, Christopher, 'Reforming the Electricity Power Industry', in Worldwatch Institute, *State of the World 1986*, W. W. Norton, 1986.

Green, P. et al., *Trawsfynydd, Power at a Price*, FoE, 1987.

Hansard, 2 November 1987; 17 February 1988.

Health and Safety Executive, *The Tolerability of Risk from Nuclear Power Stations*, 1988.

International AEA, *Nuclear Research Reactors in the World*, Reference Data Series no. 3, May 1987.

Moss, Norman, *The Politics of Uranium*, André Deutsch, 1981.

OECD, *Costs of Coal Pollution Abatement*, OECD, 1983.

Oxford Economic Research Associates, *The Privatisation of the Electricity Supply Industry*, CBI, 1988.

Patterson, Walter, *Nuclear Power*, Penguin Books, 1983.

Pollock, Cynthia, 'Decommissioning Nuclear Power Plants', in Worldwatch Institute, *State of the World 1986*, W. W. Norton, 1986.

Sivard, Ruth Leger, *World Military and Social Expenditures*, World Priorities, 1986.

Sweet, Colin, *The Price of Nuclear Power*, Heinemann, 1983.

UKAEA, *The Nuclear Share of Electricity Production*, Nuclear Energy Brief, 1986.

UNEP, *Radiation: Doses, Effects, Risks*, 1985.

'Critical Mess', *LINKS*, no. 26, Third World First, 1986.

Environment Digest, no. 17, October 1988, no. 9, February 1988, and no. 21, February 1989.

'Greenhouse warming: comparative analysis of nuclear and efficiency abatement strategies', Keepin, Bill, and Gregory Kats, in *Energy Policy*, Vol. 16, no. 6, Butterworths, December 1988.

Hansard, 23 February 1989.

Milne, R., 'Breaking Up is Hard to Do', *New Scientist*, 11 December 1986.

Openshaw, Stan, and John Fernie, 'How Far are You from a Reactor?' *New Statesman*, 16 May 1986.

Tucker, Anthony, 'The Conventional Worries for Nuclear Power', *Guardian*, 20 February 1987.

New Scientist, 10 December 1988.

CONTACTS

Campaign for Nuclear Disarmament (CND)

Cumbrians Opposed to a Radioactive Environment (CORE)

European Proliferation Information Centre (EPIC)

Friends of the Earth

Greenpeace

Scottish Campaign to Rid the Atomic Menace (SCRAM)

Socialist Environment and Resources Association (SERA)

Third World First

World Information Service on Energy (WISE)

British Nuclear Fuels Ltd (BNFL)

Department of Energy

Department of Environment

International Atomic Energy Agency

Ministry of Defence

Nirex

United Kingdom Atomic Energy Authority (UKAEA)

Nuclear Weapons

THE ARMS RACE

A 1960s study by the US Defense Department concluded that just a few hundred large nuclear warheads could destroy Soviet or American society for good. Today there are 60,000 nuclear warheads in the world, of which 50,000 are deployed. Their explosive power is equivalent to a million Hiroshimas – 2,700 times the explosive energy released in the Second World War, when 38 million people died. Nearly all of these weapons belong to the two superpowers.

The nuclear arms race has had a number of effects on the environment. Atmospheric testing in the 1950s and 1960s led to the deposition of a number of nuclear isotopes in the stratosphere, which gradually return to earth and are still being absorbed, especially by people living in the northern hemisphere.

The process of mining uranium, enriching it and disposing of both nuclear waste and spent nuclear reactors has led to air, land and water pollution.

Nuclear weapons research has distorted national energy programmes: those countries dominating the nuclear arms race have also adopted atomic power as a viable energy system, with economic losses and environmental pollution as a result. Four-fifths of world nuclear electricity output is provided by eight countries (see NUCLEAR ENERGY).

Superpower rivalry has led to a massive increase in worldwide military spending, both in the developed world, and in the developing countries, where East–West wars are often fought by proxy. Since 1945, 18.5 million people have died in 120 conflicts, mainly in the Third World: and the increasing militarization of these areas means that the opportunity to improve water, sanitation, health, infant mortality and environmental protection is lost in the places that need it most (see MILITARY SPENDING, WORLDWIDE).

It is one of the ironies of the arms race that all countries agree there are too many nuclear weapons in the world: the problem is how to reduce them, or get rid of them altogether. International developments in 1987 to 1989 appear to have increased the chances of a substantial reduction in global nuclear weaponry; whether this will be achieved depends on the internal politics of the USA and USSR.

History of the arms race

The first uranium reactor was built in 1942 in Chicago, and led to intensive research programmes to try and develop an atomic bomb. In the summer of 1945, the USA had enough material for three bombs: one was tested in New Mexico in June, and the other two – one uranium bomb, one plutonium – were dropped on Hiroshima and Nagasaki.

There are two views as to this double bomb drop: the first, that they were both justified on military grounds, and that nothing less would frighten the Japanese into submission; and the second, more cynically, that the military wanted to compare the effects of the two different types of weapon.

The Japan bombings used up all the world's available atomic weapons. By July 1946 the US had nine more B-3 bombs, of the type that wiped out Nagasaki. Two years later they had 50.

In *The Unsinkable Aircraft Carrier* (1984), Duncan Campbell outlines the mechanics of military planning during the late 1940s. The first detailed US plan for atomic war, 'Broiler', in 1947, listed 24 Soviet cities for destruction along the lines of Hiroshima and Nagasaki. The last plan to be made before the Soviets exploded their first atomic bomb, 'Offtackle', planned the dropping of 220 atomic bombs on 104 Soviet cities, with 72 bombs remaining in reserve.

It was a time of great international tension, heightened by the USSR blockade of Berlin which led to the Berlin airlift. The North Atlantic Treaty (NATO) was signed on 4 April 1949, with 12 signatories guaranteeing mutual protection in the event of attack. As part of the preliminaries to this arrangement, US nuclear-capable aircraft were stationed in Britain in 1948.

In 1949 the USSR exploded its first atomic bomb: in 1950 the USA decided to develop the hydrogen or thermonuclear 'H' bomb. In the context of the Korean War, with the USA struggling to maintain its lead in nuclear weaponry, and the USSR desperate to catch up,

Hiroshima

The Hiroshima bomb was rated as a 12.5 kiloton bomb (i.e., equivalent to 12,500 tons of TNT high explosive). It was dropped on the morning of 6 August 1945: people had taken shelter, but when only two planes were seen, the all-clear was sounded. The bomb exploded about 630 yards above the Shima Hospital, above the centre of the city.

It created a fireball 18,000 feet across, with a temperature of about 100 million degrees Fahrenheit at the centre. People who looked at the fireball were blinded. More than four square miles of this city of 130,000 people were obliterated. Houses collapsed from blast pressure or were gutted by the fire that burned for two days. About 88,000 buildings were destroyed. Some people near the centre of the explosion literally evaporated, others were charred corpses. Survivors experienced burns that caused their skin to peel off immediately.

Other survivors killed themselves to relieve the pain. Children were hurled hundreds of feet in the air by fierce winds, people were trapped in collapsed structures, others had their skin literally hanging off their fingertips. Those who lived to tell the story said that the victims looked like ghosts.

The numbers of casualties were never properly calculated. The thirty-year report to the United Nations in 1975 estimated immediate fatalities at Hiroshima and Nagasaki as 240,000. Long-term cancer figures were more difficult to estimate, although acknowledged to be occurring in large quantities. More than 2,000 cancer deaths of survivors in 1978 were attributed to the 1945 bombing.

Source: Rosalie Bertell, *No Immediate Danger*, 1985

there were few possibilities for arms limitation talks. The stage was set for the arms race.

Three other countries are acknowledged to have nuclear bombs: these were tested by the UK (1952), France (1960), and China (1964), respectively. In each case, the research and development preceding the first 'test' shot was done under great secrecy. In 1974,

India also exploded a nuclear device, but it was termed a 'peaceful' nuclear explosion by the Indian government. Not surprisingly, neighbouring Pakistan disagreed. The five 'nuclear powers' are the permanent members of the United Nations Security Council, which has responsibility within the UN for international peace and security: although it is very questionable as to whether in reality only five countries have nuclear weapons.

The arms race was of considerable size by 1970, but took off during the 1970s and 1980s, as detente became less successful in spite of the SALT I and SALT II arms treaties. Over this period, the number of American strategic weapons almost doubled, with Soviet strategic weapons increasing by a factor of three. By 1986 the two powers were approaching parity in their strategic nuclear arsenals, with the Americans still in the lead.

Nuclear arms: who owns what

It is difficult to state with certainty who owns what because of the secrecy involved on the part of all nuclear nations: also, some weapons may be retained beyond their 'useful working lives' purely as bargaining chips. Most observers say that the USA and USSR own between 95 and 97 per cent of the world's nuclear arsenal, with a rough numerical parity – although either side would point to the other's superiority in certain spheres.

A country's position in the arms race depends on the perspective from which it is viewed. The USA is able to 'target' the USSR from land-based Intercontinental Ballistic Missiles (ICBMs), from forward deployed sea-, land-, or aircraft-based weapons within Europe or from submarines in the various oceans, so has been able to concentrate on these attack modes. The USSR has no forward bases near the Atlantic USA, so it builds up its long-range weapons. Both countries, if they want to increase their nuclear arsenal, can select the superiority of their opponent in a given technology, and use that as the justification for upgrading.

Looked at from Western Europe, the Soviet Union has an overwhelming advantage in nuclear and conventional weaponry over the European states – if the armed forces of the USA are discounted. Looked at from the Soviet Union, the USSR has to arm itself not only against the USA, but also against NATO forces in Europe – at the same time protecting its flank against China, or even against Israel's nuclear weapons (see below). Looked at from the USA, the Soviet Union represents a Communist threat that wants to take over the world: looked at from the USSR, the USA has already established its position in a number of parts of the world, and wants further to increase its power. Until the deadlock is broken, the arms race will continue. Development of 'glasnost' and 'perestroika' in the USSR has given hope in the late 1980s of a 'build-down' towards nuclear

---

The UK

The *Nuclear Dictionary* (1985) gives a useful summary of Britain's position in the arms race:

Strategic

Four Polaris submarines each armed with 16 Polaris A-3 missiles carrying up to six non-independently targetable warheads (which are released together and fall on or around a target like a scatter bomb). The number of potential targets is linked to the number of missiles – 64.

These are to be replaced by four Trident submarines in the 1990s, each of which carries 16 Trident D-5 missiles, each with up to 14 multiple independently-targeted re-entry vehicles (MIRV), which can all hit different targets. The number of available targets under this system increases to a theoretical 896.

Tactical

Up to 650 nuclear-capable aircraft; at least 60 Lance missiles stationed in Germany; at least 100 M-109 field guns capable of firing a 2-kiloton shell some 24 km: 16 M-110 field guns capable of firing a 10-kiloton shell some 29 km.

In terms of the USA and USSR, the UK is very much a second-class nuclear power: but the upgrading of strategic weaponry represented by the purchase of Trident could represent a stumbling block to nuclear arms reduction negotiations. So, too, could the development – perhaps with France – of a new air-launched 'stand-off' nuclear missile.

disarmament, especially as the US administration has been more flexible than hitherto in responding.

For reasons of space it is not possible in this book to tabulate the different arms possessed by the nuclear powers, as they are different weapons systems, of different ages, in vast numbers. Readers are referred to *The Military Balance* or the *SIPRI Yearbook* for specific figures.

ENVIRONMENTAL EFFECTS

There are a number of environmental effects related to the increase in the world's nuclear weapons. Some of these are related to the nuclear fuel cycle – extracting uranium, enriching it, running it in reactors for submarines or for plutonium production, and then disposing of the waste (see NUCLEAR ENERGY) – but nuclear weapons also have other environmental effects because of the way in which they are tested and the circumstances in which they are used. Nuclear weapons production also creates considerable chemical waste and toxic materials pollution, apart from radioactive releases. The fact that so much time and money has been put into this area of research has also precluded effort being put into more environmentally beneficial work. In the US, clean-up costs presented from the nuclear programme in December 1988 run to more than $40 billion (see NUCLEAR ENERGY).

Atmospheric testing

For the last 40 years, everyone in the world has been exposed to radiation from fallout from nuclear weapons, according to *Radiation: Doses, Effects, Risks* (United Nations Environment Programme, 1985). Very little of this comes from the bombs dropped in Hiroshima and Nagasaki: almost all is the result of atmospheric nuclear explosions carried out to test nuclear weapons.

There were two peaks to the testing: first, between 1954 and 1958, when the USA, the USSR and the UK were all exploding devices, with the USA tests dominating; and second, in 1961–2, when the USA and USSR were the main contributors, and the USSR tests dominated. In 1963 these three countries signed the Partial Test Ban Treaty, agreeing not to test in the atmosphere, oceans or outer space. Since then France and China have conducted some smaller atmospheric tests. All tests now are conducted underground.

An enormous amount of radioactive debris is thrown up in an atmospheric nuclear explosion. Some returns to the ground relatively quickly, but most is pushed up into the stratosphere, where it stays for many months before descending to earth. Several hundred different radionuclides are involved.

The northern hemisphere, where most of the testing took place, received most of the fallout. The UNEP publication shows that caesium-137 in the diet of the Danish people, and strontium-90 in the diet of New Yorkers, leapt by a factor of six after the atmospheric tests of the early 1960s.

The four most important pollutants are carbon-14, caesium-137, zirconium-95 and strontium-90 (see CHERNOBYL): the zirconium, with a half-life of 64 days, has already delivered most of its dose. Caesium-137 and strontium-90 both have half-lives of about 30 years, and will have deposited most of their doses by the end of the century. Carbon-14, however, has a half-life of 5,730 years, and will stay active into the distant future, albeit at low dose rates. By the year 2000 it will have delivered only 7 per cent of its eventual contribution.

The two decades of atmospheric nuclear testing will continue to affect the world's population for millennia: what is less clear, however, is exactly what these effects will be.

In *No Conceivable Injury* (1986), Robert Milliken reviews some of the literature relating to the human effects of atmospheric testing. One health damage estimate has come from Robert Alexander of the US Nuclear Regulatory Commission, a government agency in charge of regulating standards for America's nuclear industry. As Milliken says, the NRC tends to be conservative in its outlook, but Alexander has estimated, on the basis of the average radiation to the world's population from these atmospheric tests, that the results will be up to 84,500 cancer deaths, and up to 168,000 genetic defects, 7,200 of which are classified as 'serious'.

Professor Joseph Rotblat of London University has made a similar estimate. Rotblat reckons that past tests of nuclear weapons are likely to give rise to nearly 100,000 additional deaths from cancer in the world, plus half that number of premature deaths due to genetic damage.

The nations conducting the testing have repeatedly stated that the impact of their testing programmes is minimal, although these reassurances are less than wholly convincing in the light of the casual spirit in which the British, for example, tested weapons in Australia and the Pacific Islands in the 1950s. The tests were carried out hastily and often in the wrong conditions; servicemen and civilians were exposed to radiation unnecessarily; and large parts of Australia were polluted – some for thousands of years – by fallout (see Blakeway and Lloyd-Roberts, *Fields of Thunder*, 1985, and R. Milliken, *No Conceivable Injury*).

In May 1984, a federal judge in Salt Lake City found that radioactive fallout from American atmospheric tests in the 1950s had been responsible for the deaths of nine people and that the US government had been negligent in its conduct of the tests. The US government was ordered to pay $2.66 million to the families of the victims and the sole survivor. In the US at least, this opened the doors for a number of other radiation claims.

Underground testing

Underground testing is generally assumed to give rise to little fallout, of the kind that followed the atmospheric tests. Rosalie Bertell, however, points out that all underground tests leak radionuclides into the air, and all have left deadly pollutants on the land. The US government admits to venting of radioactive gases and particulates from some underground tests (the other testing countries – the USSR, UK, France and China – give little information about tests).

Nuclear tests 1945–85

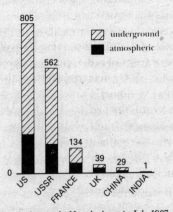

The UK's 41st nuclear test took place in the Nevada desert in July 1987.
Source: *World Military and Social Expenditures*, 1986.

Bertell also questions the wisdom of US testing in Nevada, as, in the words of a former Governor, 'Nevada is in a region of seismic activity and its citizens face a very real and growing earthquake hazard.'

The USSR discontinued its underground testing for 21 months between 1985 and 1987, in an apparent attempt at simultaneously ending US tests. The gesture was not reciprocated, and Soviet testing resumed in February 1987. The *Bulletin of the Atomic Scientists* (April 1989) lists 1,793 known nuclear tests worldwide since 1945 – an average of one test every nine days. The USA has conducted 910 tests, the USSR 635, the UK 41, France 172, and China 34.

Military nuclear reactors

The environmental threat posed by the reactors of nuclear-fuelled ships are of a similar nature to those posed by civil reactors (see NUCLEAR ENERGY) with the added complications that military reactors are moved around most of the time, often in extremely adverse conditions, and frequently near large centres of population.

Ports which would react with horror to the construction of a civil nuclear reactor in the middle of town accept the same implicit threat with equanimity when it is carried inside a submarine. Yet the consequences of a nuclear accident would be catastrophic.

Public libraries throughout Devon and Cornwall, for example, have been given a little-known naval emergency plan to be enacted in the 'unlikely' event of an accident on a nuclear-powered submarine in the refitting yards at Devonport. People will be evacuated from the area; iodine pills will be given to local inhabitants, who will be advised to take the same precautions as they would take in the event of a large civil nuclear accident; TV and radio warnings will be given; crops in the area would be in danger of radiation contamination.

Of the approximately 900 nuclear reactors in the world, nearly 550 are at sea, propelling US, Soviet, French, British and Chinese vessels. Since the first one was launched in 1954, nuclear-powered vessels have regularly run aground, sunk, suffered fires, floods, mechanical breakdowns and collisions with other ships.

In *Nuclear Free Seas* (1987), Greenpeace report one reactor meltdown at sea, five nuclear reactors being abandoned on the ocean floor, over 20 nuclear missiles being lost in the oceans. According to the US Navy, there were 628 'incidents' and two 'accidents' involving nuclear weapons aboard its ships between 1965 and 1985. In May

1989, Greenpeace and the US Institute of Policy Studies published the results of a search of naval records under the US Freedom of Information Act. This revealed that the US Navy alone had lost at least 48 nuclear warheads and 9 nuclear reactors at sea in accidents since World War II. This included the loss of a one-megatonne hydrogen bomb off Japan in 1965 when an A-4 warplane fell off an aircraft carrier.

The Americans have described the Soviet record of nuclear accidents at sea as 'horrible', with at least 200 accidents over the last ten years, some of them very serious. One of the most recent of these was in October 1986, when an explosion ripped through an SS-N-6 missile on a Soviet 'Yankee' class submarine in the Atlantic. Three days later, the submarine sank while being towed away. A complete nuclear reactor and at least 15 nuclear weapons went down, striking the ocean floor at an estimated velocity of 200 kilometres per hour. The latest in a series of accidents occurred in April 1989, when a nuclear-powered Soviet submarine sank in the Norwegian Sea, with serious loss of life and fears of severe radioactive pollution.

Nuclear war

A nuclear war between the two superpowers would produce the most adverse environmental changes in the history of humanity. The proponents of the nuclear winter believe that the dust created by a series of nuclear explosions would blot out the sun for a year, creating arctic conditions. This would be followed by a period of intense radiation burns from the sun for any people still surviving, as a result of the depletion of the ozone layer.

There is inevitably some disagreement about whether a nuclear winter would occur – the only way to find out being to try it – but there is general agreement as to the catastrophic consequences of nuclear war (for specific information, see Glasstone and Dolan's *The Effects of Nuclear Weapons*, 1980; P. Goodwin, *Nuclear War: the Facts*, 1981; and AMBIO, *Nuclear War: the Aftermath*, 1983). In the UK, the Home Office calculates that a full-scale attack on Britain – reckoned as being 200-megaton – would result in 26 million deaths from the blast effects alone. A further 2 or 3 million would die of radiation burns. Many of the 6 million others who were injured would die within days or weeks.

The northern hemisphere would suffer the greater initial damage, as the war would presumably be fought in that area. It is unlikely that any country would escape the effects, however. Stratospheric deposition of radionuclides would circle the globe, in unquantifiable amounts with completely unforeseeable results.

One of the countries that would expect to be least affected, New Zealand, has attempted an analysis of the consequences of nuclear war in the northern hemisphere (*New Scientist*, 27 August 1987). The 1987 report of the New Zealand Planning Council points out that the country depends on the north for all its medical supplies. Within six months, deaths from asthma, diabetes and epilepsy would multiply.

Unemployment would soar to 50 per cent as northern hemisphere export markets dry up. If an aggressor bombed the three Australian military communication bases, then electromagnetic pulses could arrest computer and electronic control equipment in the country. Telephones, television, radio, the banking system and the electrical grid would be crippled. There is no country in the world that would be untouched by nuclear war between the superpowers.

Opportunity costs

It is difficult, as Norman Moss points out in *The Politics of Uranium* (1981), for generations raised in a world of nuclear arsenals and the ever-present possibility of military annihilation to appreciate the impact that the Hiroshima and Nagasaki bombs made on people's thinking.

Nuclear physics became the most glamorous, and the best-funded, area of scientific research – both in the ten years after 1945 when the nuclear option was investigated almost exclusively for its weapons potential, and since the mid-1950s, when the chimera of economically viable nuclear power has been vigorously pursued. Even now, the money spent on nuclear research in the UK dwarfs that invested in alternative sources of energy.

During and since the Second World War, some of the world's best scientific brains have been researching nuclear weaponry and its offshoot, nuclear power. This appears to be an enormous waste of money and expertise. The armaments industry that has sprung up since the Second World War has done so at the expense of the environment and people's lives (see MILITARY SPENDING, WORLDWIDE).

The development of sophisticated nuclear weapons has also changed the nature of military research: it is now the technicians, not the military, who determine the next generation of military hardware.

Jonathon Porritt (in *Seeing Green*, 1984) quotes Lord Zuckerman, a former UK Chief Scientist:

It is he, the technician, not the commander in the field, who starts the process of formulating the so-called military need. It is he who has succeeded over the years in equating, and so confusing, military destructive power with military strength, [with the result that] the men in the nuclear weapons laboratories of both sides have succeeded in building a world with an irrational foundation, on which a new set of political realities has in turn to be built.

MODERNIZATION

A meeting of the NATO Nuclear Planning Group in Montebello, in October 1983, agreed to modernize NATO's weapons. 'Modernize' is a word that could have many different meanings. According to a report from the British American Security Information Council (BASIC), it entails *inter alia* the deployment of at least twice as many new nuclear warheads in Europe as those negotiated away under the INF agreement.

The new weapons will not violate the INF Treaty, but would enable the NATO forces to hit exactly the same targets as the Cruise and Pershing missiles to be removed under the treaty. The report suggests – using US Congressional and Pentagon sources – that the NATO nuclear armoury by the mid-1990s could include 1,300 air-launched Cruise missiles, 600 ground-launched ballistic or Cruise missiles, and 400 nuclear artillery shells. They would all be new weapons currently under development.

The system would not breach INF because air-launched Cruise were not included in the treaty; the new ground-launched Cruise would have a range of less than 500 km, thus being outside the range limits of INF (see below): the same exclusion would apply to the artillery shells. The total number of new warheads, at 2,300, would greatly exceed the number of NATO warheads to be removed by INF: yet, because of retirement of old or obsolete systems, NATO could claim that its total number of warheads in Europe was being reduced.

Similar ratcheting-upwards of the arms race is being achieved by the development of a new, more aggressive generation of missiles. Trident-2 has a range of 10,000 km, and is capable of penetrating a hardened silo to an accuracy of within 400 feet. It can therefore be used as a 'first-strike' weapon, designed to take out the opponent's command system and weapons silos. The Russians and French are perfecting similar weapons, also designed to be 'first-use'.

In the case of the UK, the adoption of Trident involves an increase in the number of targets that could be hit by more than 1,000 per cent.

The arms race moves to sea

The history of the arms talks shows that those items omitted from discussions are frequently the ones that are most important.

In *New Scientist* (19 November 1987), Leggett and Lewis point out that the US has not agreed to Soviet requests to include sea-launched Cruise missiles in reduction talks. The US Army had planned the European deployment of 464 Tomahawk ground-launched Cruise missiles, capable of delivering 150 kilotons of explosive power up to 2,500 km, by the end of 1988: after INF this is no longer possible. The US Navy, however, has not been blocked in its plans to deploy 758 nuclear Tomahawks at sea.

These weapons are similar to the ground-based Tomahawks, except that they would be launched from the Norwegian Sea rather than Greenham Common. The navy already has 125 of these missiles: the total 758 will be dispersed on 198 ships and submarines, about one-third of the American fleet. The situation will be exacerbated by the 3,200 conventional Tomahawks fitted with conventional (or even chemical) weapons that are also to be installed – thus making nuclear verification extremely difficult.

The Soviet Union, meanwhile, has already installed short-range nuclear Cruise missiles, with a range of up to 550 km, on its ships. According to the Pentagon, the Soviet Navy in 1987 installed its own versions of the Tomahawk, the SS-NX-21 and SS-NX-24, with a range of 3,000 km: if this happened, the Russian missiles would be following their American counterparts by three years, and another arms race would be in progress. By the mid-1990s, the Soviets could carry nearly 1,500 of these missiles on their boats.

There are also political reasons why nuclear arms are moving to sea. Carrying nuclear weapons on ships does not involve the high-profile controversy involved in, for example, shipping Cruise missiles to British airfields: and in removing these weapons from the public gaze the nuclear powers may be hoping to remove the heat from the issue.

Some nations have tried in response to declare their ports and oceans 'Nuclear Free Zones', but this has been circumvented by navies refusing to say whether their ships are carrying nuclear weapons or not, for 'security reasons'. Iceland and New Zealand have banned nuclear weapons from entering their territorial waters: Sri Lanka and Egypt restrict entry of nuclear ships. Countries such as Canada, Australia, Spain, Denmark, Sweden and Japan, although having 'non-nuclear' policies, have agreed not to challenge the ships of nuclear powers upon entry into their territorial waters. Nations like New Zealand, which have argued strongly for the Nuclear Free Zone ideal, have been threatened with economic or diplomatic penalties.

Naval nuclear armaments are not subject to international control by treaty. The Antarctica Treaty (1959) explicitly excludes restrictions on naval operations; the Latin American Nuclear Free Zone Treaty (also known as the Treaty of Tlatelolco, 1967) has been agreed to by the US, USSR, UK and France, but the effect of this has been minimized by their statements elsewhere that they will not accept any restrictions on the operations of their nuclear-armed navies; and the South Pacific Nuclear Free Zone Treaty (Treaty of Rarotonga, 1985) avoids restraining the passage of nuclear-armed or nuclear-powered vessels.

Risks of nuclear war at sea   Nuclear planners believe that nuclear war at sea might be 'contained' and involve few, if any, civilian casualties. 'It can be argued that the restricted use of nuclear weapons at sea carries neither the degree of moral stigma nor the threat of further escalation that applies to their use against land targets,' said the report of the Atlantic Council Working Group on Securing the Seas in 1979.

Other analysts have argued, however, that nuclear conflict at sea is more, not less, likely to end in world war: naval nuclear weapons, in both NATO and Warsaw Pact stockpiles, are allocated for 'first-use' (i.e., they can be used before the other side uses nuclear weapons), as a support to conventional warfare. This may greatly increase the risk of nuclear conflict, as does the fact that submarine commanders are not in continuous communication with headquarters, with contact being made as infrequently as every 12 hours. Once combat orders are given to a submarine, it can be very difficult to countermand them.

As the nuclear option shifts to sea, those nations offering base facilities will become targets in the event of war. The US operates nuclear-related land and sea facilities in 41 countries, including Japan, the Philippines, Diego Garcia, Spain and Italy; the Soviet Union has facilities in 11 countries, including Vietnam, Angola, Ethiopia and Cuba: Britain has nuclear-related operations in 12 countries; and France in 9.

REDUCTION TREATIES

The number of nuclear weapons deployed in the world has increased from zero to more than 50,000 in the space of 40 years, in spite of a number of successfully negotiated treaties to reduce them. Nuclear powers have had their operations restricted in some areas, only to expand them in others. If the number of nuclear weapons is to be effectively reduced, the treaty negotiation system needs to be more comprehensive.

The Non-Proliferation Treaty (NPT), 1968

This treaty was regarded at the time as a breakthrough in slowing down the arms race. The signatories include the UK, the USSR and the USA, the states which negotiated the NPT, and a number of non-nuclear nations (by 1989 there were 138 signatories). The treaty committed the signing nations to three main pledges:

- nuclear-weapons states would not make nuclear explosive devices available to non-nuclear states, or to other nuclear-weapons states;
- non-nuclear states would not try to acquire nuclear weapons, and would accept international safeguards established by the International Atomic Energy Agency which would attempt to regulate this promise;
- nuclear-weapons states would enter into genuine negotiations at an early date for arms control and reductions of nuclear weapons, and eventually conventional weapons, under strict verification procedures.

Although the treaty was a significant step forward, it was deficient for two reasons: (1) the two superpowers and the UK did not deliver their promise to negotiate significant weapons reductions; and (2) a number of important countries refused to sign. Among these were:

- *China* and *France*, which already possessed nuclear weapons;

Other treaties

Antarctic Treaty, 1959   (30 states)
Bans military uses of Antarctica, including nuclear tests.

Partial Test Ban Treaty, 1963   (112 states)
Bans nuclear weapons tests in atmosphere, outer space, and under water.

Outer Space Treaty, 1967   (82 states)
Bans nuclear weapons in earth orbit and stationing in outer space.

Latin American Nuclear Free Zone Treaty, 1967   (24 states)
Bans testing, possession, deployment of nuclear weapons, requires safeguards on facilities.

Seabed Treaty, 1971   (74 states)
Bans nuclear weapons on the seabed beyond the 12-mile coastal limit.

ABM Treaty (SALT I), 1972   USA–USSR
Limits anti-ballistic missile systems to two deployment areas on each side. Limited in 1974 to one area.

SALT II Treaty, 1979   USA–USSR
Limits numbers of strategic nuclear delivery vehicles, bombers with long-range Cruise missiles, launchers of MIRV'd missiles. Bans testing of new types of Intercontinental Ballistic Missiles. Not ratified by US Senate: set aside by President Reagan in 1986.

South Pacific Nuclear Free Zone Treaty, 1985   (3 states)
Bans testing, manufacture, acquisition, stationing of nuclear weapons. Requests five nuclear weapons states to ban use or threat of nuclear weapons and testing. (Eight states required for ratification.)

INF Treaty, 1987   USA–USSR
See p. 324

Source: Ruth Leger Sivard, *World Military and Social Expenditures*, 1986

- *India*, which tested an atomic bomb in 1974, and has the capability to make more, a bipartisan US survey reporting in 1988 that India had the capacity to produce 'more than 100' Hiroshima-sized bombs by 1990;
- *Israel*, apparently assembling atomic weapons during the 1973 war, and according to the revelations of a dissident Israeli scientist, Mordechai Vanunu, in 1986, possessing between 100 and 200 nuclear warheads;
- *South Africa*, which was ready to carry out a nuclear test in 1977, but was dissuaded from doing so by the USA and USSR. South Africa is the Western world's third largest producer of uranium;
- *Pakistan*, revealed by the *Observer* in March 1987 to have a secret uranium enrichment plant, and the technology to make nuclear bombs. The bipartisan US survey mentioned above reported that Pakistan could have 15 Hiroshima-sized bombs by 1990.

There are a number of countries with the know-how and the capacity to make nuclear weapons. It is a recurring risk of international relations that these weapons will be developed and deployed in times of tension. On the positive side, the treaty included many countries who appear genuinely to wish to forgo the opportunity of joining the nuclear club – including Australia, Canada, New Zealand, East and West Germany, Japan, Sweden, Iraq and Libya.

Ways of avoiding treaty commitments

Part of the problem of arms control treaties between the superpowers, as Leggett and Lewis point out in *New Scientist* (19 November 1987), is that in the past they have succeeded only in changing the direction of the nuclear arms race rather than reversing it. The treaties have stopped expansion in one area, only to allow it in another. As examples they cite the Limited Test Ban Treaty of 1963, which stopped atmospheric testing but failed to halt underground tests; and SALT I, 1972, which limited the number of long-range missiles but did not prevent the superpowers from installing multiple warheads on those missiles.

Stephenson and Weal, in the *Nuclear Dictionary* (1985), take an even more jaundiced view:

Arms limitation talks tend to be a distillation of the current state and direction of the arms race. Agreements are either about matters that pose no problems to either side because they never contemplated them anyway, or about matters that are not technically achievable at the time of signing, or which have become unnecessary to the development of the superpowers' own programmes. Talks are often a public relations exercise to convince populations and other states that 'efforts are being made'. Sufficient time is allowed for both sides to develop fully the armaments likely to be limited by a treaty before it is signed, while huge loopholes are left in the treaty itself for the development of newer and more dangerous weapons after its signature. In this sense, arms talks serve as a spur to the arms race they are meant to control and reverse. Secondary questions, such as verification, can always be wheeled out if the talks look like achieving something.

Strategic nuclear weapons deployed

(thousands)

Source: *World Military and Social Expenditures*, 1986

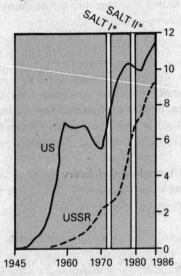

* Strategic Arms Limitations
Treaties of 1972 and 1979

The graph from *World Military and Social Expenditures* shows how strategic nuclear weapons have increased in number, to a total of more than 21,000 – some with a travelling capacity of 10,000 miles. The increase has been maintained in spite of SALT I and SALT II – the Strategic Arms Limitation Treaties, which were greeted with much enthusiasm in 1972 and 1979.

In this context, the achievements of the INF Treaty (1987) need careful scrutiny.

The INF Treaty

The INF (Intermediate Nuclear Forces) Treaty was signed by Mikhail Gorbachev and Ronald Reagan in December 1987. The

Simplified nuclear weapons glossary

Ballistic missiles   Missiles which are powered for the first 10–15 per cent of their flight, and are then left to 'freewheel' to their destination. The term is usually used for weapons that leave the earth's atmosphere during part of their flight. Ballistic missiles capable of travelling very long distances are called ICBMs (Inter-Continental Ballistic Missiles). They can carry extremely large nuclear weapons between continents in about 20 minutes.

Cruise missiles   Powered through all their flight, with internal guidance systems or remote control to guide them to their target. Cruise missiles are accurate to within 100 yards over substantial distances, are cheap and, in contrast to ballistic missiles, fly at low altitudes. They can be launched from land, from the sea or from aircraft, and can deliver an explosion of up to 150 kilotons (about 12 times as great as Hiroshima).

Nuclear launch and delivery systems are generally classified according to range:

'Strategic' weapons   Large nuclear weapons that form part of a country's main war plan (i.e., strategy). Refers to the ICBMs and weapons launched from bombers or submarines, that have a range greater than 5,500 km.

'Intermediate' weapons   The subject of the INF Treaty, having a range of 500 to 5,500 km. Subdivided into Short-Range Intermediate Forces (SRINF – 500 to 1,000 km) and Long-Range Intermediate Forces (LRINF – 1,000 to 5,500 km). All land-based SRINF missiles are to be destroyed by mid-1989, with the LRINF disappearing by 1991.

'Tactical' nuclear weapons   Also called 'battlefield' weapons, these are composed of artillery shells, short-range missiles, nuclear depth bombs, free-fall bombs and mines. A nuclear artillery shell usually delivers 1 to 2 kilotons (about an eighth of the power of Hiroshima). Missiles and mines are larger.

treaty will outlaw an entire section of the superpowers' nuclear arsenal – all ground-launched nuclear missiles with a range of 500 to 5,500 km.

The number of weapons eradicated will be small in comparison with the world total – around 2,000, approximately 4 per cent of the global figure: but the verification procedures agreed were a breakthrough in nuclear negotiations. If the success of the INF negotiations can be carried into other areas of the nuclear armoury, then the INF Treaty will be seen as an important milestone.

The INF Treaty was successful, first because both the Russians and Americans actually wanted to achieve a reduction in nuclear arms, instead of merely going through the motions; and secondly because the intermediate class of weapons was the easiest, from a practical point of view, to destroy.

A limited number are deployed, embracing only seven types of weapons (on the Soviet side, the SS-20, SS-4, SS-23, and SS 12/22; on the US side, Pershing 1A, Pershing 2, and ground-launched Cruise missiles).

INF Treaty 1987: weapons destruction commitments

USSR: 731 missiles 1,613 warheads 445.3 megatons in total
USA: 350 missiles   520 warheads   94.6 megatons in total

1 megaton = 1,000 kilotons = 1 million tons equivalent of TNT. Total US and USSR commitment: 539.9 megatons (= 40,000 Hiroshimas)

Source: *New Scientist*, 19 November 1988

The amount of weapons to be scrapped was only one-twenty-fifth of the world's total. The next stage in arms reduction talks, in which the USSR and USA have put forward the idea of a 50 per cent reduction in the number of strategic weapons, would involve a more substantial cut: still not large enough in the eyes of many observers, but a step in the right direction. The success of this Strategic Arms Reduction Treaty (START) depends on the internal politics of both the USA and USSR.

START negotiations

The first step in a START programme would be to agree how many missiles and warheads are deployed by each side (figures vary according to who makes the analysis and in what forum); whether the weapons of the UK, France and China are to be placed on one side of the disarmament scales; and whether the East and West are satisfied that there are roughly equal conventional forces on both sides.

Once there is agreement as to who actually owns what weapons, the next question is whether their removal would give conventional or chemical weapons superiority to either side. Again, estimates vary according to who is presenting the figures. It is generally stated in the West that the Warsaw Pact has overwhelming conventional superiority over NATO forces in Europe: in the USSR, it is usually stated that NATO's mobile and flexible advance battlefield weapons give it a dangerous offensive capacity. The USSR may have the greater forces quantitatively – but qualitatively, the situation is very different.

The East has more tanks than the West, but the average firing rate of Western tanks is twice that of the Soviets. NATO has three times as many helicopters as the Warsaw Pact. NATO has a score of aircraft carriers, the USSR three. The bomb tonnage of central front tactical air forces at 100 miles favours NATO by 3:1, at 200 miles by 7:1.

These figures are not intended to imply NATO superiority in conventional forces over the USSR, but to point up the difficulties of establishing conventional force equality. Overall, it is generally assumed that an invading conventional force needs three times the strength of a defending force to guarantee success: this is certainly not the case for either side, either in European or world deployment of conventional weapons.

The US has technical superiority over the USSR in a number of important areas, according to the annual US Joint Chiefs of Staff Report, 1986.

Agreement as to the relative possession of nuclear and conventional forces is the first step in a long journey. To achieve START, a number of factors have to be negotiated: the numbers and types of weapons to be dismantled; how it can be proved that the new treaty is being adhered to (here the verification procedures agreed in the INF Treaty would be very helpful); whether remaining weapons can be modernized, and if so, how; and what is to be done with the nuclear materials accruing from the destruction of weapons.

Relative US–USSR Standing in Basic Technologies, January 1986

20 most important basic technologies	US Superior	US–USSR Equal	USSR Superior
Aerodynamics/Fluid Dynamics		◆	
Computers & Software	←◆		
Conventional Warheads (incl. all chemical explosives)		◆	
Directed Energy (laser)		◆	
Electro-Optical Sensor (including infrared)	◆		
Guidance & Navigation	◆		
Life Sciences (human factors/ biotechnology)	◆		
Materials (lightweight, high strength, high temperature)	◆→		
Micro-Electronic Materials & Integrated Circuit Manufacturing	◆		
Nuclear Warheads		◆	
Optics		◆	
Power Sources (mobile) (includes automated control)		◆	
Production/Manufacturing (includes automated control)	◆		
Propulsion (aerospace and ground vehicles)	◆→		
Radar Sensor	◆→		
Robotics & Machine Intelligence	◆		
Signal Processing	◆		
Signature Reduction	◆		
Submarine Detection	◆→		
Telecommunications (includes fiber optics)	◆		

Prepared by the US Joint Chiefs of Staff and published annually, the latest comparison of US/USSR standing in military-related technologies shows the US superior in most, the USSR ahead in none.

Source: *World Military and Social Expenditures*, 1986

The process is complicated and technical, as well as being linked to other areas such as Star Wars (see below) and Modernization (see above). A successful treaty is by no means a foregone conclusion.

The rest of the world needs to watch the negotiations carefully, also, to make sure that reductions in one area are not accompanied by increases in another. The successful accomplishment of INF (covering 2,100 warheads) and START (21,000 warheads) will not place controls on the entire nuclear arsenal. As an example, the base at Fairford in Gloucestershire has long been prepared to take air-launched Cruise, with B-52s flying in on regular visits. A single wing of 48 B-52s would carry between 572 and 960 missiles, the lower figure being higher than all the land-based missiles negotiated away by the US under INF. There is also a strong possibility that the arms race at sea is about to escalate (see above).

STAR WARS

'Star Wars', formally known as the Strategic Defence Initiative or SDI, was announced by President Reagan on 23 March 1983. In simple terms, SDI conceives of a large impenetrable 'shield' being placed over the USA, through which enemy ballistic missiles would be unable to penetrate. The shield envisaged would consist of satellite space stations, particle beams of high energy, nuclear weapons and pulsed X-ray lasers, which would shoot down all opposing missiles before they reached the USA.

This was presented to the world as an important contribution to world peace: the previous concept of MAD (i.e., Mutual Assured Destruction: if either side used nuclear weapons, both would be obliterated in the ensuing war) would be replaced by MAS (i.e., Mutual Assured Security: both sides, protected from the other side's aggression, could afford to run down their existing supplies of nuclear weapons). At the time of the announcement, the President even offered to share the technology for Star Wars with the Soviet Union, once it had been developed. SDI continues to be described by the US government (but not the US Congress) as a defensive initiative which does not adversely affect the arms race.

The initial presentation has changed, however. The offer to share the technology with the Russians has been redefined, to the extent of being practically withdrawn: SDI's potential relies on an unprecedently sophisticated system of computerization, which the USA will not under any circumstances release to the Soviet Union. The export of advanced technology of all kinds to the USSR has long been rigorously controlled by the USA.

Similarly, the 'astrodome' concept of SDI (in which all citizens are protected under the astrodome roof) has been changed. It has now been admitted by the director of the SDI programme that a perfect astrodome protection cannot be achieved – some missiles will get through. What is now more likely is a defensive shield placed round ICBM silos, Trident nuclear submarine bases, major bases used by strategic air bombers and military command centres.

The technology of SDI has not been fully achieved, although some advances have been made, particularly in laser weapons and high-velocity projectiles, and the project has been ridiculed in some quarters, as it involves the identification and interception of thousands of missiles, and possibly thousands more decoy missiles, in the space of a few minutes.

In terms of the arms race, however, SDI has an extremely de-stabilizing influence. It is not a new project – research into SDI began in the 1950s, and was first expressed in the unsuccessful attempt to build an American anti-ballistic system ('Safeguard') in the 1970s. Neither is it underfunded: Star Wars activities were allocated $30,000 million in the period 1985–9, according to Frank Barnaby (in *What on Earth is Star Wars?*, 1986). The possibility of one side developing this kind of protection forces the other to follow. The USSR, like the USA, has been researching anti-ballistic systems for three decades: SDI, however, represents a significant increase in pressure.

The Americans have repeatedly stated that they would find it destabilizing if the USSR developed its own anti-ballistic missile shield, rather than the more rudimentary ABM network currently in place around Moscow. The reason for this is that the Soviets would then be able to strike against the USA, knowing that it would be protected from a retaliatory attack. The reverse, however, should not be feared, according to then Secretary of Defense Caspar Weinberger: 'The reason the Soviets have no need to worry is that they know perfectly well that we will never launch a first strike.' The idea behind this – that one side's nuclear weapons can be trusted, while the other's cannot – is an extremely simplistic analysis. It is also unworkable politically and diplomatically, particularly as NATO has indicated a readiness for 'first use' of its nuclear arms.

See also ENERGY; MILITARY SPENDING, WORLDWIDE; NUCLEAR ENERGY; RADIATION

REFERENCES

AMBIO, *Nuclear War, the Aftermath*, Pergamon Press, 1983.

Arkin, William, *The Nuclear Arms Race at Sea*, Neptune Papers, no. 1, Greenpeace / Institute for Policy Studies, October 1987.

Barnaby, Frank, *What on Earth is Star Wars?*, Fourth Estate, 1986.

Bertell, Rosalie, *No Immediate Danger*, Women's Press, 1985.

Blakeway, Denys and Sue Lloyd-Roberts, *Fields of Thunder*, Counterpoint, 1985.

Bulletin of the Atomic Scientists, *Nuclear Notebook*, April 1989.

Campbell, Duncan, *The Unsinkable Aircraft Carrier*, Michael Joseph, 1984.

Glasstone, Samuel and Philip Dolan, (eds), *The Effects of Nuclear Weapons*, Castle House, 1980.

Goodwin, Peter, *Nuclear War, the Facts*, Papermac, 1981.

Greenpeace, *Nuclear Free Seas*, 1987.

IISS, *The Military Balance 1987–1988*, 1987.

Kidron, M. and R. Segal, *The New State of the World Atlas*, Pluto Press/Pan Books, 1984.

Milliken, Robert, *No Conceivable Injury*, Penguin Books, 1986.

Moss, Norman, *The Politics of Uranium*, Deutsch, 1981.

Plesch, D., *NATO's New Nuclear Weapons, 2*, British American Security Information Council, January 1988.

Porritt, Jonathon, *Seeing Green*, Basil Blackwell, 1984.

Radical Statistics Nuclear Disarmament Group, *The Nuclear Numbers Game*, BSSRS, 1982.

Sivard, Ruth Leger, *World Military and Social Expenditures*, World Priorities, 1986.

Stephenson, Michael and John Weal, *Nuclear Dictionary*, Longman, 1985.

Stockholm International Peace Research Institute (SIPRI), *SIPRI Yearbook*, 1986.

Thompson, E.P., *Star Wars*, Penguin Books, 1985.

UNEP, *Radiation: Doses, Effects, Risks*, 1985.

Arkin, W. M. and J. Handler, *Naval Accidents, 1945–1988*, Neptune Paper No. 3, Greenpeace, June 1989.

Baker, David, 'The Making of Star Wars', *New Scientist*, 9 July 1987.

'Everyman's Guide to Doomwatch at Devonport', *Guardian*, 26 July 1987.

Leggett, Jeremy and Patricia Lewis, 'Lifting the Lid on the Arms Treaty', *New Scientist*, 19 November 1987.

Lowry, Dr David, 'Hanford's Hidden Hibakusha', *Environment Now*, July 1988.

'"More than 48" atomic warheads litter ocean bed', *Guardian*, 10 May 1989.

'New Zealand prepares for the apocalypse', *New Scientist*, 27 August 1987.

'Nuclear Update Will Wipe Out Arms Cuts', *Observer*, 24 January 1988.

Walker, M., 'Radiation fear over "lost" sub', *Guardian*, 8 April 1989.

CONTACTS

Bertrand Russell Foundation

British American Security Information Council

Campaign for Nuclear Disarmament (CND)

European Nuclear Disarmament (END)

European Proliferation Information Centre

Greenpeace

International Institute of Strategic Studies (IISS)

Nuclear Weapons FREEZE

Stockholm International Peace Research Institute (SIPRI)

The Ozone Layer

Ozone (O_3) is a gas, and a variant of oxygen (O_2). Although it is present in very small amounts in the atmosphere, significant reductions or increases in this gas can have important environmental consequences.

Ozone occurring in that part of the earth's atmosphere nearest the ground (the troposphere) is frequently industrially-caused, and can damage human and plant health (see ACID RAIN).

Ozone occurring higher up in the atmosphere, between 15 and 55 km above ground level (i.e., the stratosphere) forms a protective barrier called the ozone layer, shielding the earth from extreme heat radiated by the sun. The ozone layer has recently become the subject of much concern because it appears to be becoming thinner. If this continues, the consequences could be disastrous for the planet.

An international treaty signed in 1987 has restricted the production of some of the substances that have been eroding the ozone layer. Because of the long life of the pollutants involved, however, those already in place will continue to be there for the next century. A further pollution load will be deposited in the stratosphere by substances already manufactured, which will be released when the products they inhabit are scrapped. Additional loading will be created by substances permitted to be manufactured until the end of the century, and by substances not yet scheduled for abolition.

Ozone in the stratosphere

Ozone is a minor constituent of the earth's atmosphere; found in varying concentrations between sea level and a height of some 60 km. Most of the atmosphere's ozone is found in its two lowest layers: the troposphere, which extends up to 12 km above the earth's surface, and the stratosphere above it, which extends up to about 50 km.

The majority of ozone is found between 20 and 50 km above the ground, with the highest ozone concentrations occurring between 20 to 25 km – but even here, only about one molecule in every 100,000 is ozone.

If all the ozone in the earth's stratosphere were brought down to ground level and spread evenly around the globe, it would be a layer only about 3 millimetres thick.

Oxygen and ozone in the stratosphere absorb ultraviolet (UV) radiation from the sun, preventing it from reaching the earth. UV radiation between 100 and 200 nanometres in wavelength is mostly absorbed by oxygen, whereas ozone absorbs UV radiation with wavelengths between 200 and 280 nanometres. Between 280 and 320 nanometres (UV-B radiation), most, but not all, is absorbed by ozone.

The ozone does not appear to be particularly stable, breaking down into its constituent parts as a result of absorbing radiation, or as a consequence of reactions with various gases found in small quantities in the atmosphere. This is balanced, however, by a number of other processes which create ozone in the stratosphere. The result of all this activity is that an equilibrium is achieved, in which about 10 to 50 millionths of the oxygen in the stratosphere exists as ozone.

If radiation absorption did not occur, the consequences could be fatal for humankind. Ultraviolet light of wavelengths between 280 and 320 nanometres is capable of decomposing living substances: a strong dose to human skin causes cancer, and the small quantities that get through the ozone shield are an important cause of cancer in people. If we are to continue being able to walk around in the sunshine, then the stability of the ozone layer is essential.

Ozone in the atmosphere is broken down when it absorbs UV-B radiation. This natural process can be disrupted by the presence of pollutants. Chlorine speeds up the breakdown of ozone molecules, thus leading to a depletion of the ozone layer. Chlorine is one of the constituents of CFCs. Bromine, a constituent of halons, fulfils a similar role.

1930 – The birth of CFCs

CFCs, or chlorofluorocarbons, do not occur in the natural environment. They were invented in the late 1920s. In the 1930s they began to be used as cooling liquids in refrigerators, instead of ammonia.

CFCs are various compounds built up from atoms of chlorine,

fluorine, and carbon. Non-toxic, they do not react with water, animal, or plant matter, and are non-flammable.

Use of CFCs was relatively limited for the first 30 years of their existence. The two best-known CFCs – CFC 11 and 12 – have always dominated the market, and now account for almost 80 per cent of CFC manufacture. From 1960 to now, production of CFC 11 and 12 has mushroomed:

Manufacture of CFC 11 and 12, in tonnes	
1931	5,000
1941	6,600
1951	45,300
1961	169,000
1966	357,000
1971	604,000
1976	750,000
1981	638,000
1964	694,000

Source: Chemical Manufacturers' Association, 1985

CFCs had other useful qualities in addition to the ones mentioned above. They last a long time (CFC 11 has a lifetime of 78 years, with CFC 12 lasting 139 years, and CFC 115 even longer at 380).

They are also cheap to make. A kilo of CFC 11 costs around $1.25, and CFC 12 some $2.00 – roughly the same price as a packet of sugar.

Not surprisingly, they began to be used in other industrial products. Aerosols using CFCs as propellants first went on the market in 1950: by 1974, 1.4 billion CFC aerosols were being made every year in North America alone.

CFCs were also used as blowing agents in foam (to make hamburger cartons, insulation material for houses, and as packaging); in air conditioning and refrigeration systems; and as solvents, for cleaning electronic machinery.

Fears about the wonder chemicals began in the early 1970s, after scientists Sherry Rowland and Mario Molina worked out that CFC releases of 800,000 tonnes a year (the rate of release in 1972) would result in half a million tonnes of chlorine being deposited in the atmosphere over 30 years, destroying between 20 and 40 per cent of the ozone layer.

Because of their fears for the ozone layer, the US government banned CFCs from all aerosols (with a few minor exceptions) in 1978. Similar action was taken by Sweden, Norway, Finland, and Canada.

The aerosol ban dented the market for CFCs, but production picked up as other CFC usage took up the slack. In the mid-1980s, production of CFCs 11 and 12 began to approach the peak years of the 1970s.

Nowadays, total annual manufacture of CFCs exceeds 1 million tonnes per year, in a trade worth more than £1 billion annually. Some 39 manufacturers make the substances under various trade marks, including 'Freon' (Du Pont), 'Arcton' (ICI), 'Isceon' (RTZ Chemicals – ISC Division, Avonmouth), 'Frigen' (Hoechst), and 'Kaltron' (Kali Chemie).

1982 – the discovery of the Antarctic ozone hole

Meanwhile, evidence of ozone layer depletion began to be seen. In 1982, British Antarctic Survey scientists detected a fall in ozone concentrations above the southern ice cap.

The results were so unexpected as to be almost unbelievable. For two years the scientists checked and rechecked their findings. By October 1984, the 'hole' over Halley Bay showed a 30 per cent reduction in ozone.

Checks on the NASA satellite monitoring the area showed that it too had detected the ozone reduction, but the data had been automatically discounted by the computer as not credible.

1984 to 1986 – scientific uncertainty continues

While there was little doubt as to the existence of the Antarctic hole, controversy raged as to the cause. Was it a natural event, or caused by CFCs? The producers of CFCs defended their ground fiercely, and there was little in the way of conclusive evidence to prove the case either way.

Then, in 1986, a number of scientists proposed the idea that Polar Stratospheric Clouds (PSCs) may be linked to ozone depletion. These clouds, forming at high levels over the Antarctic during the winter, could be implicated in the release of ozone-eating chlorine. Experiments in late 1986 apeared to bear this out.

1987 – Montreal Protocol – 50 per cent cut agreed (September)

It was decided to fly a converted U-2 spy plane over the Antarctic in 1987, in order to resolve the scientific doubts. Before the results of this research were available, however, 46 countries signed the Montreal Protocol on Substances that Deplete the Ozone Layer.

The Montreal signatories agreed to limit the consumption and production of eight different chemicals – five 'fully-halogenated' CFCs, and three halons (used for fire-fighting). The intention was to reduce consumption of these products by 50 per cent by the end of the century.

The Montreal Protocol was signed on 16 September 1987. On 30 September, preliminary results from NASA's Antarctic flights were released. The NASA flights found that:

- the hole was about the size of the USA, and the height of Mount Everest;
- in the centre of the hole at certain altitudes, 97.5 per cent of the ozone was missing;
- chlorine monoxide – one of the breakdown products from CFCs – was present at up to a thousand times the 'background' concentration at lower altitudes.

The presence of chlorine monoxide was the 'smoking gun' that connected CFCs with the ozone hole. Scientists were quick to react, pointing out that the Montreal cuts would not be enough to protect the ozone layer.

1987 – 85 per cent cut called for (November)

Joe Farman, the British Antarctic Survey scientist usually credited with the discovery of the Antarctic hole, wrote in *New Scientist* (12 November 1987):

A 50 per cent cut in the world consumption of CFCs will not be enough to save the ozone layer. For every six tonnes of CFC that we allow into the atmosphere, 5 tonnes will still be there at the end of the year ... The emissions of CFC are so large, and their rates of loss so small, that they are accumulating rapidly. If we wish the amounts of CFCs to remain constant, we must cut emissions so that they are equal to the losses, that is to say to roughly 15 per cent of their current level.

Farman, and other scientists involved in the field, advocated an 85 per cent reduction of CFC emissions just to stabilize the amount of CFCs in the atmosphere.

This stabilization would be at mid-1980 levels – that is, at levels sufficient to cause depletion of the ozone layer. Greater reductions of CFC emissions are necessary, if the ozone layer is to be protected.

1988 – the call for 100 per cent reductions in CFCs

By 1988, CFCs were positively identified as the main or only cause for ozone depletion. In September 1988, the UK Stratospheric Ozone Review Group (SORG) commented that 'Man-made chlorofluoro-carbons are responsible for the Antarctic ozone depletions'.

The Review Group also commented that the Antarctic hole would continue to appear each year until chlorine levels in the stratosphere (derived from CFCs) fell to the levels of the mid-1970s. 'Even if no more man-made chlorine were to be released into the atmosphere, this would take centuries.'

In September 1988, the US Environmental Protection Agency issued a report which looked at various scenarios for phasing out CFCs. The EPA were also concerned with limiting the amount of chlorine in the atmosphere – this being the agent of ozone depletion.

Findings of the 1988 US EPA report:

- To maintain stratospheric chlorine at current levels would require a 100 per cent phaseout of the Montreal CFCs with 100 per cent participation worldwide.
- If there were a 95 per cent phaseout by 1998, instead of 100 per cent phaseout by 1990, the result would be 50 years of chlorine levels in excess of the peak chlorine level arising from the faster CFC phaseout.
- While an 85 per cent reduction is sufficient to stabilise chlorine levels from one compound (i.e., CFC 12), it is not sufficient if the production and use of other compounds are taken into account.
- If there is 100 per cent phaseout with 100 per cent partici-pation in 1990, chlorine levels will return to 1985 levels by 2050.

Both the UK and US research indicated that *even with 100 per cent phase-out of the Montreal CFCs*, stratospheric chlorine levels would take decades to return to 1985 levels. The US research went further than this: for protecting the ozone layer, anything less than 100 per cent reduction in CFC use is unsatisfactory.

Are India and China threatening the ozone layer?

It has been suggested that India and China are seriously depleting the ozone layer. This is untrue. According to a French Ministry of the Environment analysis:

- total production of CFCs 11 and 12 between 1931 and 1985 was 14 million tonnes for companies in the northern hemisphere and 700,000 from the southern hemisphere. Northern hemisphere countries have been responsible for 95 per cent of production.

- in 1984, the main producers of CFC 11, 12, 22, 113 and 114 were:

	thousand tonnes	% of world production
USA	445	37.4
West Europe	440	36.2
Japan	150	12.4
Communist countries	120	9.9
Rest of world	50	4.1
Total	1215	

Source: *The CFC Story*

- in 1985, the main consumers of CFCs 11, 12, 113 114, 115, and Halons 1211 and 1301 were:

	thousand tonnes	% of world consumption
USA	299	29
USSR/E. Europe	145	14
Other developed countries	424	41
China and India	18	1.7
Other developing countries	148	14.3
Total	1034	

Source: *The CFC Story*

The UK has a production capacity of 150,000 tonnes. Operating at 70 per cent capacity, this would result in CFC production of 105,000 tonnes. In 1988, the UK exported 48,000 tonnes and imported 9,000 tonnes. As defined by the Montreal Protocol, the unexported 66,000 tonnes is the UK's consumption for 1988.

Calculated world consumption of CFCs is estimated in the range of 1 million to 1.2 million tonnes, depending on which substances are included. The UK's 66,000 tonnes represent some 6 per cent of world consumption. The UK, with 60 million citizens, uses 3 times as many CFCs as China and India, who have 1,800 million citizens.

Even after the UK meets the terms of the Montreal protocol, it will be a larger user of CFCs than China and India combined.

Even if the UK reduced its CFC consumption by 90 per cent, its CFC use would be larger than India's 4,600 tonnes.

1989 – ozone depleting substances found over the Arctic

In late 1988 and early 1989, NASA-coordinated flights over the Arctic continued the 1987 programme that pinned down the causes of the Antarctic hole.

The key findings of the Airborne Arctic Stratospheric Expedition were:

- large quantities of chlorine monoxide were found in the Arctic lower stratosphere (the 'smoking gun' that identified CFCs as the cause of the Antarctic hole);
- the chemical composition of the Arctic polar stratosphere was highly perturbed, over a wide range of altitudes;
- overall, there was a consistent picture similar to the one drawn from the Antarctic data in 1987: no loss of Arctic ozone had occurred to date, but a considerable portion of the air was primed for ozone destruction.

There may not yet be a hole in the Arctic ozone layer, but there is depletion of ozone in the northern hemisphere. From December to March, the area suffering the largest loss of ozone is between 53°N and 64°N – where a 6 per cent loss occurs. This area includes all of Britain north of Nottingham. South of this, all areas down to 40°N (northern Spain) suffer a 4.7 per cent depletion.

At sea level, the world's ozone layer would weigh some 3,000 million tonnes, so these losses are substantial. In 1987, US EPA calculations showed that 40 million more skin cancers, 12 million eye cataracts, and 800,000 deaths would occur in the US over the next 90 years if current production rates were maintained. UNEP figures indicate that a one per cent decrease in the global ozone layer would result in a six per cent increase worldwide in skin cancers.

There would also be (as yet unascertained) threats to wildlife, agriculture, and marine life as a result of increased UV-B radiation exposure.

The ozone layer and the greenhouse effect

There are a number of connections between the ozone layer and the greenhouse effect:

- CFCs are greenhouse gases, as well as ozone depleters. A molecule of CFC 12 is 10,000 times more effective as a greenhouse gas than a molecule of carbon dioxide.
- Depletion of the ozone layer allows more radiation to hit the earth, thus increasing the input of heat to global warming.
- Some of the substitutes for CFCs are themselves greenhouse gases (e.g., the hydrocarbons, and some partially halogenated CFCs).
- Because of the quantity of CFCs in the stratosphere, CFCs will contribute to ozone depletion and global warming long after their production and use has been banned.

Developments in 1989

In March 1989, the number of signatories to the Montreal Protocol increased, and the EC and USA agreed to phase out CFCs altogether by the end of the century. This still involves an element of risk – continued CFC production and use will increase atmospheric loading of chlorine by a significant amount. This may lead to ozone depletion as is currently being experienced – or it could cross a threshold of environmental destruction, with unforeseen results. For the latter reason, the environment movement is calling for the abolition of all ozone depleters as quickly as possible (target dates vary from immediately to 1995). They also want the abolition of substances that deplete the ozone layer but are not listed in the Montreal Protocol. Methyl chloroform and carbon tetrachloride are two such substances.

CFC TRADE FROM THE UNITED KINGDOM

Figures refer to tonnes of CFC's exported from the UK in 1988

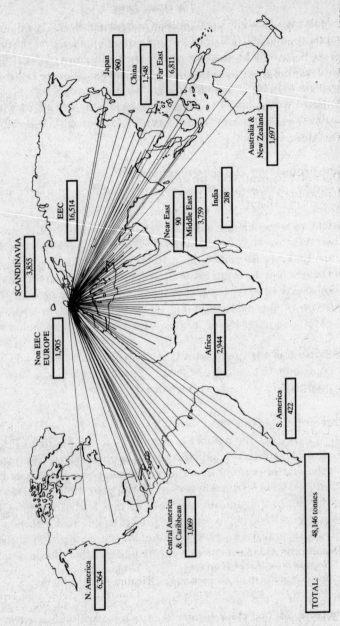

N. America
6,364

Central America
& Caribbean
1,069

S. America
422

Non EEC
EUROPE
1,905

SCANDINAVIA
3,855

EEC
16,514

Africa
2,944

Near East
90

Middle East
3,759

India
208

Japan
960

China
1,548

Far East
6,811

Australia &
New Zealand
1,697

TOTAL:
48,146 tonnes

Source: Greenpeace International, February 1989

The UK government claimed much credit for its role in abolishing CFCs from aerosols – a 60 per cent national reduction, achieved ten years before the Montreal due date. In fact, government action was irrelevant to this process: a very successful consumer boycott organized by Friends of the Earth achieved the aerosol CFC phase-out. During this time, the UK was the leading exporter of CFCs in Europe, exporting to 117 countries in 1988, 81 of which were not signatories to the Montreal Protocol.

Decrease in stratospheric ozone

Unfortunately, however, there are signs of a decrease in stratospheric ozone levels, at least in certain parts of the world. In 1985, British scientists found a 'hole' in the ozone layer over Antarctica. Checking their records, the British Antarctic Survey found that from the 1950s until 1979, the ozone layer was stable throughout the winter. Since then, in a four-week period between September and November, the total ozone concentrations has fallen each year to an increasingly worrying low.

See also ACID RAIN; GREENHOUSE EFFECT

REFERENCES

Breuer, *Air in Danger*, Cambridge University Press, 1980.

Chemical Manufacturers' Association, *Production, Sales and Calculated Release of CFC-11 and CFC-12 through 1984*, Washington, DC, 1985.

Curwell, S. R., R. C. Fox and C. G. March, *Use of CFCs in Buildings*, Fernsheer Ltd, December 1988.

Department of the Environment, *Response to the House of Commons Select Committee on the Environment's Report on Air Pollution*, December 1988.

ENDS, *Reports*, nos 139, 140, 142, 1986.

Faucheux, S. and J. Noel, *Enjeux economiques, techniques et ecologiques de differentes politiques alternatives de controle de l'evolution de la couche d'ozone*, Groupe de Prospective, Ministère de l'Environnemente, Paris, March 1988.

FoE, *The Aerosol Connection*, 1987, 1988.

Greenpeace, *The CFC Story*, 1989.

Gribbin, J., *The Hole in the Sky*, Corgi, 1988.

Heating and Ventilating Contractors' Association report, *Safe disposal of refrigerants – an urgent problem*, 23 January 1989.

Hoffman, J. and M. J. Gibbs, *Future concentrations of stratospheric chlorine and bromine*, US Environmental Protection Agency, July 1988, Prologue.

House of Commons Environment Committee hearing on Air Pollution, *Memorandum submitted by ICI*, 9 March 1988.

Johnston, Kathy, *Into the Void, a Report on CFCs and the Ozone Layer*, FoE, 1987.

Montreal Protocol on substances that deplete the ozone layer, Final Act, 1987.

National Swedish Environmental Protection Board, *CFCs/Freons, proposals to protect the ozone layer*, Report 3410, 1987.

Rose, C., *Ozone depletion and the greenhouse effect*, August 1988, unpublished Greenpeace research document.

Royal Commission on Environmental Pollution, Tenth Report, 1984.

UK Met. Office, *Airborne Arctic Stratospheric Expedition, Preliminary Findings*, 17 February 1989.

UK Stratospheric Ozone Review Group, *Second Report*, Department of the Environment, 1988.

UNEP/GEMS, *The Ozone Layer*, 1987.

UNEP/OzL. Alt. 1/4, *Workshop on Substitutes and Alternatives to CFCs and Halons*, UNEP, October 1988.

World Resources Institute, IIED, *World Resources 1986*, Basic Books, 1986.

Beggs, D. and J. Hughes, 'The Dark Side of Sunlight', *New Scientist*, 21 August 1986.

Electronic Manufacture and Test, January 1989.

Erlichman, J., 'A Spray of Self-righteousness', *Guardian*, 12 March 1987.

Farman, Joe, 'What Hope for the Ozone Layer Now', *New Scientist*, 12 November 1987.

Glenny, M., 'America Attacks Europe over Stratospheric Ozone', *New Scientist*, 5 March 1987.

Lean, G., 'British Block World Deal on Pollution', *Observer*, 15 March 1987.

Tucker, Anthony, 'The Hole in the Heavens', *Guardian*, 25 July 1986.

CONTACTS

Friends of the Earth (FoE)
Greenpeace

PCBs

'PCB' is scientific shorthand for polychlorinated biphenyl, a substance obtained by adding chlorine atoms to biphenyl. There are 209 different ways in which this can be done: if the result contains a high proportion of chlorine, the product is known as a highly chlorinated PCB. Products with smaller proportions of chlorine are called lower chlorinated PCB.

PCB was invented in Germany in 1881 and was first manufactured by the Swan Co., USA, in 1929. At room temperature the various substances, also known as askarels, are oils, viscous liquids or sticky resins. Fire-retardant and very stable, with a high boiling point, they soon became used in a number of different processes, as lubricants, softeners, laminating agents and hydraulic fluid. They were added to cement, plaster, sealing liquid, adhesives, plastics and carbonless copy paper. They had applications in heavy industry, being used in large quantities in electric capacitors, transformers and heat exchange units (in which a hot liquid enclosed in a metal pipe is used to warm another liquid). In short, while PCBs were considered safe, they were in widespread and daily use.

PCB disasters
Some scientists had warned of the possible toxic effects of the industrial wonder-liquid, but these warnings were ignored throughout the 1950s and 1960s. In 1968, however, a heat-exchanger was being used in the production of rice-oil in western Japan. There was a pin-hole leak in the exchanger, resulting in a PCB being transmitted into the oil, which was then used for human consumption: 13,000 people were subsequently found to have symptoms of poisoning which ranged from skin disorders to respiratory problems.

The outbreak became known as the 'Yusho epidemic'. Later research into Yusho victims revealed reproductive difficulties, including stillbirths, underweight births, spontaneous abortions and toxaemia (i.e., blood-poisoning) of pregnancy. Tests on animals indicated that PCB is carcinogenic (i.e., cancer-forming). Post-mortems on deceased Yusho patients have revealed an excess of malignant tumours.

Other outbreaks have occurred, mainly as a result of contaminated food. In 1971, problems arose in the poultry industry in the USA when large numbers of chicken eggs failed to hatch. The cause was eventually traced to the fishmeal they were eating: PCBs in a heat-transfer fluid in the feed plant had leaked into the chickenfeed. As recently as 1979, poultry and eggs in Idaho, USA, were found to be contaminated with PCBs, through leakage of insulating fluid from a transformer. The source was traced to a meat-packing plant in Montana, but not before the contamination had spread to 16 other states. A further outbreak of human poisoning by PCBs, involving 2,000 individuals in Taiwan and again attributable to contaminated rice-oil, has recently been reported.

PCB problems

One problem with PCBs is that they have been widely dispersed, and do not easily disintegrate in the environment. They are capable of staying in mud or water for long periods of time.

They are then absorbed by water insects and small animals, which are eaten by small fish, which in turn are digested by large predators. In 1969, the deaths of over 12,000 birds in the Irish Sea was attributed in part to high levels of PCBs in their livers. Other research has identified high PCB levels in the livers of seals in the Baltic Sea and around the Dutch coast.

As the pollutant is passed along the food chain, concentrations of PCBs increase up to a hundredfold each time it is assimilated by a new predator. The length of the food chain means that final concentrations in an animal's liver can be 10 million times as great as the PCB levels in the water. PCBs have been found to be ubiquitous contaminants of freshwater fish in English and Scottish rivers and lochs. Pregnant and lactating women who consume large quantities of fish will pass PCB traces to their infants in their milk – although PCB levels in human milk and fat in the UK are considered generally to be low. People who consume fish livers – especially children fed cod or halibut liver oil – run the risk of high intakes of PCBs.

The other problem with PCBs is that they are extremely difficult to handle or destroy. Special incinerators are used, capable of burning the material at 1,100 to 1,200 degrees C: but before this happens, the material has to be extracted from the transformer or other machine in which it is located. The pollutant can be inhaled or absorbed through the skin, and should be handled only by people wearing gloves, goggles and protective clothing. The US National Institute of Occupational Safety and Health has made these recommendations:

- PCBs should be handled in isolated areas of a factory, with efficient ventilation systems to remove airborne contamination.
- Accidental leaks or spills should result in immediate evacuation of all personnel from the area.
- Entry into enclosed spaces such as tanks which have contained PCBs should be authorized only by signed permits, with any worker entering the tank having access to an oxygen supply, and being connected by a lifeline harness to an outside worker. This stand-by support should also be equipped for entry and have access to a third person.

Because of the small number of incinerators capable of handling PCBs, they have to be transported long distances. This is also not without danger. In April 1985, a truck carrying a PCB-filled transformer leaked 200 litres of PCBs along a motorway in Ontario, Canada. When the leak was discovered, the authorities responded by closing 100 km of the Trans-Canada Highway for a week (equivalent to shutting down the motorway connecting London to Cambridge), and advising all motorists who had passed the infected area to clean their cars and dispose of the cleaning rags in plastic sacks. The highway was cleaned and re-asphalted in all the danger zones. The incident provoked a rush of new laws concerning the transportation of PCBs in Canada.

PCB pollution has surfaced in the UK. The *Guardian* reported (26 February 1987) that a bucketful of PCBs fell out of a transformer being removed from the workings of the Channel Tunnel in 1973. The pollution was discovered when the tunnel was reopened for the new tunnel diggings: the scrap merchant had not notified the Department of Transport about the spillage and could not be traced. The UK government faced a bill of £1 million to clear the polluted 100-yard site, and negotiations over the Channel were blocked until the site was satisfactorily cleared.

In 1988, it was revealed that transformers in the oil rig Piper Alpha contained PCBs: they went to the sea bed along with much of the wrecked oil rig, and are now presumably leaking PCBs into the North Sea. In 1989, Canadian exports of PCBs to the UK were blockaded by Greenpeace, who believe that developed countries should store their own toxic waste rather than dump it on other countries. A number of UK ports refused to accept the PCB shipments.

PCB combustion

The controversy over PCBs has occurred over the way in which they are incinerated. If PCBs are inadequately burnt, dioxins like 2,3,7,8 trichlorodibenzodioxin (2,3,7,8 TCDD) are produced – one of the most potent, toxic, carcinogenic and genetically damaging synthetic substances known. If chlorobenzine (a solvent frequently found with PCBs) is similarly burnt, dioxins can also be released.

There is only one incinerator in the UK capable of dealing with solid PCBs, run by Rechem in Pontypool, Gwent (the sister plant in Bonnybridge, Scotland, closed in late 1984 for economic reasons). Greenpeace UK became concerned about possible emissions from the plant. They received information from a Pontypool farmer detailing various allegations. He had been farming successfully for ten years, but in 1982 experienced severe problems with his livestock. A small number of midget and deformed lambs were born; others developed arthritis, meningitis, lost their wool and grew large scabby sores. Fifteen top-grade Charolais calves, newly purchased, failed to thrive, and died. The farmer then found that Mr Andrew Graham, a farmer located near the Rechem plant in Scotland, had been having similar problems. He apparently believed that there was a massive emission of pollutants from the plant in spring 1982, and later in spring 1984. This is strongly denied by Rechem, and no proof was furnished that such events occurred.

Andrew Graham has two farms near Bonnybridge. In 1980, cattle which had been put out to graze near the plant suffered weight loss, and by 1983 he was noticing an increase in calving problems. More than 100 cows and 90 calves had either died or been slaughtered by July 1983, and Mr Graham noted the birth of 45 deformed calves (including some born blind or with eye defects). Forty-five other calves were small and slow to grow.

Mr Graham called in Dr Alastair Hay, an expert on dioxins based at the University of Leeds, who believed that the symptoms in Mr Graham's cattle were very similar to those poisoned by poly-brominated biphenyls (PBBs) in Michigan, USA, in 1973. The Michigan cattle had eaten a contaminated food mix: thousands died or were destroyed.

Cyclops children

The *Observer* newspaper subsequently drew attention to the existence of 'Cyclops children' near the two Rechem plants: children born with only one eye, tiny eyes, almost completely closed eyes, or blindness or partial sight in one eye. The *Observer* had details of four such babies in the Bonnybridge area and three around Pontypool. A number of eminent environmental specialists called for public inquiries into whether emissions from the Rechem plants were responsible for the animal and human casualties. Although concern among local farmers and citizens was genuine, it would be premature to assume that there was a direct causal link between emissions from the plant and locally observed environmental disturbances.

Inquiries have been carried out, by the Atomic Energy Research Establishment, an independent ophthalmologist, the Welsh Office and the Scottish Office. None has found evidence that Rechem emissions have caused the localized ill-health to cattle or human beings. The Scottish Office inquiry suggested dietary deficiency as the cause of cattle death: the Welsh Office report concluded that the number of babies born with malformations in the Pontypool area was below the average for Wales. It should be emphasized that no proven connection has been made between emissions from the plant and adverse environmental or health effects. The controversy continues, however. In 1989, Rechem successfully took out a High Court injunction forbidding the local council from publishing a report on alleged emissions of PCBs from its Pontypool plant.

The size of the problem

The difficulty posed by PCBs is that a substance previously thought to be harmless is now considered to be extremely toxic. Manufacture of

PCBs has been run down since the early 1970s, with production stopping altogether in the USA and UK in 1977.

There is still a large number of PCBs to be disposed of, however. Estimates vary, but the UK Department of Agriculture calculate that between 1 and 2 million tonnes of the substance have been produced worldwide since the 1930s. Finding them may be the first problem. Before 1971, there was no legal requirement in the UK to label items which contained PCBs. Some manufacturers have now contacted all their customers, going back to the 1940s, to give them instructions as to adequate disposal. Others have gone out of business, lost records or not been able to trace some machinery. In some cases, transformers have been sold as scrap without the scrap merchants realizing the toxic nature of what they were buying.

Untraced, the PCBs represent an environmental timebomb. In 1986, the French government ordered that all plant containing more than 30 litres of PCBs should be notified to the authorities, and meet certain safety requirements. These rules, applying to 100,000 items of electrical equipment, were implemented after two fires within 18 months had released PCBs into the atmosphere: the first, in Rheims, contaminated an apartment block with PCBs, dioxins and furans, and the second resulted in PCB contamination of an aquifer to levels well in excess of EC water laws.

Once located, the PCBs have to be adequately disposed of. In the past, the pollutant has been dumped on landfill sites, in the UK in quarries at Maendy and Brofiskin in Wales, though this is no longer regarded as acceptable. Incineration or expensive long-term storage appear to be the only options.

Between 1980 and August 1981, 227 tonnes of PCBs were incinerated in the UK at a cost of £600 per tonne. The amount of PCBs to be disposed of is expected to rise dramatically before the end of the century, as large electrical equipment built in the 1950s and 1960s reaches the end of its working life. In addition, there will be a substantial amount of waste arising from PCB handling and transfer, and large quantities of lower-chlorinated PCBs (for example, starter motors of fluorescent lights and fractional horsepower motors used in domestic electrical equipment: older models contain 50 grammes of PCBs, with no label identifying the PCB content. There are upwards of 100 million fluorescent lights in use at the moment.)

The authorities' dilemma is this: to get rid of the PCBs, they incinerate them; but incineration is dependent on proof that the process does not harm inhabitants near the disposal plant. The argument still continues.

Trade names for PCBs (askarels) include:

1. Apirolio (Italy)
2. Aroclor (UK and US)
3. Asbestol (US)
4. Bakola 131 (US)
5. Chlorextol (US)
6. Clophen (FRG)
7. Interteen (US)
8. Kanechlor (Japan)
9. No-Flamol (US)
10. Pyralene (Fr)
11. Pyranol (US)
12. Pyrochlor (UK)
13. Saf-T-Kuhl (US)
14. Solvol (USSR)

See also CHEMICAL WASTES; PESTICIDES; SEVESO

REFERENCES

Department of the Environment, *PCB Wastes: Waste Management Paper no. 6*, 1976.

Environmental Data Services, Reports 137, 139.

Greenpeace UK, unpublished PCB research.

Health and Safety Executive, *Use of Polychlorinated Biphenyls in Electrical Apparatus*, 1983.

Koeman, J.H., *PCB in Mammals and Birds in The Netherlands*, PCB Conference II, 1983.

Ministry of Agriculture, *PCB Residues in Food and Human Tissues*, 1983.

Environment Digest No. 17, October 1988.

Guardian, 10 September 1984; 8 February 1985; 26 February 1987.

Hansard, 2 December 1988.

Observer, 20 January 1985; 10 February 1985.

Powers, Jane, 'Poison Raining Down from the Sky', *Green Cuisine*, Spring 1986.

'Rechem stops council publishing waste report', *Guardian*, 2 September 1989.

Toronto Globe and Mail, 14 to 20 April 1985.

CONTACTS

Friends of the Earth (Scotland)
Greenpeace

Department of Agriculture

Department of Environment
Health and Safety Executive
Rechem

Pesticides

'Pesticides' are a variety of chemical substances used to kill unwanted insects, vegetation, fungus, rodents or other species. They are mainly used agriculturally, but are also sold for garden or household application. Most current pesticides have been developed since the Second World War, and the market has expanded rapidly. About 800 pesticides have been approved for use in Britain, of which some 400 are commonly used in approximately 4,000 different formulations.

The arguments in favour of pesticides are that they are essential if crops are to be protected from damaging pest attacks, particularly in the Third World. The arguments against are varied, and include allegations that pesticides are grossly overused, leading to a decline in their effectiveness and an unacceptable level of environmental pollution; that the clearances given to some of the older pesticides are unsatisfactory; that not enough is known about the effects of pesticides on humans and on the environment, especially when they are used in combination with other substances; and that many of the pesticides are so poisonous, carcinogenic or in other ways dangerous that we should not even be producing them, let alone spreading them on our fields.

PESTICIDE TYPES

About a billion gallons of pesticide-containing liquid are sprayed on the fields, gardens and parks of Britain every year. There are many types of pesticide: insecticides (which kill all, or specific species of, insects); herbicides (all or certain types of plants); fungicides (fungus); acaricides (spiders and mites); rodenticides; molluscicides; and some others. Most of the pesticides used in Britain are herbicides (65 per cent), fungicides (20 per cent) or insecticides (5 per cent).

Modern pesticide research started in the last century, with the development of an insecticide which checked the spread of Colorado beetle in the USA. At the beginning of this century, several substances were found which prevented pests – in Germany, for example, seeds were dressed with a compound of mercury. The rapid growth of pesticide research occurred before and during the Second World War, and the current generation of pesticides have been developed within the last 40 years.

Insecticides

Pete Snell, in *Pesticide Residues and Food*, classifies five different types of insecticide: organophosphorous compounds, organochlorines, carbamates, pyrethroids, and others. For fuller information, the reader is referred to his book, but his classifications can be summarized as follows:

Organophosphates Around 100 have been marketed, varying widely in their physical and chemical properties. Used as fumigants, contact poison or systemic poisons (in which treatment of one part of the organism makes the whole of it poisonous to the target insect), they work by interfering with signals sent between nerve cells in the body. As a byproduct of research into organophosphates in the Second World War, nerve gases were developed for military use.

Some organophosphates: **mevinthos**, **malathion**, **dimethoate**.

Organochlorines Organochlorines are largely combinations of carbon, hydrogen and chlorine: **DDT** is probably the most famous member of this family. Chemically stable, the organochlorines are also soluble in water, and thus tend not to break down in the environment but to pass along the food chain and accumulate in body fat. For this reason, DDT has been banned or restricted in many countries.

Other organochlorines include **BHC (lindane)**, **aldrin**, **dieldrin**, and **chlordane**.

Carbamates About 20 carbamates have been marketed as insecticides, often for use where organophosphates are not effective. However, they are twice as expensive as the organophosphorous compounds, and are used only when all others fail.

Some carbamates: **carbofuran**, **aldicarb**.

Pyrethroids Pyrethroids were originally produced naturally from chrysanthemums, and have been used for the last century. They are capable of knocking down insects very quickly, although they are rapidly destroyed by the presence of light. Synthetic pyrethroids were originally developed in 1949, and are now both more toxic and more stable. Poisonous to fish, they are relatively indiscriminate in their effects, and will also kill bees where they are applied.

Herbicides

Herbicides can be non-selective (i.e., kill all types of plants – commonly used to clear garden paths of weeds) or selective (i.e., can be applied to a crop in order to kill unwanted weeds, without damaging the crop itself). Snell's book identifies two types of herbicide: those that work by foliar application and those that are applied to the soil. The former are divided into two groups: seven systemic groups, which include **2,4,5-T**, **paraquat** and **glyphosate**; and four contact herbicides, including **ioxynil**, **dinoseb**, and **pentanochlor**.

There are nine groups of soil application herbicides, including **diuron**, **atrazine** and **nitrofen**.

Many of these herbicides are specifically toxic to plants, but behave in such a way that they do not endanger animal or human life (because they attack processes unique to plant life, but not shared by mammals). Others, for example paraquat, are intensely poisonous to humans. The exact status of other herbicides (for example 2,4,5-T) is the subject of bitter controversy.

Fungicides

Snell categorizes three groups of fungicides: heavy metal and inorganic; non-systemic; and systemic fungicides. The intention of a fungicide is generally to prevent the fungus occurring, as once a fungus is established on a food, it is either difficult to eradicate or has already irreparably set back plant growth. For this reason, fungicides tend to be long-lasting once they have been applied.

Some fungicides include **captan**, **maneb** and **pentachlorophenol**.

The growth of the pesticide market

Over the last 40 years, there has been a 20-fold increase in the tonnage of pesticides used worldwide, according to the House of Commons Agriculture Committee. With the UK's entry into the Common

Market, sales of herbicides and insecticides have leapt, as farmers switched to subsidized crops and intensified production. Sales of fungicides have also soared, to prevent the resulting food mountains from rotting.

Money spent on pesticides by UK farmers (£ millions)

	1973	1976	1979	1983
Herbicides	27.5	56.8	134.1	188.3
Fungicides	6.6	9.0	34.2	77.3
Insecticides	3.6	12.8	23.0	30.8

Source: J. Erlichman, *Gluttons for Punishment*, 1986

On the one hand, there has been a remarkable growth in the number of products on the market, and on the other hand, the practice of using pesticides has increased dramatically. Between 1979 and 1982 the crop area treated with pesticides doubled overall: pesticide sales rose by 21 per cent in the UK in 1982–3. As mentioned above, about 1,000 million gallons of pesticide-containing liquid are distributed over the UK's land area per year: this figure is achieved not just by expanding the area of pesticide-applied land, but also by increasing the number of applications.

The mean number of sprays per season on hops in 1979 was around 23. One lettuce crop in 1982 was sprayed 46 times with four different pesticide products. According to Ministry of Agriculture figures quoted by Friends of the Earth, 97–99 per cent of all our vegetables and cereals are sprayed by one or more pesticide. Most crops receive not just one spraying, but several.

Worldwide, the industry has grown from a position of almost zero after the war, to sales of £15,000 million per annum. In the UK, the manufacturers of pesticides have an estimated 6,000 salespeople, either working directly for the firms concerned, or travelling round the country on behalf of agricultural wholesalers. In 1985, five companies were estimated to control 55 per cent of the UK pesticide market: ICI (15 per cent), Bayer (15 per cent), FBC (10 per cent), Ciba Geigy (9 per cent) and Monsanto (6 per cent).

Pesticides and the Third World

A pesticide can cost a manufacturer up to £20 million to produce, so when it is banned in the home country there is great commercial pressure to export it. The developed countries are becoming more aware of the dangers of pesticide misuse, so banned pesticides are most frequently directed at the Third World.

It is often said by the agrochemical industry that no one has died from pesticide misuse in the UK for the last ten years. This may be true, though lack of diagnostic experience and worthwhile reporting procedures make this hard to determine. It is certainly not the case in the Third World. In 1972, the World Health Organization estimated that there were around 500,000 cases of pesticide poisoning every year, with approximately one per cent of these resulting in death.

Current calculations are that up to 1 million pesticide accidents occur every year, causing 10,000 to 20,000 deaths. Most Third World accidents are caused by lack of knowledge as to the effects of the pesticide concerned.

The United Nations has resisted attempts to enforce a system of 'prior informed consent', in which exporting countries have to notify the importing nation of any domestic restrictions on pesticide use. The onus is still on the purchaser to find out the harmful effects of the substance that is being bought. In March 1987, thallium sulphate killed several hundred people in Guyana after it was used as a poison to keep rats away from the sugar crop. Thallium sulphate has been outlawed in Britain and other developed countries for more than 20 years.

Pressure from the pesticide manufacturers prevented the implementation of prior informed consent: but pressure from domestic consumers may lead to its eventual introduction. Some imported food is beginning to carry pesticide residues of a type and quantity considered to be unacceptable in the domestic market.

BANNED OR SUSPECT PESTICIDES

Pesticides are banned when research shows them to have deleterious effects on health. There are four general classifications:

- **Carcinogenic** capable of producing cancer
- **Mutagenic** capable of mutating human cells, causing genetic damage
- **Teratogenic** capable of damaging a foetus
- **Allergenic** capable of producing an allergic response. This varies from hayfever symptoms to suppression of the immune systems in

the body (as occurs in AIDS), to interference with the nervous system.

When the London Food Commission produced its first version of *Pesticide Residues and Food* (1986), the authors, while admitting that their research was not complete, identified 49 possible carcinogens, 32 suspected teratogens, 61 suspected mutagens, and 90 possible allergens in pesticides cleared for use in Britain. Government response at the time was to dismiss the report and state that no chemicals with long-term health effects are allowed to be sold in the UK. Since that time, two pesticides, **ioxynil** and **dinoseb** have been banned because of their risk to human health. On 5 December 1986, dinoseb could be used in large-scale commercial spraying operations: on 6 December, it could not.

Some 20 pesticides have been withdrawn in the UK after being cleared for widespread use. Perhaps more alarming, however, is the number of substances still used in Britain, but banned or severely restricted elsewhere: 38 pesticides, according to Nigel Dudley (in *This Poisoned Earth*), sold as over 500 pesticide products. Some of them are listed below (see The Dirty Dozen): others include **dichlorvos**, **thiram**, **pentachlorophenol**, **parathion**, **aldicarb**, **captan** and **dieldrin**. Clearance for dieldrin has been withdrawn in the UK, but outstanding stocks can still be sold.

The House of Commons Agriculture Committee has pointed out that 'no government agency appears to have made any serious attempt to gather data on the chronic effects of pesticides on human health'. Reassurances routinely given by the Ministry of Agriculture appear to be based on testing of acute rather than long-term effects, and there has been almost no research into the 'cocktail effect' of a mixture of pesticides being applied.

What is more, the clearances given to some of the longer-established pesticides were given under criteria that would not be regarded as satisfactory today. Such pesticides are being reviewed, but the review period is so long as to create substantial unease.

The clearances themselves do not always stand up to scrutiny. One company, Industrial Bio-Test, was put on trial in Chicago in 1983, charged with fraud. Staff, while testing new pesticides on behalf of the authorities, had fabricated laboratory procedures – to the extent of removing dying laboratory rats and replacing them with new ones.

The US Environmental Protection Agency estimated that one-sixth of the 800 animal tests supplied by IBT for 140 pesticides were invalid. The people responsible were imprisoned – but up to 24 of the pesticides involved in the case continue to have clearance in Britain.

The UK authorities maintain that the pesticides in question had also been tested by other procedures. This is impossible to verify, because of the arbitrary secrecy surrounding pesticide safety: pesticide data on clearances given before 1986 are excluded from public scrutiny on the grounds of commercial confidence. Data after 1986 are available on a 'reading room' basis, with criminal charges awaiting any observer who tries to use any knowledge acquired to further public debate. It is interesting that our system appears to value commercial confidence above public safety.

Recent research by the London Food Commission has established that pesticide residues are turning up in our food. In a survey of 1,649 fruit and vegetable samples analysed between 1981 and 1984, 43 per cent contained detectable residues, even though the tests used were not capable of analysing all the pesticides that may have been present.

The Food Commission has pointed out that only 20 pesticides are routinely tested for as residues in British food, out of a total 400 pesticides in use. In the absence of such testing, preventative legislation would appear a logical protection – as in the USA, where the Delaney Clause forbids the inclusion in any food of any chemical identified as a possible human carcinogen. The British have no similar legislation.

In February 1989, a report published in the USA by the Natural Resources Defence Council (NRDC) argued that pre-school children faced unacceptably high risks of cancer because pesticide standards were based on adult, rather than child, criteria: they ignored children's heavy reliance on fruit and vegetables, and their vulnerability to toxic chemicals.

The most potent carcinogen identified was unsymmetrical dimethylhydrazine (UDMH), a byproduct of the apple growth-regulator, Alar. UDMH occurs in apple juice and sauces; Alar cannot be detected by sight and cannot be removed by peeling or washing the fruit, as it penetrates the flesh of the apple. Alar is banned in New Zealand; the US Environmental Protection Agency intends to ban it in the USA. Alar was considered by the Advisory Committee on Pesticides in the UK, and cleared for use in May 1989.

The question of safety

One reason given for the continued use of controversial pesticides in the UK is that they are safe *provided that the manufacturers' instructions are followed*. The Health and Safety Executive (HSE) leaflet *Crop Spraying* lists four categories of hazardous pesticide, for which operatives are required by law to wear protective clothing – in some cases respirators, in others aprons, boots and face-shields.

Inadequate policing of the regulations, coupled with 'soft' advertising that underplays the dangers of the pesticides involved, has led to a less than rigorous approach to following manufacturers' instructions. Aldicarb is one example. According to the HSE, this should be handled with rubber gloves, rubber boots, a face-shield, coverall and rubber apron. The periodical *Garden News* (6 March 1982) reported that members of one gardening society were carrying home plastic bags of aldicarb in their pockets for home use.

All pesticides should be treated as what they generally are – dangerous substances. This includes pesticides sold for garden or home use. These international hazard symbols will often give useful information about a particular product:

International Hazard Symbols

Source: Nigel Dudley, *This Poisoned Earth*, 1987

The London Food Commission's Spring 1986 Newsletter contains a Pesticide Hazard Checklist, detailing 92 pesticides, and describing whether they are possible carcinogens, teratogens, mutagens or allergens.

The Dirty Dozen

The Pesticides Action Network (PAN) was founded in 1982 by church, environment, consumer and trade union groups to establish considerations of human safety and environmental protection as a priority when permission for pesticide use is given.

On 5 June 1985, the UK branch of PAN, which included Oxfam, Friends of the Earth and the Soil Association, launched the 'Dirty Dozen' campaign, with the intention of stopping the manufacture and use of 12 particularly controversial pesticides: **2,4,5-T**, **endrin**, **aldrin**, **paraquat**, **chlordane**, **lindane**, **DDT**, **camphechlor**, **chlordimeform**, **ethylene dibromide**, **DBCP**, **dieldrin**, **ethyl parathion** and **pentachlorophenol**. (There are actually 14 substances here, but three – aldrin, endrin and dieldrin – are collectively known as 'the drins'.) All these substances can be manufactured in Britain, imported or exported: the first six are still cleared for use in the UK.

PAN also published background information on the six substances still cleared for British use.

2,4,5-T A herbicide which gained notoriety in the Vietnam War – it is a component of 'Agent Orange', a defoliant used to clear large areas of the Vietnamese countryside. The manufacturers of Agent Orange were sued by 45,000 Vietnamese veterans and paid $180 million in compensation.

2,4,5-T is banned in nine countries, including the USA and USSR; it is severely restricted in eight others. It is a possible carcinogen, mutagen and teratogen. It is classified as 'moderately hazardous' by the World Health Organization (WHO).

Sold under 11 trade names, including Farmon brushwood killer, Kilnet and Nettleban.

Endrin An insecticide used in agriculture, it is banned in seven countries, severely restricted in 12 more. Environmentally persistent, it wipes out beneficial insects as well as targets and can cause nerve and brain damage to humans. Classified as 'highly hazardous' by the WHO; the World Bank recommends that it not be used.

Sold as Endrin 19.2 EC.

Aldrin An insecticide related to Endrin. Environmentally persistent, it too wipes out beneficial insects as well as targets. It is banned in eight countries, and severely restricted in 11 others. It can cause cancer. Classified as 'highly hazardous' by the WHO; the World Bank recommends that it not be used.

Sold as Alderstan, Adrex, various names including the word 'aldrin'. In the UK, three uses of aldrin are still permitted: approval will be revoked in 1992.

Paraquat   A herbicide widely used as a weedkiller when establishing crops. Extremely poisonous when ingested, toxic when inhaled or absorbed through the skin, *paraquat has no known antidote*. It is used throughout the world, and is severely restricted in seven countries. The WHO classifies paraquat as 'moderately hazardous'; US Environmental Protection Agency has restricted use to certified applicators, because of its extreme toxicity.

Sold under 13 trade names, including Farmon PDG, Gramazine, Grammanol 5, New Weedol, Pathclear, Cleansweep, Dextrone X, Gramoxone 100, Scythe, and Speedway.

Chlordane   Chlordane and its variant **heptachlor** are persistent organochlorine pesticides used for structural insect control (e.g. termites) in industrial countries, and in agriculture in the Third World. It can cause cancer and birth defects and is very toxic. It accumulates in human fat tissues and is transferred across the placenta from mother to child. It is banned in six countries, severely restricted in 15 others. Classified by the WHO as 'moderately hazardous'; recommended by the World Bank not to be used as a pesticide.

Sold under 11 trade names, including Nippon Ant & Crawling Insect Spray, Earthworm Killer, Sydane 25, Miscible, and RCR No 30 Concentrate.

Lindane   A toxic variant of **HCH**, lindane and HCH are organochlorine insecticides, used in agriculture, veterinary medicine, indoor pest control, and for killing human head lice. Banned in the US because of suspected carcinogenicity, HCH is aggressively marketed for agricultural purposes in the Third World. Lindane is carcinogenic in test animals, can cause spontaneous abortions, can damage the nervous system of humans and animals. It is toxic to non-target insect species, and is persistent in the environment. Banned in nine

countries, severely restricted in 13 others, both substances are classified by the WHO as 'moderately hazardous'.

More than 130 products on the market contain lindane, including
Fisons Greenfly and Blackfly Killer, Murphy Pest and Disease Spray,
Doom Flea Killer, Lifeguard Dustbin Powder, and Rentokil Smoke
Pellets.

The *Observer* reported (11 December 1988) the closure of an infant
school in Warwickshire after the children and all their teachers
became ill. Victims suffered severe headaches, vomiting, rashes, sore
throats and diarrhoea. The cause was determined to be a mixture of
lindane and tributyltin oxide, applied by workmen as a wood preservative. Even minimal precautions were ignored, with the
preservative being applied while the children were in school.

ENVIRONMENTAL EFFECTS

Pesticides were not launched on a public that was mistrustful and
suspicious: rather the reverse. When DDT was discovered in 1939 to
have insecticidal properties, it was hailed as a new 'wonder drug', and
the scientist responsible, Paul Muller, won the Nobel Prize. In the
war, DDT was used to dust thousands of soldiers free of lice: in the
decades after the war, it was widely used as an insecticide, and is still
employed in certain areas as a control for malaria-carrying mosquitoes. DDT is claimed to have saved many lives by controlling such
diseases as malaria, river blindness and yellow fever. It is cheap, very
effective, and apparently safe to humans.

In the long term, however, the picture was not so attractive. The
insecticide does not easily break down in the environment, but builds
up in the body fat of those who consume it. Insects coated with DDT
are eaten by birds, who accumulate the substance in their body
tissues. If they are eaten by a predator, the DDT will pass into the
predator's body and continue to accumulate along with other DDT
residues. When enough pesticide has collected, the animal dies. This
process caused the widespread destruction of sparrowhawks, per-
egrines and golden eagles in the UK in the period of maximum DDT
application after the war.

DDT also poses a risk to people. Contaminated grass is eaten by
cows, which pass some of the pesticide out in their milk, which is then
absorbed by us. This will accumulate together with DDT from

vegetables and meat. Mothers pass the DDT in their bodies on to babies through their milk.

Scientists believe that persistent chemicals like DDT have spread virtually throughout the world. As Nigel Dudley points out in *This Poisoned Earth*, Adelie penguins in Antarctica have detectable levels of DDT in their blood: how it got there, nobody knows. A side-effect of the widespread use and persistence of DDT is that certain pests are becoming immune to it: a total of 229 species by 1980.

For these two reasons, DDT has been widely banned or restricted throughout the developed world. The UK, after operating a voluntary ban for several years, officially proscribed it in 1984. Some suppliers continued to sell DDT illegally, however, and DDT misuse wiped out a large heronry in Evesham in 1985. In the birds' bodies, Nature Conservancy Council pathologists found the highest levels of DDT that they had ever observed.

Environmentalists argue that the DDT story is typical of the dangers represented by pesticide overuse. A substance is developed that has no obvious acute (i.e., immediate) effects; it is widely used as an additive to large areas of land; some years afterwards, long-term effects begin to become apparent, and the substance has to be withdrawn from the market. In the meantime, the damage done is incapable of being accurately calculated, because of the chronic, insidious way in which the chemical has operated.

Rachel Carson points to the central problem of pesticides in *Silent Spring* – they are mainly all synthetic, and the environment has had no previous experience of how to deal with them. The normal process, of assimilating and accommodating a new substance over a period of generations, has been bypassed by the chemical shock wave suddenly arriving in our fields.

There are immediate observable environmental effects, of which the first is the virtual disappearance of wildflowers from the sprayed areas. This has implications for wildlife survival, as restriction of habitats leads to a cut in the variety of species able to survive in that part of the country.

Another obvious effect is the growing uniformity of the countryside. Output is increased by having larger fields (see COUNTRYSIDE IN THE UK) and drenching them with a succession of chemicals. The result: large areas of similarly cropped farmland, in contrast to the mixed farming that used to be much more common in Britain. In the past, outbreaks of pest could be contained to certain areas, because there was not enough opportunity for the pest to migrate. As Chris Rose points out in *Green Britain or Industrial Wasteland* (1986), this has now changed. Pests such as BYDV, otherwise known as the Barley Yellow Dwarf Virus, have been able to 'walk' from one crop to the next. BYDV has now arrived in the north of England and the Midlands, where it had never been seen before.

There are other environmental consequences, not least of which is the contamination of drinking water. This seems a strong probability in view of the large amount of pesticides in use, but because of lack of funding, analytical techniques have not been developed which are capable of measuring the concentration in water of most common pesticides.

The EC recommends a Maximum Admissible Concentration (MAC) of 0.1 microgrammes per litre for individual pesticides, with an MAC for combined pesticides of 0.5 µg/l. The government has used the lack of available analytical techniques to advise water authorities to 'ignore' EC limits for pesticides in water (see WATER).

The Anglian Water Authority has found evidence of contamination of both ground and surface water supplies. Principal pesticides detected in surface water were **mecoprop**, **atrazine**, **simazin**, **Dimechoate** and **lindane**, which were found regularly at each of their monitoring sites. As the House of Commons Agriculture Committee observed in May 1987, there have been few systematic studies of pesticides in drinking-water in the UK, and the Department of the Environment's current monitoring proposals do not amount to a coherent national policy.

Overuse and inefficiency

Nigel Dudley has pointed out in *This Poisoned Earth* (1987) the paradox that, while chemicals for application to the land are increasingly complex and sophisticated, the machinery which is used to apply them has not changed much in the whole of the twentieth century. Pesticides are not particularly efficient at hitting their targets:

In a lecture to the Royal Society in 1977, I. J. Graham-Bryce stated that less than one per cent of insecticide applied is actually effective in killing pests. Virtually all the insecticide is wasted. Even with herbicides, where efficiency is far greater, 70 per cent or more is routinely 'lost'.

To achieve the desired end, massive overuse of pesticides has become standard practice. Conventional hydraulic nozzles force the pesticide out under high pressure, in a range of droplet sizes (varying from droplets which are too large, and bounce off the plant, to droplets which are too fine, and are carried away by the wind). The surplus pesticide ends up in water courses, in the soil, in the air, or in other parts of the countryside, sometimes with disastrous effects.

A couple of techniques have been developed to overcome this problem: electrostatic spraying, a yet undeveloped application that can 'fix' the pesticide to the target plant; and Controlled Droplet Application (or CDA) in which the droplet size is calibrated by the farmer. CDA is used extensively in parts of Europe, and when used in the UK has been claimed to reduce the amount of pesticide needed by 80 per cent or more. Introduction of CDA has been resisted in the UK by various interests, among whom could be included the pesticide manufacturers. CDA, it is argued, would substantially reduce the amount of pesticides that are sold.

The overuse of pesticides has been criticized, not just because of its effect on the surrounding environment, but because of the effects on the pests. Many insecticides wipe out not just the target species but all insects that they come into contact with – including the natural predators of the target insect. The target insects that have escaped regroup, breed anew and recolonize the sprayed area – which has now been cleared of predators. The farmer has to respray again, only this time the target population may be even larger.

In the course of time, a mutant species develops which is capable of resisting the insecticide. This takes over from the original species, and the farmer has the same problem as before: only this time a different insecticide needs to be found. Dudley quotes Michael Dover and Brian Croft, of the World Resources Institute (*Getting Tough: public policy and the management of pesticide resistance*, WRI, 1984):

From the early 1900s to 1980, 428 species of arthropods are known to have become resistant to one or more insecticides or acaricides . . . Among plant pathogens of agricultural crops, over 150 resistant species are known. An estimated 50 herbicide-resistant weed species have now been reported.

As Dudley points out, the rate with which resistance develops has increased rapidly over the past 20 years. What is more, some of the more resilient species are becoming resistant to more than one chemical. Some of these multiple resistant species, which include major problem pests like house flies, mosquitoes, cotton boll worms and spider mites, have overcome the toxic effects of nearly all the chemicals to which they have been extensively exposed.

Spray Drift

A frequently occurring problem related to the massive use of pesticides in farms is 'spray drift' – where the pesticide misses its intended target and ends up in someone else's field or garden. This can have calamitous consequences.

The majority of reported crop damage incidents are due to hormone herbicides, used to control broadleaved weeds. Damage symptoms include leaf curling and scorching, deformation of shoots and fruits, malformed leaf systems and even death of plants. Susceptibility varies, according to the chemicals used and the plants affected: susceptible British crops include brassicas (almost half the reported cases), lettuce, tomatoes, beet, tree fruit and flowers.

The consequences of spray drift should not be underestimated. According to the Soil Association, one farmer lost a million brassicas after seeing spray drifting across his crop. It is not uncommon for growers to lose £25,000 worth of produce in one drift incident and total claims for the Evesham area were ten times that amount in 1981.

Private residents who see spray drifting across their property should immediately ensure that children and pets are kept inside the house – and they should be kept away from the sprayed area for at least twenty-four hours, preferably until the farmer has been contacted and the name of the substance ascertained. Nigel Dudley's *This Poisoned Earth* gives a list of 200 hazardous pesticides, and Pete Snell's *Pesticide Residues and Food* lists over 400: these publications could be useful for checking pesticide effects.

The majority of complaints relating to spray drift are connected with aerial spraying, even though aerial spraying is only 2–3 per cent of the total spraying operation. The regulations for spraying from the air were tightened up in 1986: the *Control of Pesticides Regulations* lays down strict requirements as to prior notification of local authorities, local residents, hospitals, schools, etc. Pesticide campaigners point out that these requirements are not as strict, however, as in many other countries, and they want the practice banned altogether.

There is a scheme for commercial growers to claim damages in spray drift incidents, but it can be expensive, time-consuming, and not always successful, involving all the risks and evidential requirements of a civil court case. For private householders, the legal route is almost never worth the expense. Complaints to the farmer concerned, the police, the local authority and the press may be successful in preventing a repetition of the incident.

The official view of spray drift is that it is a relatively rare occurrence (153 aerial spraying incidents reported in 1983) and not an issue of great public concern. This attitude is almost certainly the result of inadequate monitoring and reporting procedures. The Friends of the Earth's *First Incidents Report* lists over 100 pesticide incidents reported to FoE in 1984, some of them very harrowing episodes involving extremely unpleasant substances, with consequences ranging from cattle dying, to severely ill or hospitalized children. Death of pets also occurred.

See also BHOPAL; FOOD IN THE UK; COUNTRYSIDE IN THE UK; SANDOZ; SEVESO

REFERENCES

Carson, Rachel, *Silent Spring*, Penguin Books, 1982 (first published 1962).

Dudley, Nigel, *This Poisoned Earth*, Piatkus, 1987.

Elkington, John, *The Poisoned Womb*, Penguin Books, 1986.

Environment Digest, No. 22, March 1989.

Erlichman, James, *Gluttons for Punishment*, Penguin Books, 1986.

Health and Safety Executive, *Crop Spraying*, 1985.

Hansard, 7 December 1988, 3 May 1989.

House of Commons Agriculture Committee, *The Effects of Pesticides on Human Health*, 12 May 1987.

London Food Commission, *Pesticide Hazard Checklist*, 1986.

Ministry of Agriculture, *Pesticides: Guide to the New Controls*, 1987.

Pesticides Action Network (PAN), *Pan Information on Relevant Pesticides*, 1985.

Rose, Chris, *Pesticides, the First Incidents Report*, FoE, 1985.

Rose, Chris, 'Pesticides, an Industry out of Control', in Goldsmith and Hildyard, *Green Britain or Industrial Wasteland?*, Polity Press, 1986.

Snell, Pete, *Pesticide Residues and Food*, London Food Commission, 1986.

Soil Association, *Pall of Poison, the 'Spray Drift' Problem*, 1984.

'Cloud of poison closes school', MacDonald, Eileen, *Observer* 11 December 1988.

CONTACTS

Farm and Food Society
Food and Agriculture Organisation
Friends of the Earth
Greenpeace International
Oxfam
Pesticides Action Network
Pesticides Trust
Soil Association
Transport & General Workers'
   Union

World Health Organisation

Ciba-Geigy
Health and Safety Executive
Hoechst
ICI
Ministry of Agriculture, Fisheries
   and Food
National Farmers' Union

Population

The population of the world has increased rapidly in the twentieth century, and continues to do so.

- The world's population first reached 1,000 million in 1830;
- 2,000 million around 1930;
- 3,000 million in 1960;
- 4,000 million in 1974;
- 5,000 million in 1987.

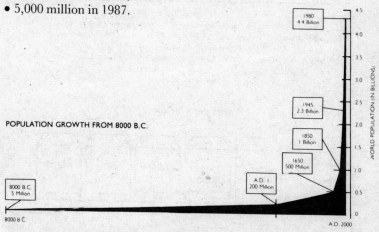

POPULATION GROWTH FROM 8000 B.C.

Source: *World Conservation Strategy in Action*, 1982

It is very difficult to estimate the future growth of the human race, as this is dependent on a number of factors including the supply of food and water, use of birth control, education, fertility, mortality, war and natural disasters. UN estimates for the year 2000 indicate a possible world population of 6,000 million.

After this, estimates vary, depending on world circumstances. A total of 8 billion people should be achieved between the year 2015 and 2045 – an increase of 50 per cent within the lifetime of the present generation.

Population Projections

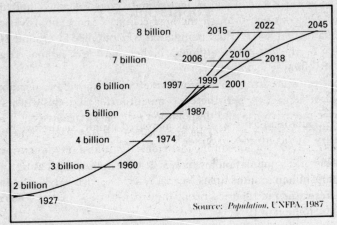

Source: *Population*, UNFPA, 1987

The long-range projections of the United Nations indicate that the world's population will stabilize at the beginning of the twenty-second century. Its ultimate size will range from 7.5 billion to 14.2 billion. According to the medium variant projection, stability will be achieved at 10.2 billion, slightly more than double the current world's population, about a hundred years from now.

Population Division, DIESA United Nations

World population, 1984

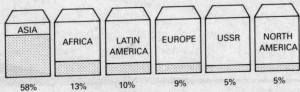

Source: *UN Demographic Yearbook*

Global population, projected to 2000

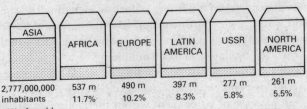

Source: UNFPA, 1987

The world is becoming an increasingly crowded place, and this trend will continue through the next century. The United Nations calculates that the world's population will stabilize at around 10.5 billion by the year 2110, although higher and lower estimates vary from 8 billion to 15 billion.

The resulting stress on environmental resources will be enormous. People need to eat: where there is competition for land, this will result in over-intensive use and despoliation (see DESERTIFICATION). They need heat, which can only be supplied by cutting down trees (see DEFORESTATION) or consuming fossil fuels (see ACID RAIN; GREENHOUSE EFFECT). They need land, which will be achieved by taking over previously uninhabited areas (see WETLANDS). Their need for money will result in rare species being hunted into oblivion (see SPECIES EXTINCTION).

There will be an enormous impact in terms of human misery. Population Concern points out that, at the moment, 450 million people are thought to be acutely malnourished, with 10 million of these on the verge of starvation. The number of acutely malnourished people is expected to rise, not fall, by the end of the twentieth century.

The disproportionate number of young people being born in Asia

The world's largest cities, 1950 and 2000

1950		2000	
City	Population (millions)	City	Population (millions)
1 New York	12.3	1 Mexico City	31.0
2 London	10.4	2 Sao Paulo	25.8
3 Rhein-Ruhr	6.9	3 Tokyo	24.2
4 Tokyo	6.7	4 New York	22.8
5 Shanghai	5.8	5 Shanghai	22.7
6 Paris	5.5	6 Beijing	19.9
7 Buenos Aires	5.3	7 Rio de Janeiro	19.0

Source: *Global Snapshots*

and Africa means that there will be land shortages; 42 per cent of Africa's population will be suffering shortage of land by the year 2000, with similar problems being experienced by 82 per cent in the Far

East and 87 per cent in the Near East. Between 1950 and 1985, the developed world's population increased from 0.8 billion to 1.2 billion; the populations of the Third World leapt from 1.7 billion to 3.7 billion. The economic problems of the less-developed countries will be exacerbated by the demands of ever-increasing numbers for water, food, accommodation and a minimal standard of living.

The lack of land, and pressures to find some sort of income, will continue to force people off the land into the cities. This migration will drastically change urban environments, with a new race of 'super-cities' whose population will be larger than that of some medium-sized countries.

It is impossible to predict how all these changes will be accommodated, and what the effects on the global environment, or even on international relations, will be.

Suggested remedies

'Population growth' has been an area of political concern for some years, with a number of suggested remedies being put forward. A popular Western argument has been that the world cannot afford to feed all these new people, and that the less-developed countries should respond to the problem by introducing rigorous birth control schemes. Developed countries, the argument goes, are achieving population stability, and the Third World should do likewise.

This is a simplistic approach, as it ignores the reasons for large families in some Third World countries. People living in a poor economy with few social services, no pension and the prospect of a bleak old age will deliberately have a large family in order to help with house and agricultural work, and to support the parents when they are no longer able to look after themselves. It costs the family little to feed an extra mouth which may make the difference, for the parents, between survival or death in later years. The situation is complicated by the high rate of infant mortality (12.15 per 1,000 in the industrialized world, 100 per 1,000 in the less-developed countries). People wanting large families overproduce to insure against one or more children dying.

The attitude of expecting the Third World to accept responsibility for the population boom has also been criticized. According to the UN, the average density of world population is 34 people per square kilometre of land. China, with a population density of 106 people per sq. km, and Middle South Asia with 145, would both under these criteria qualify as overcrowded. Western Europe, however, has a density of 153 people per sq. km, and Japan has 318, but no one is advocating a large-scale reduction of population in these areas.

Similarly, Western arguments about there not being enough food for everyone have been questioned. To meet human nutritional requirements, the world needs to produce an average of 2,300 calories per person per day, roughly equal to 500 lb of grain per person per year. On average, the amount of grain sold annually in the world is about 1,300 million tonnes – enough to provide the necessary 500 lb for almost 6 billion people. A quarter of this, however, is fed to livestock to produce meat for the developed world. More grain is consumed by the world's livestock than by the entire population of China and India together.

There is enough energy to supply all the world's people; enough wood for everybody's fuel needs, provided that the developed countries modify their consumption (see DEFORESTATION); and the money needed to supply contraceptives to all the people who want them could be found by diverting ten hours' worth of global expenditure on armaments (see MILITARY SPENDING, WORLDWIDE). Poverty-stimulated population growth will stop when the citizens of the developing world feel secure in their future prospects: this will happen when the developed world makes this possible.

The need for birth control

The questionable logic of the West towards the solution of over-population, however, should not disguise the human need in less-developed countries for smaller families. Approximately half the Third World's women, according to Population Concern, want no more children: yet only half of these have access to efficient family planning methods, and not all use their opportunities for birth control. It is estimated that the prevention of unwanted births could bring birth rates down by between 25 and 40 per cent.

Population growth is sometimes discussed in terms of the rate of growth, as this can be used to forecast future figures (populations growing at 2 per cent will double in 35 years, at 3 per cent in 23 years). In 1970, the world's population grew by 2.06 per cent, but the rate of growth has slowed since then. The current rate is about 1.67 per cent, or an extra 80 million people a year.

Lester Brown points out in *Stopping Population Growth* that some developing countries, such as Bangladesh, face population increases of 3 per cent per year, which yields a 20-fold increase per century. This rate of growth is viewed with alarm in the countries involved, who are only too aware that their natural resources will not be able to provide for all citizens. For that reason, birth control measures are becoming increasingly promoted.

This only becomes possible, however, given an improved standard of living, to alleviate the perceived necessity of having large families; better education for women, so that they understand the mechanisms of contraception, and, equally importantly, feel empowered to exert control over their own reproduction; education for men, to remove the traditional attitudes that are condemning women to bearing many more children than they wish to have; and full availability of family planning information and services. These provisions entail social changes which are not occurring in many Third World countries.

See also ACID RAIN; DEFORESTATION; DESERTIFICATION; GREENHOUSE EFFECT; MILITARY SPENDING, WORLDWIDE; NORTH—SOUTH RELATIONSHIP; SPECIES EXTINCTION

REFERENCES

Brown, Lester, *Stopping Population Growth*, State of the World / Worldwatch Institute, 1986.

George, Susan, *How the Other Half Dies*, Penguin Books, 1977.

Population Concern, *Global Snapshots*, undated.

UN Demographic Yearbook, 1982.

Worldwatch Institute, *State of the World, 1986*, 1986.

World Resources Institute, IIED, *World Resources 1986*, Basic Books, 1986.

Hogg, Sarah, 'Counting the Cost of the Baby Boom', *The Times*, 11 July 1984.

IUCN, UNEP, WWF, 'World Conservation Strategy in Action', May 1982.

Lean, Geoffrey, 'My Five Billionth Baby', *Observer*, 5 July 1987.

UN Fund for Population Activities (UNFPA), *Population* (newsletter), February 1987.

CONTACTS

International Union for the Conservation of Nature (IUCN)
Oxfam
Population Concern
Save the Children
Survival International
Third World First (TWI)
United Nations Environment Programme
War on Want
World Wide Fund for Nature (WWF)

Radiation

'Radiation' means:

1. energy or particles emitted by radioactive materials as they decay into more stable elements;

2. the energy waves found in the electromagnetic spectrum (a system for classifying energy sent out – 'radiated' – from various sources): these include radio waves, microwaves, visible light, X-rays and gamma rays;

3. the process of emitting (1) or (2).

'Radiation' is a confusing word to use because it has different meanings. In its most general sense, it refers to the energy waves found in the electromagnetic spectrum:

Electromagnetic spectrum

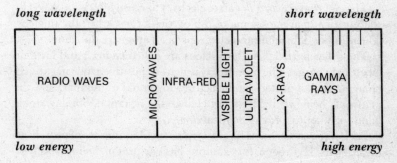

Visible light waves are the most familiar part of this range, but they are a very small part of the spectrum. Other waves vary from radio waves (long wavelength, low energy) to high-energy gamma rays and X-rays. Infra-red and ultraviolet light are also located in the spectrum – so sunlight is a source of radiation – as are microwaves.

Radioactivity

A more frequent use of the word 'radiation' nowadays refers to the energy emitted by radioactive materials.

The atom

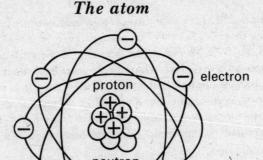

An atom can be visualized as having a central *nucleus*, consisting of a number of particles clinging tightly to one another, surrounded by *electrons* which circle round it rather like planets round a sun.

The electrons carry a negative electric charge, which is balanced by the positive charge of some of the particles (*protons*) in the nucleus. The number of protons and electrons in an atom are the same.

The other particles in the nucleus are called *neutrons*, and have no electrical charge. The atom itself is neither positively nor negatively charged, as the protons and electrons are equal in number, and the neutrons, being neutral, do not change the equation. Similar atoms bond together to form a chemical *element*.

Each different element has its own particular number of protons in the nucleus. Hydrogen, for example, has one proton, helium has two, lithium has three. If an atom loses or gains a proton, then the new formation becomes an atom belonging to another element.

On the other hand, an element can occur in a variety of forms, with varying numbers of neutrons. These different forms are called *isotopes*: uranium-238 has 92 protons and 146 neutrons (92 + 146 = 238), whereas uranium-235 has 92 protons and 143 neutrons (92 + 143 = 235). The atoms of isotopes are called *nuclides*.

A number of nuclides are *unstable*: because of their atomic formation they are trying to change to something else and so become stable. This is done by throwing off a chunk of the atom; if a proton is lost, then the element changes to another element.

As an example:

- Uranium-238 throws off two protons and two neutrons, thus becoming thorium-234 (new atomic structure: 90 + 144 = 234).
- Thorium-234 is also unstable. A proton in the nucleus turns into a neutron, so a negatively-charged electron is released and escapes. With one proton fewer, the thorium-234 turns into protactinium-234 (new atomic structure: 89 + 145 = 234).
- The process continues until lead-206 is formed. Lead-206 is a stable element, and the process of metamorphosis stops.

This process of transforming is called *radioactive decay*, and the unstable nuclides are *radionuclides*. The time taken to change from one radionuclide to another varies between a fraction of a second and millions of years. After a certain period of time, half of the substance will have changed. This is called the *half-life* of the element. Uranium-238 has a half-life of 4.47 billion years, Bismuth-214 a half-life of 19.7 minutes (i.e., in 19.7 minutes, half of it will have changed, in another 19.7 minutes, half of the remainder will have changed, etc).

As each change occurs, energy – *radiation* – is emitted from the atom. The type of radiation depends on the type of transformation that takes place. There are three kinds of radiation in radioactive decay:

1. 'alpha' radiation, which is the emission of a chunk of the nucleus containing two protons and two neutrons;
2. 'beta' radiation, which is the emission of an electron;
3. 'gamma' rays, which are pure energy emitted from very excited nuclides.

Radiation from radioactive decay can be extremely dangerous to human health. Alpha and beta radiation, and high-energy electromagnetic radiation such as gamma rays or X-rays, produce electrically-charged particles (*ions*) in material that they strike. This process (*ionizing radiation*) frequently results in changes to living

Radioactive decay

Type of radiation	Nuclide	Half-life
	Uranium-238	4.47 billion years
α	↓	
	Thorium-234	24.1 days
β	↓	
	Protactinium-234	1.17 minutes
β	↓	
	Uranium-234	245,000 years
α	↓	
	Thorium-230	8,000 years
α	↓	
	Radium-226	1,600 years
α	↓	
	Radon-222	3.823 days
α	↓	
	Polonium-218	3.05 minutes
α	↓	
	Lead-214	26.8 minutes
β	↓	
	Bismuth-214	19.7 minutes
β	↓	
	Polonium-214	0.000164 seconds
α	↓	
	Lead-210	22.3 years
β	↓	
	Bismuth-210	5.01 days
β	↓	
	Polonium-210	138.4 days
α	↓	
	Lead-206	stable

Source: *Radiation*, UNEP, 1985

tissue, which can injure it. Non-ionizing radiation, such as radio or ultra-violet waves, does not normally have this effect.

Penetrating capacity

The forms of ionizing radiation have different abilities to travel. Alpha particles, with their bulky chunk of two protons and two neutrons, can be blocked by a sheet of paper and will not penetrate the skin. Alpha-emitting nuclides pose a serious health risk if they get into the body through an open wound, or are breathed in or eaten. Once inside the body they continue to be radioactive and are particularly damaging.

Penetrating capacity of radiation

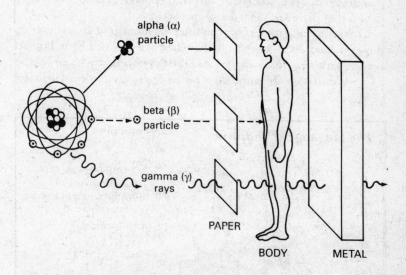

Beta particles are more penetrating, but can be stopped by relatively thin layers of water, glass or metal. Beta emitters can also be hazardous if taken into the body.

Gamma rays travel at the speed of light and will go through almost anything before being absorbed. The rays can be screened by a thick layer of lead or concrete. X-rays have similar penetrating abilities.

A fourth type of ionizing radiation is associated with nuclear reactors (see NUCLEAR ENERGY). Neutron radiation, as it is called, is also very penetrating but can be screened by thick layers of concrete or water.

Measuring radiation

The systems for measuring radiation and radiation damage are complex. This complexity is not simplified by the fact that there are two measurement systems in existence – the traditional method, and the newer SI (Système Internationale) method. If the two systems are used together, it is rather like talking in feet and inches and metres and centimetres. (Usage seems to depend on whim. This dictionary uses the SI system, and where the old system is quoted, gives equivalents.)

When a radioactive substance decays, it undergoes a number of decays each second. In the SI system, one *becquerel* refers to one disintegration per second of any radionuclide; 3,000 becquerels means that there are 3,000 decays per second.

This is merely a system for counting the number of atomic events, however, and does not indicate how harmful this will be to human beings. To assess this, a system has been developed which looks at the effects of radiation. The amount of radiation energy absorbed in living

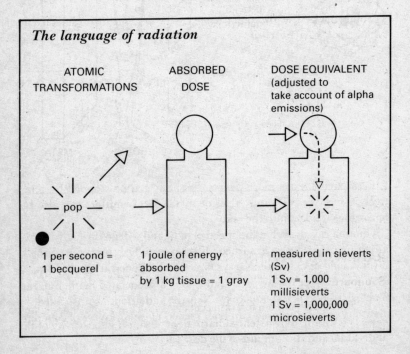

The language of radiation

ATOMIC
TRANSFORMATIONS

— pop —

1 per second =
1 becquerel

ABSORBED
DOSE

1 joule of energy
absorbed
by 1 kg tissue = 1 gray

DOSE EQUIVALENT
(adjusted to
take account of alpha
emissions)

measured in sieverts
(Sv)
1 Sv = 1,000
millisieverts
1 Sv = 1,000,000
microsieverts

matter is called the *dose*. This can be received from one radionuclide or several, inside or outside the body. The dose is measured in units called *grays*. One gray equals one joule of energy absorbed by one kilogram of tissue.

Even now, however, another adjustment is necessary. A dose of alpha radiation is about 20 times more damaging than the same amount of beta or gamma radiation. The dose needs to be adjusted to take this into account, and the final calculation is referred to as the *dose equivalent*, which is measured in *sieverts*.

Other items of jargon which may be useful to understand are:

- the *effective dose equivalent*, also measured in sieverts, which calculates the effect of a given radiation dose to different parts of the body (the breast, say, being more vulnerable than the thyroid, the dose is multiplied by a weighting factor to take this vulnerability into account);
- the *collective dose equivalent* describes the dose equivalents received by a number of people, rather than just one person.

Some books use the older systems for measuring radioactivity, which are shown overleaf:

Equivalents, old and new systems

1 Curie = 37,000,000,000 becquerels	100 rad = 1 gray	100 rem = 1 sievert
		1 rem = 10 millisieverts
		1 millirem = .01 millisieverts
		(10 microsieverts)

RADIATION EFFECTS

Summary:

1. There is no known tolerance level for ionizing radiation, i.e. any dose is harmful. The extent of harm depends on the sensitivity of the individual and the amount of the dose received.

The early language

ATOMIC
TRANSFORMATIONS

ABSORBED
DOSE

DOSE EQUIVALENT
(adjusted to
take account of alpha
emissions)

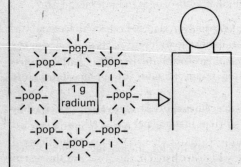

the base unit is the number of nuclear transformations occurring per second in one gram of radium (this is called **1 Curie**)

1 Curie = 1,000 microCuries
= 1,000,000 picoCuries

1 rad = the absorbed dose of radiation equal to that which releases 100 ergs per gram of matter

base unit = **1 rem**. Defined as the amount of radiation that would cause the same amount of biological damage as a specific amount (**1 roentgen**) of X-rays or gamma rays.
For external radiation, rads and rems can be used interchangeably, but to indicate the greater damage done by alpha emissions inside the body, rads are multiplied by 20 to give the rem dose.

2. Most radiation received by the population at large comes from natural background sources.

3. Most artificial radiation received by the population at large comes from X-rays.

4. An additional, though by comparison small, radiation loading is imposed on the public by the use of nuclear weapons and nuclear power.

5. Exposure to radiation should be treated as a risk, to be quantified against the benefits to be gained by such exposure. Any unnecessary exposure to radiation should be avoided.

No known tolerance level for radiation

The remark 'there is no known tolerance level for radiation' was made by the radiologist R. M. Sievert at a conference in 1950, and has since passed into radiation lore. A tolerance (or threshold) level is a level below which no damage occurs.

The effects of a high dose of radiation to the whole body are a matter of scientific agreement: death. The United Nations Scientific Committee on the Effects of Atomic Radiation has determined the effects of different whole-body doses, which are listed in the box. (For the rest of this section, equivalents in sieverts are given, assuming a one-to-one relationship between sieverts and grays.)

- Doses of 100 grays   *(100 sieverts)*:
  death through central nervous system damage in hours or days.
- 10 to 50 grays   *(10 to 50 sieverts)*:
  death through gastrointestinal damage in about one to two weeks.
- 3 to 5 grays   *(3 to 5 sieverts)*:
  death for half of the people exposed in one to two months (bone marrow damage).

Lower doses have less immediately apparent effects, though long-term damage does occur. Dr Rosalie Bertell (in *No Immediate Danger*) lists these probable effects (again for whole-body dose):

- 150 to 250 rems *(1.5 to 2.5 sieverts):*
nausea, vomiting, probable skin burns, foetal or embryonic death if pregnant; long term, people in ill-health may not survive, people in good health will apparently recover, though with possible permanent health damage.
- 50 to 150 rems *(0.5 to 1.5 sieverts):*
less severe radiation sickness and burns, spontaneous abortion or stillbirth if pregnant; long term, possible benign or malignant tumours, premature ageing, shortened lifespan, genetic damage to offspring.
- 10 to 50 rems *(0.1 to 0.5 sieverts):*
most people experience little immediate reaction; sensitive people may have radiation sickness; long term, possible premature ageing, genetic effects and some risk of tumours.
- under 10 rems *(under 0.1 sieverts):*
no immediate effects; long term, premature ageing, some offspring mutation, risk of tumours.

To put these figures into context:

- When the Three Mile Island disaster occurred, instruments inside the containment building were reporting a high radiation level which would have resulted in a 10-sievert dose for two minutes' exposure: certain death. So no one dared go inside the damaged building.
- According to the UK Atomic Energy Authority, no early deaths occur from a 1 sievert exposure: presumably, 'early' here means 'short-term' or 'immediate', as one's lifespan may eventually be shortened because of cancer or other radiation-induced illness.
- Rosalie Bertell notes that some sensitive individuals experience radiation sickness at 0.5 sieverts, but not at 0.1 sieverts.
- A modern chest X-ray will result in a whole-body exposure of 0.0001 sieverts (though before 1970 some mass chest X-ray machines gave a dose of 0.03 sieverts). A year's dose from natural background radiation can be around 0.001 sieverts (= 1 milli-sievert).

10 sievert	(= 10,000 millisieverts)	death
below 1 sievert	(= 1,000 millisieverts)	no 'early' death
below 0.1 sievert	(= 100 millisieverts)	no radiation sickness in sensitive individuals
0.03 sieverts	(= 30 millisieverts)	one X-ray, certain machines before 1970
0.001 sievert	(= 1 millisievert)	one year's dose from background radiation
0.0001 sievert	(= 0.1 millisievert)	one modern X-ray

Different tolerances of radiation

All the figures above, excepting the figure for background radiation, refer to whole-body doses over a short period of time. If the dose is spread over a longer period, the body is better able to cope. Because of the natural background radiation that we are all exposed to in our everyday lives, our bodies have developed repair mechanisms for radiation damage.

According to the UK Atomic Energy Authority, a single dose of 4 sieverts would result in a one in two chance of death: the same dose delivered gradually over a year would probably be tolerated because of the body's natural repair processes, although with possible long-term consequences.

There is a variation in radiation sensitivity between the different organs of the body. Adult tissues are relatively robust: the kidneys, bladder and cartilage can take relatively high levels of radiation, though red bone marrow, eyes, testes and ovaries are more sensitive.

Sensitivity differs between individuals. Some adults, and all children, are particularly at risk. Quite small doses of radiation to a child's cartilage can slow or halt the growth of bones and lead to deformity. The younger the child, the more severe the stunting. Irradiation of children's brains during radiotherapy can cause changes of character, loss of memory and, in very young children, dementia and idiocy.

Unborn children are particularly prone to brain damage, if their mothers are irradiated between the eighth and fifteenth week of pregnancy. This danger extends to X-rays, which can cause severe mental retardation to an unborn child.

Large doses of radiation are given only to patients who are already so ill that the risk of the treatment is justified.

Dangers of radiation

Scientific consensus now exists concerning the effects of large doses of radiation, though this has not always been so. X-rays and radioactivity were discovered in the 1890s: radium was regarded as having very strong medicinal qualities, and was sold for a number of miracle cures. Its harmful qualities were first noticed by Henri Becquerel, when he put a vial of radium in his pocket and damaged his skin. Nevertheless, the dangerous qualities of radiation were not fully understood, and at least 336 early radiation workers died as a result of the doses they received – including Marie Curie, the discoverer of radium.

As more has been found out about radiation, so safety standards have become stricter. Permissible *occupational* exposure to ionizing radiation in the USA has been tightened up over the years (equivalents are now in millisieverts. 1,000 millisieverts = 1 sievert):

- 52 roentgen (470 to 520 millisieverts) per year in 1925;
- 36 roentgen (320 to 360 millisieverts) per year in 1934;
- 15 rem (150 millisieverts) per year in 1949;
- 5–12 rem (50–120 millisieverts) per year in 1959.

The allowable dose for *public* exposure is much lower than 50 millisieverts (see below).

If there is agreement about high levels of radiation, there has frequently been controversy about low-level exposure. In 1958, Alice Stewart, a co-founder of the Oxford Survey of Childhood Cancers, pointed out that children exposed to X-rays while in their mother's womb ran an increased risk of developing childhood cancers. This finding was initially derided by the nuclear medical establishment: it is now an agreed medical fact.

Stewart is currently claiming that low levels of radiation, including background radiation, are responsible for most childhood cancers. This is hotly disputed by the nuclear industry.

Potential radiation risks

Nuclear power stations, the reprocessing of nuclear fuel and the disposal of nuclear waste, all result in the emissions of various levels of radioactivity.

- The radioactivity emitted by an efficiently-run nuclear power station is small compared to natural background radiation, although people in the immediate vicinity will receive a larger radiation dose from the plant than people living further away.

- The total radioactive load to the planet is much larger when the effects of digging up radioactive raw material, and disposing of nuclear waste, are taken into account (see NUCLEAR ENERGY).
- There is a risk of a large release of radioactivity from a nuclear accident, act of sabotage or bombing during a conventional war (see NUCLEAR ENERGY).
- Releases of radiation from nuclear accidents are often belittled by expressing them as a percentage of natural background radiation. There is no scientific basis for this. Every dose of radiation is harmful, so additional doses cannot be justified by comparing them to existing levels.
- Atmospheric radiation from testing nuclear weapons is a small percentage of overall radiation levels. It has had severe localized effects, however, with global implications which will persist for hundreds of thousands of years (see NUCLEAR WEAPONS).

Risks and benefits of radiation exposure

Exposure to radiation should be treated as a risk, to be quantified against the benefits to be gained by such exposure. Any unnecessary exposure to radiation should be avoided.

This statement is accepted by the international bodies who set radiation protection limits. There are areas of common ground between the two sides of the nuclear debate.

- Radiotherapy, in which large doses of radiation are given to treat serious illnesses such as cancer, is accepted as a reasonable exposure to radiation. The risk is large, but in many cases the risk of not receiving the treatment is larger.
- The use of X-rays for medical diagnosis is also accepted as valid, provided that they are used for specific reasons and not as, say, a screening system for new employees in a firm.
- Natural background radiation is a variable about which little can be done, although a debate is opening as to how 'natural' should be defined.

There are areas which are still being discussed.

- The use of radiation for occupational purposes, e.g. for checking oil pipelines, has not created much controversy. The assumption appears to be that the radiation workers are aware of the risks and are paid accordingly.
- The proposed use of radiation for treating food has been approved by the World Health Authority, but is encountering opposition from consumer groups and the public. It is currently not approved in the UK.

And there are areas – nuclear weapons and nuclear power – in which there is no agreement whatsoever.

- The nuclear lobby argues that nuclear power is safe, necessary and cheap, and that therefore the risks of using nuclear energy are minimal compared to the advantages.
- The anti-nuclear lobby argues that nuclear power is dangerous, unnecessary and expensive, motivated by the need to make nuclear weapons, and the risks of using nuclear energy enormously outweigh the advantages purportedly gained from it.

Arguments concerning safety, necessity and cost are similar for nuclear weapons.

SAFETY STANDARDS

Safety standards for exposure to radiation are set by the International Commission on Radiological Protection (ICRP). In 1952, the ICRP issued its recommended exposure limits to radiation, which was the same standard agreed by nuclear physicists after the Second World War: 5 rem (50 millisieverts) to the whole body.

The revised limits in 1959 recommended that workers' 5 rem (50 millisieverts) whole-body exposure should be calculated by adding external and internal exposure together (internal exposure occurs by swallowing or breathing in radioactive materials). The limits have stayed the same, except for an upward revision in 1977 of exposure to certain parts of the body, to the present day.

Exposure limits for radiation workers are based on the assumption that they know the risks of what they are doing, and are healthy, fit, and capable of withstanding a relatively high exposure. The ICRP recommended that the public, for whom greater protection is necessary, should receive no more than one-tenth of the occupational exposure, i.e. a whole-body dose of 0.5 rem (5 millisieverts) over a year.

The ICRP accept that there is no threshold limit for damage from radiation exposure, and that all doses can cause some damage to the body. The 5 millisieverts exposure limit for the general public was considered the absolute maximum, while a limit of 1 millisievert was considered a better value to adopt. West Germany decided on a 0.35 millisievert limit, the USA took 0.25 to be its limit – but the UK adopted a limit of 5.0 millisieverts.

In 1987, the UK National Radiological Protection Board issued a recommendation that the public exposure over the long term should be not more than 1 millisievert per year, although in any one year it could go up to 5 millisieverts, provided that the long-term average was maintained. This safety limit has no legislative backing, however: the official limit remains at 50 millisieverts for workers in the nuclear industry, and 5 for the general public.

Legal dose limits currently in force in the UK
(Currently under examination following advice from NRPB, 1987)

Dose limit for adult employees	50 msv	in any calendar year
Investigation level for adult employees	15 msv	in any calendar year
Dose limit for members of the public	5 msv	in any calendar year
Annual average dose limit for members of the public exposed over long periods, enforced by the Authorizing Departments	1 msv	

Source: UK Health and Safety Executive, 1988

Controversy over safety limits

The ICRP, and its safety limits, are being reappraised by other bodies. Some disturbing points have been raised:

1. The ICRP is a self-elected, self-regulating body formed in 1950 out of the ashes of an organization called the International X-ray and Radiation Protection Commission. Although the ICRP is affiliated to

the World Health Organization as a non-governmental organization, it is an entirely autonomous body, responsible neither to the United Nations nor the WHO, or indeed to anybody else.

Medical participation in ICRP is restricted to medical radiologists. Paediatricians, epidemiologists, public health experts and similar specialists are excluded from the membership, which is dominated by representatives from the military, civil nuclear power and medical radiology. The environment movement has pointed out, and it seems a reasonable criticism, that the committee is mainly composed of people who have an interest in the continued use of nuclear technology. There are no nuclear sceptics, and few truly independent specialists, sitting on the body which determines acceptable risks of exposure to radiation.

2. The estimates of radiation damage were made by calculating the radiation exposure of the people in Hiroshima and Nagasaki, working out the rates of cancer that occurred, and extrapolating the figures downwards to guess the effects of lower radiation exposure.

This approach is now criticized because:

- The ICRP did not have a correct figure of what the radiation exposure was over Hiroshima. The estimates which they used have subsequently been shown to be too high, and are currently being revised downwards by the Japanese. The damage occurred at a lower level of radiation exposure than the ICRP assumed for their calculations.
- The survivors studied for cancer were assembled in 1950, when 300,000 bomb victims had already died. The exposure calculations are based on a tougher, 'survivor' population who had pulled through the bombs themselves and five years of trauma afterwards. Those people who were the more radiation-sensitive part of the population had presumably already perished.
- The risk assessments that the ICRP made were based on the number of cancer deaths that would occur from exposure to a given level of radiation – not total cancer cases, but cancer *deaths*. Many cases of radiation-induced cancer do not always kill, especially skin, breast and thyroid cancer. The risk of incurring a non-fatal cancer is three times the risk of a fatal cancer; if prevention of non-fatal cancers was built into the regulations, then the permissible exposure rate would have to be lower.

Other interpretations of international safety standards

Other bodies have looked at the subject of permissible exposure limits, and have reached different conclusions to the ICRP. Reports published by the US National Academy of Science ('Biological Effects of Radiation III') conclude that the risk of cancer unit per dose had been underestimated by ICRP by a factor of five to seven. The committee chairman, Edward Radford, subsequently suggested that the overall cancer risks were underestimated by ICRP by a factor of ten.

The United Nations Scientific Committee on the Effects of Radiation (UNSCEAR) issued a spread of risk figures, the upper range of which were four times as large as the ICRP's. Epidemiological studies of workers at the Hanford nuclear reprocessing plant, USA, and of workers in the UK Atomic Energy Authority, suggest levels of risk between five and ten times as great as those laid down by the ICRP.

If the amount of public protection that ICRP wants with its regulations is to be achieved, it looks likely that the exposure limits will have to be revised downwards to about 10 per cent of their present level. This was the argument put forward by one of the UK's biggest unions, the General Municipal and Boilermakers (GMBATU), in a statement made in November 1985:

The International Commission on Radiological Protection estimates that between 2 and 3 workers in 100 will die from radiation-induced cancer if they are exposed to the maximum radiation dose permitted over their working lifetime. In addition, it is estimated that there could be at least as many non-fatal cancers, and a significant number of cases of serious genetic damage.

This is an unacceptably high risk. Evidence that has accumulated since these dose limits were first determined (1957) has led several eminent review bodies and experts to conclude that the risk may be much higher, i.e. from 4–20 cancer deaths per worker exposed.

We therefore call upon the Government to reduce the occupational radiation dose limits by 10 times . . .

The public is also at risk from legally permissible doses of man-made radiation and between 2 and 20 people in every 1,000 exposed to the public dose limit could die of radiation-induced cancer. Therefore the public dose limit should also be reduced.

The GMBATU is a union with members in the nuclear industry, so it has jobs to protect. It realized the implications of recommending an occupational dose limit of 5 millisieverts a year: parts of the reprocessing industry, certain nuclear power stations (particularly the PWR) and some industrial radiography would have difficulty in meeting the new limits. If the gap between industrial and public exposure were to be maintained, public exposure limits would have to drop to 0.5 millisieverts a year – still more lax than current standards enforced in the USA and West Germany, but a significant improvement on current UK practice.

LOW-LEVEL RADIATION

The effects of radiation are sometimes referred to as stochastic (i.e., conjectural) and non-stochastic. Non-stochastic effects, such as radiation sickness and cataract blindness, can be easily observed, and are associated with high doses of radiation. Exposure to lower radiation levels does not normally produce immediate effects, but can have long-term stochastic effects, such as cancer and genetic damage.

Effects of low-level radiation

Fears regarding low-level radiation are founded on the reaction it has on a living cell. Cells can be killed or altered by exposure to radiation. The alteration can be permanent or temporary, leaving the cell unable to reproduce itself, make it reproduce mutant cells, or make it produce a proliferation of cells which form a tumour. As Rosalie Bertell points out in *No Immediate Danger*, the effect of radiation on a cell has been described as similar to the effect caused by 'a madman loose in a library'.

The damage done within cells by alpha, beta, gamma, X-ray, or neutron radiation (see page 379) can occur directly or indirectly. As the radiation speeds through the cells, it gives energy to the electrons in the atoms, enabling some to break free. Living organisms are made up of long strands of atoms: these strands can be torn apart by the ionization process, destroying the templates used by the body to make DNA and RNA (the information-carrying molecules in the cell). This breakdown of DNA and RNA, argues Dr Bertell, gradually makes a person less able to tolerate environmental changes, and less able to recover from diseases or illness.

Dr Bertell illustrates her argument by considering the effect of a 1 rad X-ray (10 millisieverts) on a colony of 1,000 living cells. There would be two or three cell deaths, two or three mutations or irreparable damage in cell DNA, and about 100,000 ionizations in the whole colony of cells – ranging from 11 to 460 ionizations per cell. While cells can repair some damage, no one claims that there is perfect repair even after only one such X-ray.

The effect of a series of X-rays on a young child could be temporary depression of the white blood cells; as a result, a fortnight after the radiation exposure the child could fall prey to influenza or some other infectious disease.

Ordinarily, the connection between the X-rays and the infectious disease would not be made – and, of course, it is impossible to prove that the one is the result of the other. This possible but unprovable link between cause and effect is at the centre of the 'leukaemia clusters' argument.

Leukaemia clusters

If a population is irradiated – such as at Hiroshima and Nagasaki, when nuclear bombs were exploded – leukaemia is the first cancer to emerge. It seems on average to kill about ten years after the damage was done, at an earlier stage than other cancers.

When Yorkshire TV was researching its 1983 programme 'Windscale: the Nuclear Laundry', the researchers found a childhood leukaemia rate ten times the national average at Seascale, the village nearest to the nuclear complex at Sellafield.

An inquiry under Sir Douglas Black gave a 'qualified reassurance' to residents in the area, although it subsequently transpired that crucial evidence, which may well have lessened this reassurance, was not made available to the Black inquiry.

New Socialist subsequently published an article pulling together various research studies into leukaemia clusters. They identified abnormally high leukaemia and cancer rates around Sellafield, Dounreay, and the Hunterston, Chapelcross, Sizewell A, Berkeley and Winfrith nuclear power plants. To this they have added unusually high leukaemia rates round Aldermaston and the Burghfield bomb factory, the US nuclear submarine base at Holy Loch, and Rosyth nuclear submarine dockyards. The implication made was that there was a link between low-level radiation coming from the nuclear complexes, and the leukaemia clusters.

This evidence is challenged by the nuclear industry. In the words of John Dunster, head of the National Radiological Protection Board: 'We retain an open mind on the cause of leukaemia clusters, not all of which are near nuclear installations.'

The existence of leukaemia clusters away from nuclear installations does not defeat, however, the argument that low-level radiation causes leukaemia. In some instances, the mysterious leukaemia cluster can be linked to hitherto undetected radiation hotspots in waste disposal dumps – as appears to have been the case at Capper Pass, Humberside, and Bishops Cleeve, Gloucestershire ('Dispatches', Channel 4 TV, March 1988).

The alleged link between leukaemia and nuclear installations is growing stronger. The UK Committee on Medical Aspects of Radiation in the Atmosphere (COMARE), set up as recommended by the Black Inquiry in 1985, confirmed in 1988 a statistically significant excess of leukaemia near the Dounreay nuclear complex. The authors of the official report were unable to pin down the cause, but say that the burden of proof has now shifted. Dr Martin Brobow, the principal author, said 'the leukaemia cases must be assumed to be connected with the nuclear plants (Dounreay and Sellafield) until proven otherwise'.

Another author, Dr Thomas Wheldon, commented: 'The implication is that there is an undiscovered biological mechanism by which radiation can cause leukaemia . . . (This) has profound implications for the nuclear industry . . . If you don't understand at least one of the pathways by which radiation can cause leukaemia, there is no way you can make your plant safe because you don't know what you are trying to prevent.'

Risks of genetic mutation

Rosalie Bertell describes other dangers. She believes that low-level radiation causes not only visible damage in the form of leukaemias and other cancers, but also genetic mutation. The amount of background radiation has increased, she says, because of activities related to nuclear power and nuclear weapons. As the general exposure to radiation has increased, each new generation is born weakened by radioactivity, prone to enzyme disorders, allergies and asthma directly caused by cell mutation. The implications of this, if it continues generation by generation, could be a weakening of the gene pool.

Some queries have been raised about low-level radiation from Visual Display Units on computers and word processors. The UK National Union of Journalists, in *Journalists and the New Technology*, points out that the case for or against the safety of VDUs has yet to be proven: it advises that pregnant women, or those who believe themselves pregnant, should not work at VDU screens. *Freelances and Computers* quotes American research (1988) showing a considerable increase in miscarriages among women using VDU screens for more than 20 hours a week. This may or may not be due to EMR – low-frequency Electro-Magnetic Radiation.

These types of arguments, and the theory put forward by Alice Stewart linking childhood cancer to natural radiation, (see p. 399), are currently impossible to prove or disprove. They are interpretations of data, which should be compared to the equally subjective viewpoint of the nuclear industry, in an area loaded with uncertainties, that low-level radiation does not damage human health. The anti-nuclear lobby argue the case for extreme caution: the pro-nuclear lobby argue that this caution is already being applied. Unfortunately, the record of the nuclear industry makes its reassurances less than wholly convincing.

NATURAL BACKGROUND RADIATION

Eighty-seven per cent of the radiation dose that the average citizen receives in the United Kingdom is defined as 'natural background radiation' – it comes from the environment, rather than being artificially produced.

A number of radioactive materials occur naturally and can be found all over the earth. Uranium, for example, is a thousand times as plentiful as gold, and nearly as common as tin, nickel and zinc. It combines easily with other elements, forms many compounds and is distributed in minute quantities throughout the earth's lands and seas.

Naturally radioactive materials are so widespread that they have become assimilated in our water supplies and food sources, our building materials and even the air we breathe. A good deal of radiation reaches the earth from space ('cosmic' radiation). Some areas contain rocks which are quite significantly radioactive. There is a lot of natural background radiation around.

Natural background radiation varies from place to place for a number of reasons: the higher an area is above sea level, the less atmospheric protection there is against cosmic rays, for example, so the greater the exposure to radiation. For the same reason, air travel involves a greater dose of cosmic radiation than staying on the ground.

The UK National Radiological Protection Board has published an analysis of an 'average' citizen's exposure to radiation:

Sources of radiation in the UK
millisieverts per year

0.3	Cosmic rays
0.4	Radiation from the ground and building materials
0.37	Food and drink
0.8	Natural radioactivity in air
0.25	Medical uses of radiation
0.01	Nuclear weapons testing
0.01	Air travel (from exposure to cosmic rays)
0.002	Exposure to nuclear power
2.142	TOTAL

The Box gives an indication of the relative exposures to different sources of radiation, though it is slightly misleading. The figures are arrived at by calculating the collective radiation dose received by the country as a whole, and then dividing it by the total number of people living there. This system works for radioactivity in air, as everybody breathes air. Not everybody travels by air, however, so this is an exposure to which millions of people would not be subject.

Similarly, the figure for exposure to nuclear power is an average of the population as a whole. The nearer you live to a nuclear power station, the more radiation you receive: an average figure is an underestimate of the radiation exposure of the people living downwind of a nuclear power plant.

Having said that, the radiation exposure of people in such a situation is likely to be a fraction of the background radiation they receive – provided that the plant is functioning efficiently. Emissions vary widely, even from similar installations: the levels of radioactive gases given off by boiling water reactors (BWRs) can vary more than a millionfold from plant to plant and year to year.

Variations in natural background radiation can be seen by looking at the map, produced by the UK Atomic Energy Authority, of radiation from rocks in the UK. Much of the south-east has an average background exposure of 0.3 to 0.6 millisieverts per year, with areas in Cornwall, Wales, the north of England and Scotland having a higher radiation average of 0.6 to 1.3 millisieverts a year.

The main radioactive materials in rocks are potassium-40, rubidium-87, and two series of elements arising from the radioactive decay of uranium-238 and thorium-232, long-lived radionuclides that have been on earth since its origin. Studies in France, Germany, the USA, Italy and Japan suggest that about 95 per cent of people live in areas where the average dose rate varies from 0.3 to 0.6 millisieverts a year, although there are 'hotspots' around the world where this exposure is much higher.

This radiation exposure is 'external', i.e. it comes from outside the body. On average, two-thirds of the radiation exposure received from natural sources is internal – it comes from breathing, eating and drinking radioactive substances, especially radon (see below).

Fish and seafood accumulate lead-210 and polonium-210, so people eating large quantities of these can expect to receive high doses. Reindeer meat contains substantial amounts of radioactive materials, because the animals graze on lichen which accumulate radioactive substances (this has increased dramatically since the CHERNOBYL disaster). People living in western Australia, where there are large amounts of uranium, receive up to 75 times the normal dose from the sheep and kangaroo meat they consume.

Risks of natural background radiation

Radioactivity may be natural, but that does not mean that it is benign. As with other natural phenomena like water or sunlight, it has an everyday role in our lives, but should be treated with appropriate caution. People who live in areas of high radon build-up, for example, should ensure that their houses are well ventilated.

Natural background radiation

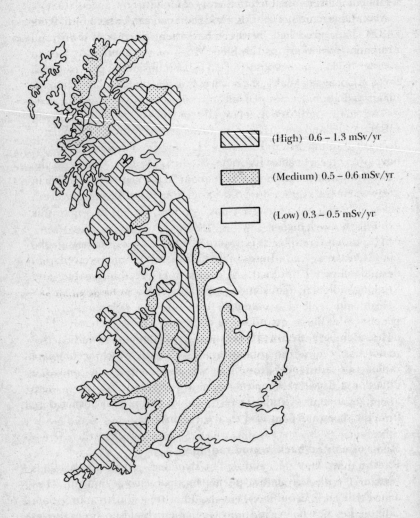

(High) 0.6 – 1.3 mSv/yr

(Medium) 0.5 – 0.6 mSv/yr

(Low) 0.3 – 0.5 mSv/yr

The role of natural background radiation in human illness is the subject of research. Alice Stewart, whose pioneering work alerted a sceptical nuclear industry to the link between foetal X-rays and childhood cancer, now believes that background radiation is responsible for most cancers among children. The belief is founded on data compiled by the Oxford Survey of Childhood Cancers (OSCC), which has records of all UK childhood cancer deaths from 1953 to 1979. These data have been compared with surveys of background radiation variations, and Dr Stewart has stated:

A single momentary exposure to a minute dose of ionising radiation – no more than the tiny amount of radiation needed to produce an x-ray photograph – may be sufficient to initiate a disease process which leads to a cancer death any time during the next ten, twenty, or thirty years . . . we have learnt, first, that all childhood cancers have foetal origins, and, secondly, that sensitivity to the cancer induction effects of radiation is much higher towards the beginning than the end of the prenatal period. From a recent Japanese survey we have also learnt that the effects of pregnancy x-rays on childhood cancers are exactly matched by effects of background radiation.

This is a controversial theory. Dr Stewart adds that the effects of background radiation, if proved, should not be used by the nuclear industry as a justification for their smaller day-to-day releases of radioactivity. If her theory is proved correct, then any release of radioactivity into the environment would have to be as small as is technically achievable – if it is to be permitted at all.

How natural is 'natural' background radiation?

Dr Rosalie Bertell raises an important question, which is how to distinguish between 'natural' and 'unnatural' background radiation. The public perception is that natural radiation comes from rocks, sunlight, etc., and artificial radiation comes from nuclear power and nuclear bomb testing; also that natural background radiation is a fixed unchanging level against which the effects of our nuclear activity can be judged. This is not necessarily the case.

Uranium, thorium, radium and radon gas are all classed as 'natural' radiation sources, as they have not been manufactured: on the other hand, they have been dug out of the ground, blasted with dynamite, and pulverized into very small particles. If we had not removed them from deep in the earth, they would not be emitting radioactivity into the air: yet they are still counted as natural background radiation.

Calculating the natural background is complicated by the secrecy surrounding nuclear power accidents and nuclear-weapons testing. If the former are not properly notified to the public – as occurred in the Windscale fire of 1957, for example – it is impossible to estimate what pollutants have been emitted into the atmosphere. The same problem is true for nuclear-weapons testing. There is even a nuclear accounting quirk which appears to distort the figures arbitrarily: radioactive releases from nuclear installations are counted as artificial radiation one year, but are included as natural background radiation the next.

Other industrial activity results in radiation releases which are counted as natural. A certain amount of radiation escapes, for example, when coal is burnt – like most natural materials, it contains primordial radioactive materials, which accumulate in the ash and can be released up the chimney. This is also included as natural background.

The cumulative effect of this, says Dr Bertell, is that background levels of radiation are steadily increasing year by year. This is disputed by the nuclear industry, who say that past readings are too inaccurate for such a claim to be made. On the other hand, the USA Environmental Protection Agency has introduced the concept of 'technologically enhanced natural background radiation' (TENR) to describe the artificially-caused contribution to radiation levels. TENR now ranks first as a source of internal radiation exposure in the States.

RADON

One of the most important sources of natural background radiation is a tasteless, odourless, invisible gas called radon. This is a 'daughter' (i.e., derived) product from the decay of uranium-238 or thorium-232, and is estimated to provide up to half of the radiation dose from all natural sources. Most of the exposure results from breathing in the gas, particularly indoors.

Radon seeps out of the earth all over the world, but levels vary from place to place. Indoor readings can be much higher than outdoors, because well-insulated houses trap the gas and it builds up. Emissions of gas from the ground can be supplemented by the use of radioactive building materials, such as certain types of granite, alum shale, calcium silicate slag (used for concrete) or phosphogypsum (building blocks, plasterboard and cement).

High radon levels

The dangers of radon build-up are gradually being appreciated. In November 1986, scientists in the Lawrence Berkeley Laboratory in California announced that immediate measures should be taken to reduce levels of radon gas in 200,000 American homes, as 400,000 people faced a risk of developing radiation-induced lung cancer. Radon activity is currently blamed for 2,000 to 20,000 lung cancer deaths per year in the USA.

In the UK, the Royal Commission on Environmental Pollution considered radon in its 1984 report. It estimated the total average radiation dose annually for each person in the country from all sources to be 2.39 millisieverts, of which 0.8 millisieverts came from radon exposure – a third of the overall dose.

The Commission reckoned that radon levels in about 100,000 British homes resulted in a radiation dose of 5 to 25 millisieverts per year, with a dose above 25 millisieverts in some 1,000 dwellings. Typically, half of this radon came from the ground, a quarter from the air and the rest from building materials.

They recommended that radon levels should be reduced in dwellings with a dose greater than 25 millisieverts a year. This can be done by improving ventilation, sealing floors or ground surfaces, or installing air-conditioning.

There was some disappointment that the Commission did not make similar recommendations for buildings with levels in the 5–25 msv range, but said merely that these premises should be 'further investigated'. The feeling among environmentalists was that public exposure outside the home was limited to a maximum of 5 msv per year, so the same should apply inside. The Commission did recommend that new homes should be designed to be within a 5 msv per year limit.

Radon risk estimates double

In 1986, scientists from the National Radiological Protection Board doubled their estimates of the threat of lung cancer posed by a given amount of radon. After smoking, they said, radon is probably the biggest single cause of lung cancer in the UK, killing around 900 people each year.

On the basis of a survey of 2,300 homes, the NRPB estimate that around 20,000 British homes are likely to be harbouring lethal levels of radon gas. The government has declared an 'action level' of 400 becquerels for radon in homes. This is four times the limit set recently for nuclear power station workers working at Sizewell B nuclear power station. A national survey would be needed to find out where these homes are, but so far funding has been withheld.

The NRPB reckoned that some 8,000 homes in Cornwall and 5,000 in Devon exceed the action level. Other affected areas include Somerset, the Derbyshire Peak District, Northamptonshire, Clwyd, West Yorkshire, Shropshire, Gloucestershire and Lincolnshire.

The map shows radon levels in the UK. Within these areas there will be individual houses which are radon 'hotspots'. The NRPB believed that there were 2,000 homes in Britain that would give their

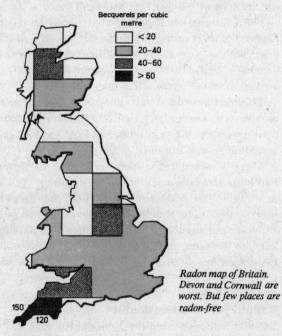

Becquerels per cubic metre

☐	< 20
▨	20–40
▥	40–60
■	> 60

Radon map of Britain. Devon and Cornwall are worst. But few places are radon-free

150

120

Radon in Britain

Source: *New Scientist*, 5 February 1987

occupants doses above 50 millisieverts (and thus a death risk of more than 1 in 20).

The perceived threat from radon appears to be growing more serious. According to *New Scientist*, the US Environmental Protection Agency reported a preliminary finding in August 1986 that one in eight American homes harbours dangerous amounts of radon. In 1987 the *Journal of the American Medical Association* reported a survey of ten States which suggested safety levels were exceeded in 20 per cent of American homes.

In January 1988, the UK NRPB again doubled its estimate of people killed by radon in Britain. It believed the figure to be 1,500 per year. In March 1989, the NRPB again revised its figures. They now believe that 2,500 lung cancer deaths are caused by radon every year. They also revised their assessment of how much the average dose of radiation exposure is – from 2.2 millisieverts in 1984, the figure is now believed to be 2.5 millisieverts. The increase is caused almost entirely by reassessments of exposure to radon.

The US EPA has set a standard of 150 becquerels per cubic metre as a safety level for radon, which is less than half the British equivalent. The Americans also believe that radon has a higher risk of causing death from lung cancer than the figure quoted by the British.

In September 1988, the EPA put radon on the same footing as cigarettes and toxic waste: immediate hazards demanding quick action. EPA surveys of 17 States in the USA indicate that radon is widespread enough to be blamed for 5,000 deaths from lung cancer in US citizens every year. Another 15,000 deaths from lung cancer among smokers should also be included – smoking increases the risk by up to 15 times.

In the same month, the UK Institution of Environmental Health Officers issued the results of a national survey of 121 local authorities in England and Wales. According to this survey, between 50,000 and 90,000 homes may have radon concentrations that exceed the government's 'action level'. This compares with the NRPB's estimate of 20,000 homes at risk. The survey calls into question the NRPB's assumption that geology is an effective predictor of radon 'hotspots'. Some homes in the most geologically unlikely areas contained dangerous amounts of radon. This, if true, would increase the number of radon deaths experienced in the UK.

As Fred Pearce points out (*New Scientist*, 5 February 1987), both

Sweden and the US, two countries with experience of radon emissions, estimate death tolls to be higher than the regulatory authorities in the UK. Using the conversion figures employed by the Environmental Protection Agency, Britain's death toll from radon exposure would be almost 7,000 per year, in comparison to the 1,500 currently thought probable.

Remedial measures

Systems for dealing with radon contamination are available, varying from underfloor fans to 'radon reservoirs' – tanks sunk in gardens which draw the gas away from homes. The systems are relatively cheap and easy to install, but are useless unless the houses at risk are identified.

X-RAYS

X-rays, like gamma rays (see p. 379) are photons – high energy light waves. Essential for medicinal diagnosis and treatment, X-rays are now routinely given in large quantities. The average British person has an X-ray once every two years. Medical radiology accounts for almost one-eighth of our annual dose of radiation, the single biggest non-natural radiation that we are exposed to.

The 1984 Royal Commission on Environmental Pollution published this chart to describe the sources of radiation exposure to the 'average' citizen:

'Average' radiation exposure

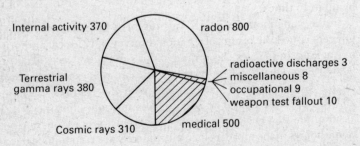

Internal activity 370 — radon 800 — radioactive discharges 3 — miscellaneous 8 — occupational 9 — weapon test fallout 10 — Terrestrial gamma rays 380 — Cosmic rays 310 — medical 500

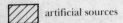 artificial sources

figures in microsieverts
(1,000 µSv = 1 mSv)

Of the notional annual dose of 2.39 millisieverts, 0.53 millisieverts is described as coming from artificial sources; and 0.5 millisieverts (21 per cent) comes from medical practices. X-rays account for 11.5 per cent of the total radiation exposure of the population.

Although these X-rays are very low-level radiation, there is a risk involved. The Radiation and Health Information Service, an independent body campaigning to limit radiation exposure in the UK, reckons that X-rays are likely to cause 1,400 cancers and 600 cases of serious genetic damage each year (these figures do not include radiation therapy). In addition, they estimate 60 children are born each year with serious defects as a result of parental exposure to X-rays. The National Radiological Protection Board dispute the figures, saying that they should be 170 fatal cancers and 100 cases of serious genetic damage per year.

Reducing the risks

Use of X-rays is not necessarily an objective medical practice: the number of chest X-rays per thousand people in West Germany, for example, is half that of Japan, and almost a third of the number in Romania. In certain countries, it is still fashionable to give large numbers of chest X-rays, in spite of the fact that these are becoming less useful as the incidence of tuberculosis falls. In places such as Sweden, the UK and the USA, the number of these examinations has fallen heavily. Other countries still examine a third of their people every year.

Since the danger of X-rays has been appreciated, the size of the radiation dose given in routine examinations has dramatically dropped. The number of X-rays given could also be reduced without affecting health care – for example, by stopping the practice of routinely X-raying new employees, using newer radiographic technology, or using alternative imaging techniques more widely. One alternative system, the rare-earth screen, can cut the received radiation dose by half, and costs no more than the traditional tungstate screens – yet they are used in only about half the X-rays done in British examinations.

X-rays are an essential medical practice, and millions are given every year. The General Municipal and Boilermakers Union has commented, however: 'It should be noted that a 10% reduction in overall medical exposures could have as much effect as completely eliminating all other sources of man-made radiation.'

See also CHERNOBYL; NUCLEAR ENERGY; NUCLEAR WEAPONS; THREE MILE ISLAND

REFERENCES

Bertell, Rosalie, *No Immediate Danger*, Women's Press, 1985.

Green, Patrick, *Low-level Radiation, Questions and Answers*, FoE Energy Campaign, 1986.

Moss, Norman, *The Politics of Uranium*, André Deutsch, 1981.

National Radiological Protection Board, *Radiation Exposure of the UK population: 1988 review*, 1989.

Royal Commission on Environmental Pollution, *Tenth Report*, 1984.

UKAEA, *The Effects and Control of Radiation*, 1985.

UK Health and Safety Executive, *The Tolerability of Risk from Nuclear Power Stations*, 1988.

United Nations Environment Programme, *Radiation: Doses, Effects, Risks*, 1985.

GMBATU, 'Statement on the Need to Protect Workers and the Public from Radiation-induced Cancer', November 1985.

GMBATU, 'Briefing Notes on Reducing Unnecessary Exposures to Ionizing Radiation in Medicine and Dentistry', November 1985.

NUJ, 'Freelances and Computers', National Union of Journalists, March 1989.

NUJ, 'Journalists and the New Technology', National Union of Journalists, March 1987.

'Concern about radon grows in Britain and America', *New Scientist*, 22 September 1988.

The Ecologist, vol. 16, no. 4–5, 1986.

Environment Digest, No. 14, July 1988.

Milne, Roger, 'Background radiation blamed for child cancers', *New Scientist*, 23 October 1986.

Milne, Roger, 'Cancers cluster around older nuclear plants', *New Scientist*, 26 February 1987.

Nuclear Supplement, *New Socialist*, October 1986.

Pearce, Fred, 'A Deadly Gas under the Floorboards', *New Scientist*, 5 February 1987.

'Radiation Agency notes the rising menace of radon', *New Scientist*, 18 March 1989.

'Radon Peril Haunts US Homes', *New Scientist*, 20 August 1987.

Read, Cathy, 'X-Rays: Dangers of Defensive Medicine', *Guardian*, 6 August 1987.

'Rising Radon Concern Sparks Tests on Homes', *Engineer*, 11 June 1987.

CONTACTS

British Society for Social
  Responsibility in Science
Campaign for Nuclear
  Disarmament
Earth Resources Research
Friends of the Earth
General Municipal and
  Boilermakers Union
Greenpeace
Political Ecology Research Group
Radiation and Health Information
  Service

British Nuclear Fuels Ltd
Central Electricity Generating
  Board
Department of Energy
Department of the Environment
National Radiological Protection
  Board
UK Atomic Energy Authority

Sandoz

The Sandoz disaster, described variously as 'Chernobasle' or 'the Bhopal of the Rhine', occurred on 1 November 1986. An electrical fault caused by an animal gnawing the wiring in Warehouse 956, in the Sandoz chemical company's Muttenz storage complex three miles from the centre of Basle, caused a fire which turned into a conflagration.

The warehouse contained 1,246 tonnes of chemicals, mostly insecticides. Although the building complied with Swiss safety regulations, the storage facility had no automatic heat sensors, sprinkler system, or containment trenches to catch potential leakages of dangerous chemicals.

The fire brigade put out the fire by applying large quantities of water, which poured into the nearby Rhine carrying with it about 30 tonnes of herbicides, insecticides and compounds of mercury. This formed a slick 30 miles long, which swept down the Rhine, killing hundreds of thousands of fish and eels, and raising doubts about drinking water supplies for riverside towns.

Two hundred miles of the Upper Rhine lost most or all of its water life, with ecological consequences which are impossible to foretell. The West German government ordered the closure of all wells along the Rhine, and supplied 25,000 people in two towns near Bonn with water ferried in by tanker. The destruction of fish, birds, insects and river flora appeared to be worst between Basle and the West German city of Karlsruhe, though the potential danger stretched as far as The Netherlands and the North Sea, as the Dutch authorities closed three sluices to divert the poisons away from the water supplies of Amsterdam, The Hague and Leiden.

The spotlight turned on the storage systems used by the chemical industry, and the implications of what might have happened became slowly apparent. Next door to Warehouse 956 was a storage shed for sodium: the roof of this was punctured by drums of chemicals thrown into the air by the force of explosions in the burning warehouse. Sodium explodes on contact with water. If one of the drums of sodium had ruptured and then been exposed to water from the fire brigade's hoses, the resulting chain reaction would have taken out the entire Sandoz plant, including tanks of deadly nerve gases.

Sandoz admitted that phosgene was stored in the complex (this was allegedly one of the substances that caused the disaster in BHOPAL, India, in 1984). A West German MP, Michael Muller, claimed that Sandoz processed organo-phosphates, which 'have a similar effect to Tabun and Sarin', the nerve gases developed by the Germans in the Second World War (see PESTICIDES). 'If the twelve tonnes of those organo-phosphates stored in Muttenz had gone up, the results would have put Bhopal in the shade.'

Authorities in Basle decided to give blood and urine tests to 600 people in and around the plant who were exposed to the foul-smelling smoke from the fire. Highly poisonous dioxin was released into the air at the time of the disaster.

Other incidents

Environmental monitoring stations along the Rhine were puzzled to find evidence of a pollutant that was not supposed to have been stored in the Sandoz warehouse. On 7 November, Ciba-Geigy, Switzerland's largest chemical company, admitted that 400 kg of the herbicide Atrazine had escaped from its production plant on 31 October, the day before the Sandoz fire, and had been slowly leaking into the Rhine.

Following that, the West German company BASF admitted that 2,000 kg of the herbicide dichloro-phenoxyacetic acid had leaked into the river from its factory at Ludwigshafen.

The West German firm Hoechst admitted spilling 850 grammes of chlorobenzol into a drain from a leaky tank: the environmental ministry of Hesse estimated the true figure as up to 50 kg.

On Thursday 20 November, Ciba-Geigy released a cloud of phenol over Basle; the following Monday, a cloud of phosgene gas leaked from a factory belonging to the Swiss firm Siegfried, in Aarau, near Basle.

The fear expressed by the environmental movement is that this apparent catalogue of disasters represented normal industrial practice, and that media attention was drawn to the releases of the toxic emissions only because of the fire at the Sandoz plant. International negotiations following the Sandoz disaster centred on establishing an early-warning system for alerting water authorities after the release of a pollutant into the river: the Basle authorities sounded the international alarm 40 hours after the fire first broke out – a day after the German Ministry of the Environment sent out warnings of its own.

The Swiss agreed to pay the costs of the pollution, provided that a cause and effect from the Sandoz fire was established. At least half a million fish are estimated to have died, with damage calculated at $2.5 to $5 million in one German state alone. Ultimate cost to the Sandoz company in compensation is likely to be about £15 million. The ecological damage to the Rhine could take a decade to recover.

Sandoz themselves appear to have taken the disaster to heart, as they faced large financial costs from the loss of business confidence in their company. Manufacture of many hazardous products, including 36 dyestuffs and chemicals worth around £2 million in annual sales, has been terminated. Higher warehousing standards are being implemented throughout the Sandoz group.

The disaster highlighted the inadequate international legislation about the safe-keeping and storage of potentially deadly chemicals. After the SEVESO disaster in Italy in 1976, the EC drew up the Seveso Directive, which regulated how these dangerous substances should be stored. By the time of the Sandoz fire, only five EC countries had adopted the Directive – the UK, Germany, Denmark, France and Eire.

See also BHOPAL; CHEMICAL WASTES; SEVESO; WATER

REFERENCES

Guardian, Observer, New Scientist, Financial Times, November 1986.

Environmental Data Services Reports, 153 and 156.

CONTACTS

Bureau of European Consumers' Unions (BEUC)

European Environmental Bureau (EEB)

Seveso

Seveso, the scene of one of Europe's worst chemical disasters, is an Italian town near Milan. On 10 July 1976, the Icmesa chemical plant at Seveso erupted, spilling a contaminated cloud of gas over the residential area nearby. As a result of this contamination, 70,000 animals died or were slaughtered, the health of 30,000 people was put at risk, and over 700 citizens were long-term evacuated. The disaster also brought to public notice one of the most toxic chemicals to have been discovered – dioxin.

History of disasters
The Icmesa plant produced trichlorophenol, a chemical used to make a bacteria-killer called hexachlorophene or a very powerful weedkiller (2,4,5-T – an active ingredient in Agent Orange, a defoliant used in large areas of Vietnam).

The plant had been bought in 1969 and modernized a year later, with the intention of manufacturing trichlorophenol. The difficulties of the production process were well-known. Trichlorophenol (TCP) is made at a temperature of 180 degrees C. If overheating occurs and the temperature rises to around 220 degrees, the process runs out of control and explodes. The manufacture of TCP involves the production of very small quantities of 2,3,7,8-tetrachlorodibenzopara-dioxin (TCDD) as a by-product. At the higher temperature leading to an explosion, TCDD is produced in much larger quantities.

Lethal quantities of TCDD for animals are measured in micrograms (i.e., millionths of a gram). Half a microgram per kilogram of body weight is enough to kill a guinea-pig. This makes a process which produces TCDD extremely dangerous. Accidents had occurred before Seveso: at a Monsanto factory in the USA in 1949 (228 workers injured); at BASF in West Germany in 1953 (53 casualties); at Philips Duphar, Amsterdam, in 1963 (50 injured); and at the Coalite factory in Bolsover, UK in 1968 (79 people affected).

The new owners of the Icmesa plant were Givaudan, a subsidiary of the Swiss drugs firm Hoffman La Roche. One reason for the decision to make TCP was the recent closure of a British TCP factory after an accident, which heightened the world shortage of the product. It was considered that the new plant, heated by saturated steam which should have guaranteed a maximum temperature of 180 degrees, was perfectly safe.

The Seveso incident

Unfortunately, this was not the case. Before July 1976, 230 production runs of TCP had taken place at Icmesa, usually lasting about 20 hours. Sometimes the plant was shut down in mid-reaction for the weekend break, a practice that had not been agreed by Givaudan – but was not expressly forbidden. 10 July 1976 was a Saturday, and the process had been stopped in mid-reaction. A maintenance crew of ten were the only people in attendance at 12.37 P.M., when the production process overheated and a safety valve blew, venting a large cloud of gas into the atmosphere. The cloud drifted slowly southwards over the town.

John G. Fuller's book *The Poison that Fell from the Sky* describes the cloud as some five miles long, dropping small white crystals like snow on the roofs and gardens below. An acrid mist stung people's eyes and skin, making it difficult to breathe. The next day, a shiny, oily coating covered houses, plants, vegetables and trees.

In the absence of any instructions from the factory, life went on as normal. People continued eating the vegetables and fruit from their gardens, children played in the streets and swam in the open-air swimming pool, chickens and rabbits kept in backyards were killed for Sunday lunch. Two technicians from Icmesa told the mayor that the contents of the gas cloud were unknown at present, but probably contained TCP. Samples had been sent to Switzerland for analysis. They suggested that maybe people shouldn't eat produce from their gardens, and this information was passed on to local press and radio, where it was featured without undue prominence.

On Monday, work resumed normally at the Icmesa plant, though the TCP reactor area was roped off. Local people began visiting their doctors, complaining of headaches, swollen abdomens, back pains. Children's faces, arms and legs began to show ugly rashes.

By Wednesday, four days after the incident, local doctors were becoming inundated with sick people seeking treatment. Many children had started vomiting. Birds were dying, falling out of the air uncontrollably. Cats and dogs were staggering around and collapsing. In the evening, the mayor received a phone call from Switzerland, saying that a 'very poisonous substance' had been detected in the gas cloud, but it had not been identified yet. The normal labour–management meeting at the factory was cancelled without explanation.

On Friday, 30 Icmesa workers were told to fix tall posts at certain locations round the factory, saying DANGER AREA. CONTAMINATED. DO NOT EAT VEGETABLES, FRUIT, OR ANIMALS THAT EAT GRASS FROM THE GROUND. The workforce asked for a meeting with the plant manager. He refused, saying that he did not have enough time. They decided to strike, and demand from the mayor that the factory be closed until safety could be guaranteed. The management issued a statement saying the workers were work-shy and were simply looking for an excuse to lay down their tools. On Friday evening a two-year-old baby was rushed to hospital with running sores all over its body: the first hospital casualty of the incident.

On Saturday, a dozen more children were admitted to hospital, and several adults. The local vets were being overrun with sick pets: animals were dying in the streets. The sickness had hitherto been confined to Seveso: now animals began dying in Cesano Maderno, two miles to the south of Icmesa.

The seven first days of the disaster are recounted above to give an impression of the developing awareness among the people of the township that things were going badly wrong. In spite of this, no official action was taken. The authorities delayed an evacuation because they were awaiting detailed information from Hoffman La Roche's scientific tests.

Within three days of receiving the first samples, Roche had identified dioxin in large quantities existing in the TCP reactor itself. The firm delayed notifying the authorities until it could define how far from the plant the poison had spread. It was on 23 July – 13 days after the accident – that they told the Seveso mayor of the existence of dioxin in the gas cloud, and of the need for evacuation. The first estimate of the amount of dioxin in the cloud was two to three kilograms: theoretically enough to kill 100,000 people. Evacuation began on 24 July.

Evacuation and extermination

The authorities declared a state of emergency, placed the directors of the Icmesa factory under house arrest, and warned nearby towns that they too might be contaminated. Then they began to work out the most affected areas, so that they could be evacuated. This was done by collecting dead animals and mapping their locations.

The poison cloud had spread in a fanlike pattern to the south-east of the factory, fortunately missing the most populated areas of Seveso. Three areas of contamination were identified – Zone A, where 90 per cent of the animals had died, a mile long and half a mile wide in Seveso itself, and stretching outside the town; Zone B, lying to the south of Zone A, where animals were sick and dying but not to such an extent; and around both these zones Zone R, the Zone of Respect, where caution should be applied.

On 24 July, 200 people were evacuated from Zone A; this number was increased to over 700 five days later, when soil sample analyses were received. An army battalion arrived, surrounded the whole of Zone A with barbed wire, and posted armed sentries. Entry was forbidden unless wearing protective clothing and masks, which were removed on leaving the zone. Roadblocks were put up to mark Zone B.

The animals were still dying. Teams of vets and volunteers moved into Zone A and Zone B, and killed every animal that was still alive – an estimated 70,000.

The problems of dioxin disposal

The authorities were now faced with enormous problems. It was known that dioxin is extremely persistent, and no system of cleaning up the poison had yet been developed. Experts who had dealt with dioxin contamination in the USA and the UK recommended complete evacuation of all the contaminated areas, to be sealed off and left, possibly for ever.

The authorities postponed any disposal procedures until they had firm advice on what to do. As time went by, the poison settled into the soil, which was then collected by Hoffman La Roche and stored in 41 large barrels.

In the short term, however, up to 30,000 people had been affected by the dioxin cloud, which had missed some houses because of upward air currents, but had also spread far outside the designated zones. The health authorities advised people not to have sexual intercourse that would produce children, because of the danger of mutation. Ninety women had abortions. The miscarriage rate increased significantly in the first quarter of 1977.

Fortunately, the enormous fatality figures that had been expected did not occur. This may have been because the dioxin spread thinly over a wide area; or it may be because dioxin has differing effects on different species, and may not affect humans as drastically as had been thought. Some have accused the Italian authorities of disguising dioxin deaths for political reasons.

There are great disparities between the claimed figures for sickness arising from the incident. Chloracne, a severe pitting of the skin that is associated with dioxin poisoning, was confirmed officially in 136 cases. Other medical opinion put the figure as at least 500, and point to liver complaints, birth defects, eye problems, heart disease, and a lack of resistance to disease. The full picture will probably never be known – Italian plans to monitor the health of 100,000 people foundered on the lack of cash available.

The lessons of Seveso

Seveso, with its science-fiction barbed wire, sentries, exclusion zones and mass extermination of animals, could have been a lot worse. It was chance, and not the result of emergency planning or safety procedures, that prevented the death of thousands of human beings. Some criticisms have been made, and it was alleged that:

1. Givaudan were over-confident in a plant known to produce very poisonous chemicals. The design of the safety valve, which vented a reactor explosion into the open air, has been particularly criticized. A design could have been implemented which vented the exploded gases into a containment building: the Dow Chemical TCP plant in Michigan, for example, incorporated this feature.

2. The notification of dioxin in the cloud should not have taken 13 days. This appears to have been a case in which commercial caution outweighed considerations of public safety.

3. The authorities should have taken independent action, and not waited for information from Hoffman La Roche. Detection of dioxin on the ground is a complex process involving specialized instruments, which is why evacuation was delayed for so long. On the other hand, the town leaders appeared to have no idea of the potential consequences of an explosion at the Icmesa plant. After the Seveso scare, other industrial plants in the Milan area were checked, and 300 were found to be breaking Italy's (not very severe) safety regulations. The attitude of the authorities towards potentially lethal industries appeared to be extremely relaxed.

There has been some tightening up of procedures after the Seveso incident. The Seveso Directive was passed by the EC and should have come into force in January 1984, but by the time of the next large accident involving chemicals in the EC, had been adopted by only five countries (see SANDOZ). The lessons of Seveso prevented neither the enormous BHOPAL tragedy nor Sandoz. Reassurances currently given by sectors of the chemical industry bear a striking resemblance to the reassurances that were given before the Seveso accident.

In 1983, five officials of the Icmesa plant – the chairman, plant designer, managing director and two technical directors, were given jail sentences of 30 months to five years. The managing director and a technical director had their five-year sentences cut to two years and 18 months on appeal in 1985; the other three were acquitted.

The 41 barrels of contaminated waste from Seveso were given to the German company Mannesman for disposal, but disappeared, prompting a Europe-wide search. They eventually turned up in a disused French slaughterhouse. The sub-contractor responsible, Bernard Paringaux, received an 18-month suspended sentence and a £20,000 fine. The waste was finally burned in a high-temperature incinerator in Basle, Switzerland, in 1985.

The long-term consequences of the disaster will become apparent with time. As the *Sunday Times* commented in August 1976, this incident is

. . . the story of how a multinational company was able to bypass local regulations, ignore the lessons of previous accidents with the same chemicals, and contaminate a populated area with a poison whose effects are still not completely understood. Indeed, as the disaster has no precedent on anything approaching this scale, its full magnitude will not be known for months, or even years.

See also BHOPAL; CHEMICAL WASTE; PESTICIDES; SANDOZ

REFERENCES

Cook, Judith and Chris Kaufman, *Portrait of a Poison, the 2,4,5-T Story*, Pluto Press, 1982.

Elkington, John, *The Poisoned Womb*, Penguin Books, 1985.

Environmental Data Services, Report 142.

Fuller, John G., *The Poison that Fell from the Sky*, Berkley Books, 1977.

'The Cost of Avoiding Another Seveso', *Economist*, 14 August 1976.

'Doomwatch Italian Style', *Sunday Times* Insight report, 1 August 1976.

Fox, Robert, 'Seveso: the Dust Will not Settle', *Listener*, 11 August 1977.

'Seveso, Lessons from an Escape', *Economist*, 17 June 1978.

CONTACTS

European Environment Bureau
London Hazards Centre

Smoking

Smoking kills an estimated one million people around the world every year, according to the World Health Organization, and damages the health of hundreds of millions more. The addiction is the single most important cause of avoidable illness and death in the UK, causing nine out of ten lung cancer deaths, and most bronchitis and emphysema fatalities. It is a substantial contributor to coronary heart disease.

Smoking in some – though not all – First World countries is decreasing steadily among males, less rapidly among females. Third World smoking is increasing dramatically, and remains a huge growth market. The tobacco industry has shrugged off overwhelming medical evidence linking its product with enormous sickness and fatality rates.

Smokers in the USA and Europe now generally accept that the habit kills other users, but tend to believe that the same fate will not happen to them. The belief is often mistaken, as James Wilkinson points out in *Tobacco* (1986): 'Of 1,000 young adults who smoke regularly, one will be murdered, six will be killed by the roads, and 250 will be killed by tobacco.' Deaths caused by smoking are often preceded by years of disablement and incapacitation.

The harmful effects of smoking have been discovered only within the last 40 years, and research into its side-effects is relatively recent. Smoking by a parent can deleteriously affect the health of foetuses, newborn babies and toddlers; the sight of a parent smoking can encourage a child to take up the habit in later life; living or working with a habitual smoker can increase a non-smoker's chances of catching lung cancer by up to 30 per cent. Research findings such as these are leading to the loss of the smoker's 'right' to pollute other people's clean air.

Lung cancer as a new phenomenon

Lung cancer is regarded as common nowadays, but at the beginning of the twentieth century it was rarely seen. In 1920, less than 250 people in England and Wales died of the disease; by 1960 the figure was 10,000, rising to 40,000 in the 1980s. Lung cancer can take 20 or 30 years to develop, so the current fatality figures reflect the popularity of smoking in the 1950s and 1960s.

The first half of the twentieth century saw an unprecedented increase in the numbers of cigarettes smoked. In the Britain of the 1920s, men were smoking on average six cigarettes a day; by 1945 consumption had doubled. In an era when smoking was regarded as harmless, fashionable and attractive, three-quarters of all British men, and half the women, were smokers. The UK had – and still has – the highest lung cancer rates in the world.

In 1959, the Royal College of Physicians set up an inquiry which reported, with devastating results, in 1962: cigarette smoking, it said, 'is the most likely cause of the recent world-wide increase in deaths from lung cancer'. This UK report was followed in 1964 by an investigation of a team of scientists under the USA Surgeon-General. After studying 6,000 articles in 1,200 publications, they concluded: 'Cigarette smoking is a health hazard of sufficient importance in the United States to warrant appropriate remedial action.'

Research into smoking and lung cancer in the 1950s had established statistical links between smokers and lung cancer victims; the inquiries in the early 1960s reviewed all the available evidence and confirmed the connection; subsequent studies initiated new research, which overwhelmingly corroborated the 1960s' findings. One such was a $10 million, 15-year programme carried out by the American Medical Association, which confirmed in 1978 that cigarette smoking played an important role in chronic obstructive pulmonary disease, and was 'a grave danger' to people with coronary problems.

In 1971, the Royal College of Physicians published its second report, in which the graphic idea of a 'lottery' was used. Non-smokers aged 35 would have a 1:75 chance of dying within the next ten years, whereas the chances for a heavy smoker would be 1:22 – more than three times as great. The Royal College's 1983 report was even more definite: one in four smokers, it said, will die of tobacco-related diseases; someone with a 20-a-day habit will lose on average five to six years of life. In the same year, the UK Department of Health's Chief

Medical Officer stated that cigarette smoking was the largest avoidable hazard in modern Britain, causing about 100,000 deaths a year.

Tobacco industry response

The tobacco industry has responded with a series of novel arguments, which have since become a model for industries wishing to defend polluting practices. The tobacco lobby position rests on the statement that science has not yet established the full cycle whereby smoking causes cancer. Statistical evidence is not good enough, neither are laboratory tests. Only when the entire process, from inhalation to tumour formation, is definitively explained will the explanation be accepted and action become necessary.

The position is unusual because it shifts the onus of proof from the producer to the consumer, even though it is not the misuse of tobacco that kills so many people, but the use of the substance exactly as the manufacturers intend it. The industry's viewpoint is not an easy one to put forward, and has become known in the USA as the 'tightrope' argument. The basic defence is that tobacco is a legal substance, and until this position changes, producers are under no obligation to interfere with their customers' free choice. There is still, say the tobacco firms, an element of doubt as to the health effects of smoking.

Peter Taylor, in *The Smoke Ring* (1985), carries a telling comment from Sir George Godber, UK Chief Medical Officer of Health from 1960 to 1972:

> I just don't believe that anybody could be unconvinced who's really taken the trouble to look at the evidence. They know they're selling death now. They're not stupid. They just don't choose to admit it. I think they're an enormous, wealthy industry in which the major decision-makers can distance themselves sufficiently far from the outcome of their product to ignore it.

The effects of smoking

Smoking a cigarette exposes an individual to over 2,000 chemical agents, many of which promote cancer. A single puff produces a mouthful of 50 millilitres of dense smoke containing approximately 50 milligrams of gas and solids. About a third of this is solid matter – tar – in the form of a million million droplets, most of which remain in the airways and lungs after the smoke is expelled. The remainder includes the addictive agent nicotine, and substances such as benzene and benzo(a)pyrene, which is strongly suspected of being carcinogenic.

The gaseous mouthful includes carbon monoxide (in relatively large quantities), ammonia, formaldehyde and hydrogen cyanide. Cigarettes even contain radioactive materials like polonium-210. One expert claims that smoking 20 cigarettes a day for 40 years can produce a cumulative dose of 38 to 97 rads of alpha radiation, which he believes causes most lung cancer. Others point to the tar, known to produce cancers on the skin of mice; the benzo(a)pyrene; or the total chemical cocktail. There are so many dangerous chemicals involved in smoking a cigarette that it is difficult to prove exactly which one produces the corpse.

Cancer

The best-known effect of smoking is lung cancer. In 1985, 40,860 people in the UK died of lung cancer, with 90 per cent of these deaths being attributed to smoking. The increased risk of contracting lung cancer has been quantified in a 1976 study:

Risk of developing lung cancer

No. of cigarettes per day	Annual death rate per 100,000 men
0	10
1–14	78 (8 times as many as non-smokers)
15–24	127 (13 times as many as non-smokers)
25 or more	251 (25 times as many as non-smokers)

Source: ASH, Fact Sheet No. 4, December 1986

There are other risks, too:

Cardiovascular disease The UK has the highest rate of coronary heart disease (CHD) in the world, with 186,598 deaths in 1985 – the leading cause of death in the UK, especially in Northern Ireland and Scotland. This is caused by a variety of factors, including inadequate diet (see FOOD IN THE UK), lack of exercise, and/or smoking. The cigarette smoker has a two to three times greater risk of having a heart attack than a non-smoker. At least 80 per cent of heart attacks in younger men (under 45) are thought to be due to smoking. At this age heavy smokers have a 10 to 15 times greater risk of heart attacks than non-smokers.

Other risks include cancer of the larynx, the oral cavity, the oesophagus, and the cervix; peripheral vascular disease (obstruction of the blood supply to the limbs, leading to gangrene and amputation); and subarachnoid haemorrhage (brain stroke).

Chronic obstructive lung disease, including chronic bronchitis or emphysema These diseases are progressively disabling and cause prolonged suffering through difficulty in breathing. The small airways in the lung break down and the lung loses its elasticity. In 1985, nearly 15,000 people in the UK died from this disease, with at least 90 per cent of deaths being attributed to cigarette smoking.

Additional risks for women Female smokers, who have an increased risk of lung cancer, CHD and obstructive lung disease, face other hazards too. Subarachnoid haemorrhage is 2.5 times more common in female smokers than non-smokers. Women smokers who also take the contraceptive pill are more likely to have a coronary attack, stroke or blood clot in the lung (pulmonary embolism) than non-smoking pill-users. The menopause occurs two to three years earlier in smokers than in non-smokers.

Childbirth Babies born to smokers are on average 200 grams lighter than those of non-smokers (smoking by the father, as well as the mother, can reduce a baby's weight at birth); tobacco use during pregnancy causes a twofold increase in the risk of spontaneous abortion; the risk of a stillbirth, or death during the first week of an infant's life, increases directly with the number of cigarettes smoked during pregnancy (20 per cent increase in risk for smokers of less than 20 a day, 35 per cent increase for people who smoke more than this). This risk is significantly greater for women who are poor, anaemic or have had several children.

Children Infants of parents who smoke have an increased frequency of hospitalization for bronchitis and pneumonia in the first year of life, and until the age of two are more susceptible to chest infections and bronchitis. Chronic cough and phlegm are also more frequent among children of parents who smoke. Children of mothers who smoked in pregnancy may have slight but measurable deficiencies in physical growth and intellectual development up to eleven years of age.

Smoking as an environmental issue

Until recently, smoking has been presented as a matter of personal choice, but it is now perceived as an environmental issue. Breathing other people's smoke is called passive, involuntary or second-hand smoking. The non-smoker breathes 'sidestream' smoke from the burning tip of the cigarette and 'mainstream' smoke that has been inhaled and then exhaled by the smoker. Nearly 85 per cent of the smoke in a room results from sidestream smoke, which contains toxic gases in higher concentrations than in mainstream smoke. The World Health Organization stated in 1986 that passive smoking 'violates the right to health of non-smokers who must be protected against this noxious form of environmental pollution'.

Passive smoking produces small but measurable changes in the air passages of otherwise healthy adults, as well as eye irritation, headache, cough, sore throat, dizziness and nausea. Adults with asthma experience a significant decline in lung function after exposure to sidestream smoke for one hour. People with other respiratory and heart ailments are often more seriously affected.

In the long term, passive smoking can be fatal. The UK government's Independent Scientific Committee on Smoking and Health stated in March 1988 that passive smoking led to an increased risk (between 10 and 30 per cent) of non-smokers getting lung cancer.

Figures produced by leading scientists say that about a third of cases of lung cancer in non-smokers who live with smokers, and a quarter of all non-smoking lung cancer cases, may be due to passive smoking. Up to 1,000 cancer deaths a year could be attributed to the effects of other people's cigarette smoke – with research currently being carried out into diseases other than lung cancer which are likely to spring from the same source.

This represents a significant environmental hazard. Smoking in one's home is a personal choice (except for children who are exposed to their parents' smoke), but smoking at work should be treated as a different matter altogether. Research has indicated that non-smokers working over a long period of time in a smoking environment suffer the same lung damage as that incurred by light smokers.

This has produced action in the USA where over 40 States have laws on smoking in the workplace and other public areas. In New York State, smoking is banned in schools, hospitals, courthouses, toilets, banks, shops, indeed any public area. All restaurants with over 50 seats have to provide 70 per cent of their space to non-smokers. In the workplace the rights of the non-smoker must prevail over any wish of the smoker to smoke.

The situation is not the same in the UK, where legislation may be necessary to enforce the rights of non-smokers. Employees have sued for constructive dismissal if a smoking ban is introduced at work.

The tobacco companies and new markets

The publicity surrounding smoking has led to a reduction in the number of adult smokers in the UK. Between 1972 and 1986 the number of adult male smokers fell by one-third and that of women by a quarter. A third of the adult population now smoke: they have been in a minority since the 1970s. Cigarette sales in the UK dropped from 130,000 million in 1972 to 95,000 million in 1986. Average weekly consumption among smokers over the same period has fallen slightly for men – but has increased for women.

Prevalence of cigarette smoking (%)

	1972	1974	1976	1978	1980	1982	1984	1986
Men	52	51	46	45	42	38	36	35
Women	41	41	38	37	37	33	32	31

Source: ASH, Fact Sheet No. 1, October 1986

The drop in adult smoking is encouraging, although it is balanced by worrying figures for young smoking. A 1984 government survey found that 30 per cent of secondary school children are regular smokers by the age of 16. This is a crucial age, as people who avoid smoking before the age of 20 do not usually become smokers at all; and the health damage that occurs to a smoker is proportionately greater the younger a person becomes addicted.

In Britain, as in most other Western countries, more teenage girls than boys are starting to smoke (24 per cent of mid-teen girls, 17 per cent of boys). This may reflect the explicit targeting of women for advertising by the tobacco giants. Design of slim-line 'feminine' cigarettes and mass advertising in women's magazines are attempts to reshape part of the market. Lung cancer has already overtaken breast cancer as the leading cause of death in Scottish women and older English women.

For smoking to continue, young smokers have to be recruited. Anti-smoking campaigners point to peer-group pressure, parental attitudes and ruthless advertising on the part of the tobacco companies, as causes for the large number of young smokers. Sponsorship of televised sport is a particularly subtle but all-pervasive way of promoting a product that has been banned from television advertising since 1965. In 1985, there were 350 hours of tobacco-sponsored sport on television, 97 per cent of which were shown by the BBC. The BBC banned the Lola racing car from carrying adverts for Durex contraceptives, but it allows the John Player Special auto, and others like it, to continue advertising cigarettes.

The tobacco companies are now aiming at the Third World, where cigarette consumption is increasing by 3 per cent per year. Bobbie Jacobson, who first pointed out the dangers to women represented by the tobacco industry's operations, has used Brazil as an indication of the new trends. Coronary heart disease is now the primary cause of death in Brazil, with lung cancer as the third leading cause of cancer mortality. Nearly one-third of Brazil's 120 million people are under 15. This has led the tobacco trade press to describe the country as 'a lucrative, growing market', where 'there are no warnings on cigarette packs, nor are there advertising restrictions'.

Cigarettes sold in the Third World usually have a much higher tar content than is permitted in the UK or USA, and are sold using very aggressive marketing techniques: 20 per cent of all television advertising time in Argentina is given to cigarettes. The tobacco trade is so well-embedded in some countries that governments would find it extremely difficult to wean their farmers away from tobacco leaf. Curing the product is also very expensive in terms of trees (see DEFORESTATION) – in Kenya annual tobacco production requires the felling of 5,000 to 8,000 hectares of forest a year. If this rate of felling continues, it will result in the country being bare of trees by the year 2000.

Economic arguments

Third World dependence on tobacco can be understood in terms of the general domination of developing by developed countries (see NORTH–SOUTH RELATIONSHIP). Surprisingly, however, the UK also appears to be strongly dependent on the cigarette trade.

UK Treasury revenue from tobacco duty and VAT in 1986 is

estimated at £5,540 million – the third largest source of national income after VAT and oil. About 21,000 people in the UK are employed in the tobacco industry, which received government grants to the tune of £27 million in the period 1979–86. The government spends £4 million a year on anti-smoking campaigns.

The industry argues that the consequences of drastically reducing tobacco consumption would be loss of national income, unemployment, reduction of sponsorship of sport and the loss of personal freedom to smoke. The threat of unemployment, and the loss of shareholders' dividends, have occasionally united backbench MPs to lobby against tax increases for cigarettes – the most established way of discouraging smoking, in a market where the real price of cigarettes is not much different than it was in 1962 when the first Royal College of Physicians' report was published.

Where the figures have been scrutinized, the tobacco argument appears increasingly threadbare. In a recent study in Northern Ireland, costs of NHS care, loss of working days, and fires (15 per cent of which were caused by cigarettes or matches) weighed heavily in the balance against smoking. The main income from cigarettes is tax – which is a transferable item that can be raised from other sources. As for sponsorship – the £8 million to £10 million invested annually in sports sponsorship, and the £1.25 million given to the arts, could easily be supplied out of the existing £5,000 million that the government receives from cigarettes (or from a fraction of a percentage increase in the tax).

Other products

Informed criticism of tobacco, though described above in relation to cigarettes, includes cigars, pipes and oral tobacco products such as Skoal Bandits. Cigar and pipe smoking is safer for long-term users who do not inhale, so take in less tar: on the other hand, cigarette smokers who change to a substitute such as cigars usually continue to inhale, and may be worse off than before. Herbal cigarettes do not contain nicotine, but produce tar and carbon monoxide. Switching to a lower tar brand of cigarette may (or may not) reduce the risk of lung cancer, depending on the individual's smoking habit. The only safe form of smoking is no smoking at all.

The British Medical Association, which is running a vigorous campaign against tobacco, points out that of those who know the results of the habit – doctors – less than 15 per cent now smoke. The medical consensus in Britain, Europe, the USA and the World Health Organization is that smoking is a disabling, disease-causing, and frequently fatal occupation. As the US Surgeon-General said in 1982: 'Cigarette smoking . . . is the chief, single, avoidable cause of death in our society, and the most important public health issue of our time.'

See also FOOD IN THE UK

REFERENCES

ASH – Fact Sheets 1–9, 1985–7.

British Medical Association, Press Releases, April to November 1986.

British Medical Association, *Smoking out the Barons*, 1986.

Jacobson, Bobbie, 'Women and Smoking', in *The Politics of Tobacco*, Cambridge Health Promotion, BMA, 1986.

Taylor, Peter, *The Smoke Ring*, Sphere, 1985.

Wilkinson, James, *Tobacco*, Penguin Books, 1986.

Ulster Cancer Foundation / ASH, *The Economic Consequences of Smoking in Northern Ireland*, 1986.

McGourty, Christine, 'Legislation needed to protect non-smokers', *New Scientist*, 31 March 1988.

Sadgrove, Judy, 'Smoking out the Ladykillers', *Guardian*, 7 October 1986.

Wintour, Patrick, 'Prohibition is Just Around the Corner', *Guardian*, 19 March 1987.

Parliamentary written answer, 13 March 1987.

CONTACTS

Action on Smoking and Health (ASH)
British Medical Association

National Society for Clean Air
Department of Health and Social Security

Species Extinction

There are over 13,000 known species of mammals and birds, thousands of reptiles and fish, some 250,000 plants, and millions of invertebrates (i.e., insects, worms and other species that do not have a backbone). Extinction is a natural feature of the evolution of life on earth, the best-known example being the disappearance of the dinosaur.

In the last 400 years, however, human activities have been responsible for the loss of most of the animals and plants that have disappeared. Gone for ever, for example, are seventeen species or subspecies of bears, five of wolves and foxes, four of cats, ten of cattle, sheep, goats and antelopes, five of horses, zebras and asses, and three of deer. These are large mammals: there are thousands of insects, plants and small mammals which have suffered the same fate.

Estimates as to the total number of species in the world vary between 5 and 30 million, with the scientific consensus currently at the lower end of the scale. The calculations vary because of the number of life-forms which are as yet unlisted.

The last dodo was killed in Mauritius in 1681; the passenger pigeon, which used to congregate in enormous flocks over North America barely a hundred years ago, was wiped out for food early this century. Current estimates are that up to a million species will disappear by the year 2000 (including a large number that we have not yet discovered); if this is true, this means the loss of one type of animal, plant or invertebrate every six minutes. E. O. Wilson in *Biodiversity* (1988) hypothesizes a smaller rate of loss – some 17,500 species per year, or one species every 30 minutes. Whichever projection is true, the current rate of species loss is appalling.

There are many causes for species extinction, most of which are examined in other sections in this book. In the majority of cases, the principal threat is the disappearance of the types of environment on which the life-form depends:

1. A crucial loss of habitat has been the destruction of the tropical rain forests, where roughly one-twelfth of the world's land area hosts an estimated half of all the world's species. Forty to fifty per cent of these forests have disappeared, much of this since the Second World War, with destruction continuing apace (see DEFORESTATION).

2. Another significant factor is the loss of WETLANDS, a fertile habitat type. The World Wide Fund for Nature estimates that half of all the world's wetlands have disappeared this century.

3. Countryside changes have also contributed, as semi-natural and natural land has been taken over by agriculture (see COUNTRYSIDE IN THE UK) and PESTICIDES have destroyed a number of habitats. In many countries, over-intensive agriculture has led to a breakdown in the vitality of the land (see DESERTIFICATION), which becomes unable to support the plants and animals that previously lived there. The process of building roads and towns itself changes the environment, making it uninhabitable for certain species (see TRANSPORT POLICY IN THE UK).

Species extinction occurs in both the developed and developing worlds. The Organization for Economic Cooperation and Development (OECD) has gathered information as to the state of wildlife in the 24 major Western industrial nations. In these countries, roughly a quarter of all mammals are classified as threatened.

Among declining mammals around the world, the large species – grizzly bear, wolf, wild cat, and the blue, humpback and sperm whale – figure prominently.

Gaps in the OECD's data have been filled by *World Resources 1987*, and the status of species in different industrial countries has been calculated. The UK, by comparison with others, has a high number of birds, mammals, and fish threatened with extinction on a national basis.

The world's habitat changes have been brought about by a remorseless growth of the human population, which has exerted enormous stress on the environment. There is another cause of species extinction, however, which is considered below: the collecting or hunting of wildlife, and the multi-billion dollar trade that this services. The Secretary-General of CITES, the treaty administering wildlife trade around the world, reckons illegal activities to be worth between $4 billion to $6 billion annually – second only in scale to drug trafficking.

The CITES agreement

CITES, the Convention on International Trade in Endangered Species of Wild Fauna and Flora, came into force on 1 July 1975 and now has 95 member countries. The signatories agree to ban commercial trade in endangered species, which are listed under Appendix I of the treaty. Among those listed are all apes, lemurs, the giant panda, many South American monkeys, great whales, cheetah, leopards, tiger, Asian elephant, all rhinoceroses, many birds of prey, cranes, pheasants and parrots, all sea turtles, some crocodiles and lizards, giant salamanders, orchids and cacti.

Other species, which are categorized as being at serious risk though not yet threatened with extinction, are listed under Appendix II of the Convention. The intention is to control and monitor trade in these species, so that over-exploitation does not lead to their extinction.

Countries which want to protect their populations of particular species can place them on Appendix III. Trade in animals and products from these populations is then regulated in the same way as for Appendix II.

Trade in both endangered and threatened species is controlled by issuing permits. Appendix I species, or products based on them, are allowed to be traded only in very exceptional circumstances (as scientific exchange; as animals genuinely bred in captivity; as personal and household effects; or because they were acquired before the Convention came into effect).

International trade in Appendix II species is permitted with proper documentation issued by the government of the exporting country. Appendix II includes, among others, all species in the following groups which are not already in Appendix I: primates, cats, otters, whales, dolphins and porpoises, birds of prey, tortoises, crocodiles, and orchids; and many others, such as the African elephant, fur seals, the black stork, birds of paradise, the coelacanth, some snails, birdwing butterflies, and black corals. All in all, CITES lists some 700 species.

Countries may enforce even stricter control than that required by CITES if they wish to give special protection to certain fauna or flora – or they may, if they wish, ban trade in all their wildlife.

Problems with species

In spite of CITES, which is a useful protection for wildlife, a number of species continue to decline. Environmental organizations attribute this to inadequate enforcement, to a low prioritization of wildlife protection in many countries, and to a changing attitude on the part of CITES itself: as Greenpeace comment in their CITES report *Endangering Wildlife*:

> The original motivation for the Convention was the protection of wildlife endangered by trade. However, a momentum has gradually developed to change the purpose of CITES to one of promoting the trade in wildlife.

CITES' Secretary-General Eugene Lapointe commented in 1986:

> We feel strongly at CITES that sometimes the only way to preserve a species is to make it economically attractive to local populations who might otherwise destroy the animal because it is a pest to agriculture, dangerous for human beings, or whatever. The elephant is a good example of this: controlled commercial exploitation of ivory tusks adds to the elephant's worth to peoples in Africa.

Without CITES, the situation for endangered species would be much worse than the critical state which now exists. There is ample room, however, for CITES to be tightened up and applied both more rigorously and on a more widespread basis. The reason for some countries' non-enforcement of CITES is simple negligence. Other countries, such as Japan, turn a blind eye to the illegal trade.

The wildlife trade is a highly lucrative business and involves a wide variety of species, both as live specimens, and as products. Millions of live animals and plants are shipped around the world each year to supply the pet trade and to meet the demand for ornamental plants. Furskins, leather, ivory and timber, and articles manufactured from these materials are all traded in large quantities.

CITES Secretariat

The Greenpeace report describes a number of ways of bypassing CITES: backdating permits, smuggling animals in aircraft baggage, hiding them inside cages of other species that do not need permits. French Guiana is singled out for particular condemnation: it has a long border with Brazil and Surinam, and so is difficult to patrol. Wildlife can easily be smuggled into the country, from where, as a *département* of France, it can be exported to any EC country with no CITES permits being necessary.

The free market conditions within the EC make evasion of CITES particularly easy. Countries with rigorous customs controls can be entered by importing the wildlife through less rigorous nations, and then sending the cargo to its original destination. The work of the smugglers is facilitated by understaffing at customs posts, lack of training in species identification, and penalties which appear not to take the offence of CITES evasion too seriously.

Greenpeace and other environmental organizations want the EC to set up a CITES enforcement agency under the control of the Commission, which would be responsible for implementing CITES in all member states.

CITES depends on the collation of adequate data on world trade in wildlife. Most monitoring is done on behalf of CITES by the Wildlife Trade Monitoring Unit (WTMU), which is part of the IUCN World Conservation Monitoring Centre in Cambridge, UK. WMTU receives data from governments, and also from IUCN/WWF TRAFFIC offices in many countries (TRAFFIC = Trade Records Analysis of Flora and Fauna in Commerce).

Animal extinctions: two examples

Some of the larger mammals are being literally hunted to death. *South* magazine has described prices being fetched for certain species: a panda skin sells for £50,000 in Taiwan; a Spix's macaw stolen from its nest in north-eastern Brazil fetched $20,000 after being smuggled into Paraguay; Taipei zoo illegally imported gorillas from Cameroon at $645,000 for two pairs.

Many observers believe that it is now too late to save the rhinoceros from destruction – and others say that the African elephant will not be far behind. Large mammals appear to be particularly threatened.

Rhinoceros There are five species of rhino, numbering about 10,000 in all. Two-thirds of them are in Africa and one-third in Asia.

The Secretary-General of CITES commented in October 1986: 'They really are in danger of extinction, and almost everywhere the populations are crashing as the poachers attack the few remaining strongholds of the species.'

The money to be made from the trade in rhinoceros horn is so great that incentives to continue trading far outweigh the threat of relatively small penalties that are often imposed. A kilogram of rhino-horn powder – fabled, erroneously, as an aphrodisiac – is worth almost as much as the equivalent weight in gold. Even in countries where rhinoceros smuggling is a great risk – in Zimbabwe, for example, game wardens have killed 20 rhinoceros poachers – the trackers are not deterred.

According to *World Resources 1986*, the black rhino population stood at 15,000 in 1980, but had dropped to fewer than half that number by 1985. (In the Central African Republic, numbers plunged from 3,000 to about 150.) The southern race of white rhino has increased slightly, but the northern race has dropped from almost 1,000 to at most one dozen.

The three species of Asian rhino, though rather better protected, are equally threatened, with the rarest – the Javan rhinoceros – numbering about 50.

Elephant   The Asian elephant is listed under Appendix I of CITES, and is therefore classified as a most endangered species.

The African elephant is widely hunted for its ivory, the price of which has increased from $5 per kilogram in the 1960s to some $50 per kilo now. The increase in ivory value was followed by a wave of elephant poaching in East Africa, where several populations were drastically reduced.

It is difficult to estimate the total elephant population of Africa, as the numbers in the Zaire basin are difficult to quantify: research by a leading expert, Iain Douglas-Hamilton, indicated approximately one million. Revised figures quoted by Keith Lindsay in *New Scientist* (November 1986) indicate between 800,000 and 900,000 animals. Populations in most African countries are falling rapidly, with up to 2,000 elephants being killed every week.

Elephants are slow to reproduce. The maximum growth rate is between 3 and 7 per cent a year, and this figure has been documented only in the Addo Park in South Africa, where a fed and fenced herd of

17 animals increased to 108 in 27 years. In disturbed conditions their reproduction rate can dwindle to 2 per cent per year.

This means that elephants are susceptible to being over-exploited, with herds unable to recover in adverse conditions. Ivory hunters exterminated the species in North Africa perhaps a thousand years ago, in much of South Africa by the nineteenth century, and in most of West Africa by the end of the twentieth century. There is evidence that the process can be reversed. In the late nineteenth and early twentieth centuries some colonial powers regulated the slaughter of the animals, and populations in certain areas recovered.

The prognosis for the elephant is not good, however. For continued survival of the species, hunting should be kept to the reproductive rate, of about 5 per cent. A 10 per cent annual kill could halve remaining populations within a decade. Contraband ivory, according to *South* magazine, has been the main reason for a 40 per cent drop in Africa's elephant population over the last seven years (this figure is difficult to verify).

With the price of ivory remaining high, the elephant is a valuable commodity. A CITES quota system began in January 1986: time will tell whether this is successful or not. Sixteen of the 35 African states with elephants are part of the system.

One theory is that the elephant population will fall to about 150,000, the number inhabiting the most protected areas, where it will then stabilize. Stabilization, however, depends on an efficient system of keeping poachers away: at the moment, most of the herds that are dwindling in number have at least nominal protected status.

In May 1989, the Environmental Investigation Agency publicized the plight of the elephant with a series of films documenting their mass slaughter. Elephant populations have plummeted in the 1980s – one estimate in 1989 was that only 350,000 are left, with large numbers dying annually. In view of the threatened demise of the species before the end of the century, a number of countries started talking about ending the ivory trade. The EC voted to ban imports of ivory in June 1989: in October 1989, CITES discussed a total ban on ivory trading.

The implications of species protection

There have been examples where a species has been rescued from the brink of destruction. The oryx, for example, was reported to be extinct in the wild in 1971. Successful breeding from the 1962 'world herd' of eight oryxes has achieved a current population of almost 800.

The tiger project, in India, is another success. In 1930 there were 100,000 tigers worldwide: by the early 1970s only 5,000 were left. In 1972 the World Wildlife Fund launched Operation Tiger to save the species, and pledged a million dollars to help countries set up tiger reserves. India reacted enthusiastically, and set up 15 reserves. The number of tigers in India has doubled since the start of the project. In addition to the tiger, a number of other species have prospered.

Successful though such schemes have been – other stories that are quoted usually include the re-establishment of the South American vicuña, nearly hunted to extinction because of its fine silky wool, and the saving of the American bison – they nevertheless provide some worrying questions.

- Breeding in captivity, though a justifiable system for saving a species, remains a second-best solution. It is damage limitation rather than damage prevention. It is also impractical to hope that zoos will be able to save more than a fraction of the world's species.
- The establishment of an animal reserve depends on an adequate standard of living among the humans who surround the reserve. True, in the short term it is possible to protect an area with rifles and game wardens: but if the reserve is to survive, it must be because the local population support the idea, not because they are frightened of being shot.

  This has long-term implications for the developed countries. If they want the Third World to protect the large share of the world's environment that it inhabits, they will have to reconsider the financial commitment they are making to ensuring that the people in the beneficiary country, as well as selected animals, have minimal resources. Erik Eckholm's comment is apt: 'As long as large numbers are denied the chance to make a decent living, the nature reserves will be in jeopardy.' A nature reserve has questionable long-term prospects if it is surrounded by people whose only potential source of food or wealth lies in the protected area.

Biological diversity

'Species extinction' is often considered in its most dramatic sense – the disappearance of recognizable animals such as the rhinoceros or whale. This is lamented on philosophical or moral grounds.

The loss of plant species, however, has extremely worrying implications for the human race. The IUCN's Threatened Plants Committee reckons that 10 per cent of the world's flowering plants are 'dangerously rare or under threat': 25,000 plants could be extinct by the end of the century.

The loss to medical research can only be guessed at. Currently, about one-quarter of all medicines still contain components derived from flowering plants: in spite of sophisticated technology, we can synthesize only seven major pharmaceuticals more cheaply than they can be produced from plants.

Scientists at the University of Illinois reckon that only 5,000 species of flowering plants have been thoroughly examined as potential sources of useful drugs – just 2 per cent of species known to exist. As around 40 of these actually provide substances of medical importance, the number of plants predicted to become extinct by the year 2000 could include 200 drug-yielding species. The genetic pool which has provided the basis for much scientific advance in the past is being seriously depleted.

This is a very human-centred way of looking at the problem of species extinction. There is a planetary dimension. We still do not understand all the complexities of the way in which the atmosphere, the sea and the land maintain their equilibrium. The biological diversity which has evolved over the centuries may be a cornerstone of this equilibrium. Humanity's extinction of hundreds of thousands of species could have undreamt-of reverberations.

See also ANIMALS; COUNTRYSIDE IN THE UK; DEFORESTATION; DESERTIFICATION; MARINE POLLUTION; PESTICIDES; TRANSPORT POLICY IN THE UK; WETLANDS

REFERENCES

CITES Secretariat, *CITES Leaflet*, undated.
CITES Convention and Appendices, 1980.
CITES, Press Releases, June and October 1986.

EC CITES, *Endangering Wildlife* (report), Greenpeace Environmental Trust, 1987.
Eckholm, Erik P., *Down to Earth*, Pluto Press, 1982.

IUCN, *World Conservation Strategy*, 1980.

OECD, *OECD Environmental Data Compendium*, 1987.

Strawberry Research, personal communication, 1988.

UNEP, *Environmental Report*, Basil Blackwell, 1987.

Wilson, E. O., (ed.) *Biodiversity*, National Academy Press, 1988.

World Resource Institute, IIED, *World Resources 1986*, Basic Books, 1986.

Environmental Investigation Agency, personal communication.

Forse, Bill, 'Elephant Decline Blamed on Ivory Poachers', *New Scientist*, 16 June 1987.

Lindsay, Keith, 'Trading Elephants for Ivory', *New Scientist*, 6 November 1986.

Smith, Malcolm, 'Where Have All the Medicines Gone?', *Guardian*, 13 September 1987.

South, October 1987.

CONTACTS

Convention on International Trade in Endangered Species of Wild Fauna and Flora (CITES)

Environmental Investigation Agency

Fauna and Flora Preservation Society

Greenpeace

International League for the Protection of Cetaceans

International Union for Conservation of Nature and Natural Resources (IUCN)

People's Trust for Endangered Species

TRAFFIC

United Nations Environment Programme (UNEP)

World Wide Fund for Nature (WWF – formerly World Wildlife Fund)

Three Mile Island

The nuclear power station accident at Three Mile Island, Pennsylvania on 28 March 1979 was the first acknowledged large-scale nuclear disaster. There had been other incidents – notably the fire at Windscale, UK, in October 1957, and an alleged major accident in the Ural mountains in the winter of 1957 – but both had been shrouded by official secrecy, with the scale of the event being minimized by the UK and USSR governments. Three Mile Island occurred in full view of 300 journalists over a period of three days, and was reported as it happened around the world. Until CHERNOBYL, TMI was regarded as the most significant example of what could go wrong with nuclear power.

The accident

Mark Stephens's book *Three Mile Island* (1980) gives a detailed account of what happened to the TMI Pressurized Water Reactor known as Unit 2. In 1979, the plant was new, having been licensed in February the year before. There was great confidence within the nuclear industry about nuclear power in general and this type of plant in particular: at the licensing hearings in 1977, the US Nuclear Regulatory Commission agreed with the power station's owners that it would be a waste of time to debate the effectiveness of reactor safety systems in the face of a large-scale accident, because such an accident could never happen.

The owners, Metropolitan Edison, had written to the local town hall in 1974: 'Even the worst possible accident postulated by the Atomic Energy Commission would not require an evacuation of the borough of Middletown . . . based upon the discussion above, it can be seen that it is unnecessary to have specific evacuation routes identified for the borough of Middletown.' At the time of the accident, there were no evacuation plans for any township or city round Three Mile Island.

The accident, when it occurred, was caused by a number of factors. At 4.00 A.M. two feedwater pumps failed in the secondary cooling system of Unit 2: there was no longer any water circulating to remove heat from the reactor, and the temperature and pressure of water inside the reactor soared. Emergency systems swung into operation: within nine seconds, the plant 'scrammed', and 69 boron and silver control rods dropped into place among the 36,816 zirconium fuel rods. These rods absorbed neutrons, and stopped a chain reaction (see NUCLEAR ENERGY: A NUCLEAR GLOSSARY).

After this, things began to go wrong. A relief valve had opened to release some of the super-pressurized cooling water; as reactor pressure dropped, this valve should have closed, retaining the vital fluid inside the reactor. However, it stayed open, allowing the coolant to escape unnoticed. At the same time, the emergency feedwater system failed, blocked by closed valves.

The four operators on duty had to make split-second decisions based on inadequate information. A crucial warning light was covered by a paper tag. Another apparently failed to operate. They were faced with events that were outside their normal training or experience.

After eight minutes, more than a hundred alarm lights were showing on their control board. The coolant was overheating, producing bubbles of steam which further reduced coolant flow. By 6.15 A.M., the reactor core, from being covered by six feet of water, was partially uncovered. The valve which had stayed open had released a quarter of a million gallons of radioactive cooling water, which was now filling the reactor and auxiliary buildings.

The operators, in trying to prevent catastrophe, removed more water from the system and exacerbated the problem. Within three hours, the core had deteriorated to the point that radiation from the damaged fuel was 'shining' – beaming through the 8-inch steel walls of the reactor vessel and the 4-foot-thick walls of the containment building. All this was unknown to the people in control, however: they called the local Nuclear Regulatory Commission to tell them that there was a 'slight problem at Three Mile Island'.

Three days of confusion

After the alarm was sounded, increasing numbers of nuclear experts were rushed to Three Mile Island. Unfortunately, it was almost impossible for them to know what was happening inside the stricken reactor, as high radiation levels precluded close examination. Walter Patterson comments in *Nuclear Power* (1983):

What followed, for the next three days, was an almost unbelievable chronicle of confusion, misinformation, contradictory advice and – for the hapless thousands of people living in south-western Pennsylvania – nightmare uncertainty, the fear that an invisible, undetectable horror might engulf them, and that those in charge were blundering around like lumberjacks attempting brain surgery.

A day after the accident, the situation deteriorated. A hydrogen bubble formed in the reactor vessel, with the possibility of exploding and showering radioactivity into the air. Experts from the Nuclear Regulatory Commission desperately tried to calculate whether the bubble would explode, and if so, what they could do to prevent it. While they were doing this, it gradually dissipated of its own accord.

The scientists' helplessness in the face of the threatened catastrophe became apparent to the governmental and media representatives who were following the situation closely. When President Carter toured the site four days after the accident, he was given two different pieces of advice from NRC representatives: one, that the hydrogen bubble was likely to explode at any time; the other, that it wasn't. The governor of the state eventually came to mistrust the assurances he was being given, to the extent of advising pregnant women and pre-school children living within five miles of the plant to evacuate the area. Within a few hours, 40,000 people had left. More than 150,000 people were eventually evacuated.

There were no direct casualties of the incident. For this reason, Metropolitan Edison and the nuclear lobby took the view that Three Mile Island proved the safety of nuclear installations. A report commissioned by the Nuclear Regulatory Commission, however, came to the conclusion that the reactor had been within 60 minutes of meltdown on the morning of 28 March: a catastrophe had been averted by sheer luck.

Lessons of the accident

It is sometimes said that orders for nuclear power stations began to be cancelled after Three Mile Island. This process, however, had started six years before, as the promised economic benefits of nuclear power failed to come to fruition (see NUCLEAR ENERGY: DIFFICULTIES AND COSTS). The accident was nevertheless a public rebuttal of the safety case being argued for the nuclear option, and had a number of consequences. Previous risk estimates of the likelihood of serious accident were re-examined and found to be fallacious. The national recommended evacuation zone of two to three miles around a nuclear reactor was upgraded to ten miles. The slow move away from nuclear power became a rush in the United States.

The people living around the plant were badly affected by the disaster. More than twenty anti-nuclear groups sprang up, and vigorously opposed the reopening of the other nuclear unit at the plant. It eventually did reopen, however, in October 1985. During its first month of operation, the plant suffered two leaks of radioactive gas.

There were other consequences. During the year after the accident, all eight of the operational Babcock and Wilcox PWRs in the United States (the same type as at Three Mile Island) were closed for regulatory reasons, for an average 27 per cent of the time they could have operated. A country that had concentrated its power production in nuclear power would have been severely inconvenienced by an occurrence such as this.

The accident was expensive. Metropolitan Edison had to purchase replacement power from neighbouring utilities for $900,000 a day. A year elapsed before the clean-up could begin – using 1,700 engineers and technicians, scrubbing the buildings with detergents and water. Clean-up costs, even before decommissioning, were $1 billion by 1989. The total bill, in replacement power, clean-up, rebuilding and legal expenses is likely, according to Stephens, to be $3 billion.

The accident may well have caused significant health problems, too: 2,000 lawsuits alleging damage to health are still outstanding. Lawyers suing the power station owners collected evidence that the death rate among elderly Americans surged in the three years after the incident. Evidence from official US health statistics showed an additional 50,000 to 130,000 deaths, mainly in surrounding states. It was alleged that there may have been a connection between low-level radiation release and suppression of immune systems. The claims were treated very cautiously by nuclear analysts.

See also CHERNOBYL; NUCLEAR ENERGY: DIFFICULTIES AND COSTS, A NUCLEAR GLOSSARY

REFERENCES

Bertell, Rosalie, *No Immediate Danger*, Women's Press, 1985.

Ince, Martin, *Sizewell Report*, Pluto Press, 1984.

Patterson, Walter C., *Nuclear Power*, Penguin Books, second edition, 1983.

Pollock, Cynthia, 'Decommissioning Nuclear Power Plants', in *State of the World 1986*, W. W. Norton, 1986.

Stephens, Mark, *Three Mile Island*, Junction Books, 1980.

Hawkes, Nigel, 'Still active after all these years', *Observer*, 9 April 1989.

CONTACTS

Friends of the Earth
Greenpeace

World Information Service on Energy (WISE)

Transport Policy in the UK

Transport decisions are rarely clear-cut from the environmental point of view. One person's urgently required bypass is another's lost landscape.

This comment, from the 1987 Department of Transport document *Transport and the Environment*, reflects the need for balance when planning the UK's transport policy. A new road can be beneficial for a small number of people, but represent an irretrievable loss to the environment: on the other hand, an industrial country needs roads. Perhaps the most telling thing about this quote, however, is that it refers to the balance between *roads* and the environment, rather than looking at transport policy as a whole. In the UK, 'transport policy' has increasingly come to mean 'Let's build more roads.'

One-sided approach
The environmental argument against Britain's current transport policy is that it is one-sided, favouring the road lobby and the private motorist to the exclusion of alternative transport possibilities. The needs of road users such as cyclists or pedestrians are minimized; public sector transport is progressively run down; environmental deterioration is tolerated or even imposed.

The commitment to roads is ideological, and will not be swayed by arguments either of logic or sound financial practice. The result is a transport policy that benefits a minority of the population at the expense of the majority. It also wastes enormous sums of money.

Internationally, British transport policy is eccentric: its rail network has tighter financial targets than in any other industrial country, company cars are subsidized more than anywhere else in Europe, and the system of bus deregulation has been adopted only in Chile, Kuala Lumpur and Kingston, Jamaica.

The consequences of this policy distortion are a deterioration in standard of living for people who do not have their own transport, or who want to use the roads as pedestrians or cyclists; the degradation of large areas of countryside and the loss of a number of habitats; pollution, noise and vibration for people living near large roads; and air pollution that threatens large sections of the environment.

Roads: costs and benefits

Of the Department of Transport's (DTp) staffing nationally, more than 10,000 people are employed in vehicle licensing, testing and taxation; nearly 2,500 work on roads; and 72 work on railways. Even allowing for the fact that BR employs its own staff, the figures give an indication of the importance of rail travel to the DTp.

The government 'invests' in roads and 'subsidizes' railways. The criteria for assessing a proposed road are different to those used for evaluating a new railway. Rail has to provide an 'economic' return in cash terms after the costs of laying track, staffing and rolling stock are taken into account. Roads are not subject to the same restraints.

A cost benefit analysis (COBA) is used to decide whether the proposed road is viable. This estimates how many people would use the road, what savings in travelling time would be achieved, and what economic value could be assigned to the result.

COBA is a subjective tool that does not produce consistent results, even on the simplest roads, and is easy to manipulate in order to produce the desired figures. To give an idea of the arbitrariness of the system, these are the economic values placed on working time in order to estimate the financial 'benefits' of a new road (1976 figures – they have since been uprated for inflation):

- Car driver – 379p per hour
- Car passenger – 332p per hour
- Bus passenger – 196p per hour

The calculations favour car drivers over other road users (figures for walking or cycling were not even calculated before 1987). What is more, the pro-car bias is being increased: in March 1987, it was announced that the 'value' of leisure motoring in the calculations is to be uprated to 58 per cent above its previous level. With the new figures, the apparent economic benefits of road schemes will now be even greater.

COBA is a circular argument. If the economic case is not strong enough, the figures can be recalculated until they are. This occurred in 1986, at the inquiry into the East London River Crossing: 134 days into the inquiry, the DTp adjusted its initial calculations and added £14.5 million in benefits to the scheme. What had been a loss-making project now appeared profitable.

Public sector transport is underfinanced on the grounds that it has to stand on its own two feet. This stipulation is not applied to road-building.

If people want to commute into London, who am I to say they shouldn't? If we believe in consumer choice, in individual freedom, why pillory drivers on the dreadful offence of congestion? . . . I make no apologies for being pro-motorist.

Nicholas Ridley, Secretary of State for Transport, 1984

Since 1979 we have increased spending on national roads by 30% in real terms.

Nicholas Ridley, 1985
(Mr Ridley subsequently became Secretary of State for the Environment)

Roads are expensive in terms of:

- *Life and limb*   5,041 people killed in 1988, and 317,000 injured.
- *Pollution*   Traffic causes 85 per cent of national carbon monoxide emissions, 45 per cent of nitrogen oxides, 28 per cent of hydrocarbons, and significant noise pollution.
- *Environmental destruction*   At least 110 Sites of Special Scientific Interest (SSSIs) have been destroyed or damaged in the last few years, or are threatened with damage, by road schemes.
- *Resources*   National spending on building and maintaining roads is more than £3 billion p.a.; NHS cost of road accidents 1985 – £2.8 billion; planned upgrading of 70 urban roads in London – £1.5 billion; over the last 20 years, billions have been spent on road schemes in London, but average road speeds in most of the capital have declined;
- *Subsidy*   £2 billion per year in tax concessions to company cars before the 1988 budget. Thereafter, approximately £1 billion per

year. 79 per cent of all cars entering central London in 1984 were subsidized (although only 16 per cent of commuters went to work by car). No other industrial country operates this subsidy on such a large scale. 58 per cent of all new cars are bought as company cars or are otherwise subsidized by the tax payer.

Percentage of company cars in national fleet	
UK	12
Sweden	8
W. Germany	6
USA	4
Japan	negligible

Source: Environmental Data Services, *Report no. 156*, January 1988

Carparking is subsidized, too. Councils overspent by 250 per cent on carparking schemes in 1985–6, 336 per cent in 1984–5, a total of £62 million. *One* new Westminster City Council carpark will lose £300,000 a year. Compare this with national government spending on cycling for the whole country in 1985 – £500,000.

1988 was the UK's fourth record year for car sales. Each year, more than 2 million new cars arrive on Britain's roads – and the UK's car population increased by 25 per cent between 1985 and 1988.

It is strongly debatable whether new roads provide value for money. The rationale is that they cut costs by reducing journey time, but transport costs are a small percentage of overall costs, usually no more than 5 per cent. Roads rarely reduce journey time by more than 10 per cent. The maximum financial saving is 0.5 per cent.

These figures are intuitive, as the Department of Transport is lax in following up the impact of its traffic schemes. In 1985, the National Audit Office found that 'regional offices often failed to send reports to headquarters . . . From 62 schemes requiring actual traffic flows to be notified only one report had been submitted.'

The State is also passing up the chance of reclaiming £100 million a year in unpaid Vehicle Excise Licence duty. This could be achieved by abolishing the tax and increasing the price of petrol to make up the revenue loss. The government refuses to do this, or to take alternative measures to clamp down on tax evasion.

The Department of Transport estimates that building motorways and trunk roads will over 30 years provide traffic benefits worth £1.50 for every £1.00 spent. The Greater London Council identified alternative expenditure which would reap much greater rewards:

Road construction	£1.50
Better fares and ticketing	£2.30
Parking enforcement	£3.00
Publicizing public transport	£4.00
Bus priority measures	£5.00
Accident remedial schemes	£7.00

More imaginative thinking would produce significant benefits. As an example, the Institution of Highways and Transportation has suggested that over 1,000 road deaths a year could be prevented by spending £10 million per year for the next 20 years on special schemes. This would be a real financial saving. The government is not interested in this kind of value for money because it wants to build roads.

The misapplication of finance has environmental consequences. Public transport is less environmentally damaging than private transport because it doesn't use up so many natural resources – clean air, raw materials and land.

Road building also has a directly negative effect, however: the sectioning of the countryside decreases the area available to small mammals, with a resultant loss of species variety. Department of Transport publicity focuses on such things as badger tunnels, toad crossings and wildlife variety on motorway verges. The habitats would have been even more attractive if the roads hadn't been built in the first place.

Similarly, the DTp claims about the number of trees that have been planted by roadsides, or the 'disguising' of motorway schemes by hiding them in cuttings or behind screens, ignores the greater benefit to the environment of not building the road scheme at all. The DTp says that 'Great care has been taken to fit the M25 into the landscape as unobtrusively as possible' (*Policy for Roads in England*: 1987). An unobtrusive six-lane motorway is a contradiction in terms. Similarly, 'A well landscaped new road can improve the environment' (*Transport and the Environment*, 1987) is a rather bizarre statement to make.

Any industrial country has to have road schemes, but it seems logical that there should be a limit somewhere. The Department of Transport is currently responsible for maintaining over 6,000 miles of motorways and trunk roads; England alone has nearly 160,000 miles of roads. In 1989, a £12 billion plan was foward to widen and extend the UK's motorway network. The road expansion philosophy is founded in the 1950s and needs to be superseded by something a little more up-to-date.

Public transport

While expenditure on roads has increased, spending on public transport has been radically reduced.

British Rail has to get official approval to invest its money, resulting in long delays in approval of new rolling stock and electrification. At 29 per cent, Britain has the lowest level of electrification in Western Europe.

BR has been set the tightest financial targets of any rail network in the industrial countries. The network is also greatly underfunded in comparison with other European countries.

Public investment in railways, 1984

Country	Investment, £ per train km	Investment as % of costs	% of costs covered by fares
Britain	0.264	8.9	71.2
Sweden	0.410	13.4	83.1
Eire	0.490	12.5	48.9
France	0.703	15.6	55.3
Norway	0.742	20.2	59.2
The Netherlands	0.789	30.0	50.0
Denmark	0.823	37.5	61.0
Switzerland	1.062	30.8	60.8
West Germany	1.284	26.1	53.0
Italy	1.453	25.1	32.0
Belgium	1.592	39.4	47.3
Finland	1.992	51.6	50.2
Austria	2.154	38.8	54.0

Source: Hash, *Government Policy and Rail Transport in Western Europe*, as quoted in *Capital Schemes?* 1987

Environmental Data Services *Report no. 156* makes the point that, in 1986–7, the subsidy to keep British Rail's rural lines open was £740 million; the bus subsidy was £440 million; London's underground subsidy was £80 million. This totalled £1,260 million, about three-fifths of the subsidy given to a small section of the population – company car drivers.

British Rail receives one-third of the amount of financial support received by the French railway system, and one-sixth that of West Germany. Its annual grant has been cut by £275 million in the mid-1980s.

This means that the money 'can't be found' for small, local rail schemes, although the DTp was able to locate £8.5 million overnight for a tunnel to facilitate the East London River Crossing road scheme.

When a road is overcrowded, the response is to widen it. When a rail line becomes too popular, British Rail is forced to raise fares in order to reduce the number of passengers. Rail fares on some popular routes increased 15 per cent in real terms from 1984 to 1987.

The same paradoxical standards have been applied to the public transport system in London. While enormous sums can be found for road-building in the capital, public transport is regarded as a drag on the public purse and funding is severely limited. London Regional Transport have made substantial cuts to meet the shortfall, with the balance of the cost falling on the ratepayers.

Central government funding for LRT (£ million)	
1984–5	175
1985–6	130
1986–7	79

In enforcing these cuts, the government has ignored the success of the previous (GLC) transport policy. As a result of the GLC's integrated ticketing and new fares policy 1982–84,

- Bus use rose 13 per cent;
- Tube use rose 44 per cent;
- Car commuting fell 21 per cent.

There were fewer cars on the roads, traffic moved more quickly, there was less pollution – and an estimated 3,500 fewer road casualties in 1983. The GLC was lambasted for throwing money at public transport, whereas in reality the level of support was rather moderate.

Proportion of public transport costs in major cities met by subsidy, 1984–5

City	Percentage	City	Percentage
Turin	87	Bordeaux	70
Rome	81	Miami	69
Rotterdam	81	Los Angeles	69
Amsterdam	80	Antwerp	66
Genoa	79	Stockholm	63
Sheffield	78	Milan	62
Seattle	70	Paris	54
Athens	70	London	30

Source: *Jane's Urban Transport Systems*, 1985, as quoted in *Capital Schemes?* 1987

In addition to overt reduction of public transport investment, the government made two administrative changes that were crucial:

1. From 1980 to 1984, the New Bus Grant was reduced from 50 per cent to zero. This had a devastating effect on UK bus manufacture.

2. In 1985, the Transport Supplementary Grant was changed. In the past, county councils used this to subsidize all forms of transport. *From 1985, it could be used only for road-building*.

The Conservatives' major public transport policy – bus deregulation – was pushed through on the basis of one very inconclusive trial area. Deregulation outside London started on 1 January 1987.

There is some evidence of bus operators competing for rush-hour times and ignoring less densely populated schedules; of operators selling new vehicles and buying cheaper, older buses to meet competition; and of some operators failing to run registered services. Transport Minister John Moore claimed £40 million in savings from deregulation; much of this amount, small in transport terms, has been achieved by wage cuts. The figures need to be examined for their side-effects in terms of reliability and availability.

Secrecy, democracy and competence

Environmentalists accuse the Department of Transport of having a hidden agenda – road-building – and of operating secretively to protect that agenda. As an example, they point out that the DTp consistently denied having extra road-building schemes for London, until the National Audit Office uncovered a £1.5 billion provision for trunking 70 miles of London roads.

The most well-documented instance of governmental secrecy, some would say deceit, is the Falloden Way scheme in north-west London. Objectors have tabulated a 'Timetable of Deception'.

17 August 1982   Letter from Transport Minister Lynda Chalker to residents, saying the DTp 'had no intention of widening Falloden Way . . . and no plans to do so'.

8 November 1982   Letter from Lynda Chalker: 'We have no present plans to widen Falloden Way. We are not working on such plans'.

27 July 1983   Residents meet Lynda Chalker, who says the Department 'has no plans for widening Falloden Way'.

10 May 1984   Letter from Lynda Chalker to local MP Peter Thomas: 'No plans exist for this section of road at present'.

25 June 1984   Department of Transport announces five possible schemes for Falloden Way, four involving road widening. The level of detail suggests many months of hard preparation.

In terms of democracy, the government's record is debatable.

- The government's own Assessment Studies found that Londoners loathe heavy lorries and commuter cars, yet there are no plans for minimizing their impact on the capital. The studies also indicated dissatisfaction with one person operated (OPO) buses, which are 5 to 25 per cent slower than the 'back-loaders': yet plans go ahead for replacement of these buses by OPOs.
- Juggernauts are a major source of public nuisance, yet gross lorry weights were increased from 32.5 to 38 tonnes after the 1983 election. The government claims credit for not bringing in 40 tonne lorries, but on the other hand has issued instructions that firms overloading by up to 10 per cent are not to be prosecuted.
- Nicholas Ridley overrode 8,000 objections from management, consumers and unions in order to deregulate buses – a highly speculative venture with almost no trialling beforehand. He also ignored constitutional convention (the ruling of an all-Party Parliamentary Committee), local objections and government policy on National

Parks, to force the Okehampton bypass through Dartmoor National Park.

- On occasion government behaviour has actually been unlawful. Mr Ridley 'directed' the GLC to hold a public inquiry into its lorry ban; the courts decided that he had acted 'unlawfully'. He appealed against the decision: and lost.

After the misdrafting of the bill setting up London Regional Transport, Mr Ridley 'directed' the GLC to pay LRT £50 million to make up a financial shortcoming. This time, the courts decided that Mr Ridley had not only acted unlawfully – he had acted 'irrationally, unlawfully, and unreasonably'.

Our transport policy is intensely political, founded in an ideology of 'private transport – good; public transport – bad'. From the point of view of an intelligent relationship with the environment, the reverse applies.

See also AUTOMOBILE POLLUTION; COUNTRYSIDE IN THE UK; CYCLING

REFERENCES

DTp, *Policy for Roads in England: 1987*, 1987.

DTp, *Roads to Prosperity*, 1989.

DTp, *Transport and the Environment*, 1987.

Environmental Data Services, *Report no. 156*, January 1988.

FoE, *Capital Schemes?*, 1987.

FoE, *Getting There*, Friends of the Earth Transport Policy, September 1987.

Greenpeace, *Air Pollution from Cars*, 1988.

Hamer, Mick, *Wheels within Wheels*, Routledge and Kegan Paul, 1987.

Secrett, C. and V. C. Hodges, *Motorway Madness*, Friends of the Earth, 1986.

CONTACTS

Bus and Coach Council
Council for the Protection of Rural England
Friends of the Earth (FoE)
Greenpeace
Institute for Terrestrial Ecology
London Cycling Campaign
Nature Conservancy Council

Pedestrians' Association
Transport 2000
Transport Users' Consultative Committee

British Rail (BR)
British Road Federation
Department of Transport (DTp)

Water

UK WATER SUPPLY

Water in England and Wales is supplied by ten water authorities, which have power over the whole 'water cycle' from upland reservoirs to disposal of waste. They supply the water, check that it is clean, and have responsibility for treating or getting rid of polluted by-products.

The water authority members are not democratically elected but are appointed by local councils and the government. With the exception of the Welsh Water Authority, their meetings are held in secret. Fred Pearce points out in *Green Britain or Industrial Wasteland?* that industrialists are being appointed in ever-increasing numbers to the boards of water authorities. The 13 members of the North West Water Authority, for example, have included senior officials from Shell, ICI, Unilever, a Cumbrian paper mill and the CBI. At the time, ICI had people on no less than four out of the ten authorities.

Membership of water authorities is important: environmentalists argue that water quality is being sacrificed in the interests of the industrial lobby. The National Water Council used to have a statutory responsibility to work for higher standards in the water industry, especially on pollution, and for advising ministers on policy. It was abolished in 1983. Now, again according to Pearce, this advisory role has been taken over by individuals from the industrial sector.

Water supply in Scotland is the responsibility of the local authorities. In Northern Ireland it is administered by the Department of Environment at the Northern Ireland Office.

Drinking water

In 1854, Dr John Snow stole the handle of the local water pump in London's Soho, and set in train the great Victorian revolution that resulted in clean supplies of drinking water. Snow suspected, correctly, that the Broadwick Street pump was causing a local cholera

Standard regions, water authorities and river purification boards

United Kingdom

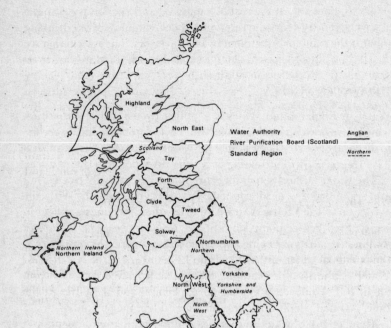

Water Authority	Anglian
River Purification Board (Scotland)	
Standard Region	*Northern*

Highland

North East

Scotland

Tay

Forth

Clyde

Tweed

Solway

Northern Ireland
Northern Ireland

Northumbrian
Northern

Yorkshire
Yorkshire and Humberside

North West

North West

East Midlands

Severn-Trent
West Midlands

Wales

Anglian
East Anglia

Welsh

Thames
South East

Wessex
South West

Southern

South West

Kilometres
0   80
0   50
Miles

The standard regions of England are those adopted on 1 April 1974 following the Local Government Act 1972. The water authorities in England and Wales came into effect on 1 April 1974 following the Water Act 1973. The river purification boards of Scotland came into effect on 16 May 1975 following the Local Government (Scotland) Act 1973. The Department of the Environment (Northern Ireland) is the sole water authority for Northern Ireland.

Source: *Digest of Environmental Pollution and Water Statistics*, 1987

outbreak. It had been contaminated by a leak from an infected cesspool.

Since the nineteenth century, Britain's water supplies have been free of the lethal organisms that plagued our ancestors. This was achieved, however, at the cost of a massive construction programme of sewers, pipe systems and reservoirs. The cleanliness of our drinking water is the result of investment by our ancestors. The system that we now have is old and in need of large expenditure if standards are to be maintained. Moreover, in addition to problems caused by leaking mains, collapsing sewers and inadequate treatment plants, modern science has identified a number of threats that were unknown to the Victorians.

Soft and hard water Hard water contains calcium and magnesium salts, whereas soft water does not. Most lowland waters of south and east England are hard: most highland waters, from Cornwall and Wales to the Pennines and Scottish Highlands are soft.

Soft water kills. That was the conclusion of a ten-year study by doctors at the Royal Free Hospital in London and scientists at the Water Research Centre into Heart Disease in 253 British towns. Their findings were published in 1980 in the *British Medical Journal* to a crescendo of silence from the water authorities and the Government. The findings suggested that perhaps 7,000 people die of heart disease in Britain because of the effects of soft water.

Pearce's excellent book *Watershed*, from which the extract above is taken, points out the connection between soft water supplies and cardio-vascular disease. Taking into account social and economic differences, different smoking rates and climatic variations, scientists are left with a 10 to 15 per cent difference in heart disease rates between those living in soft water areas and those living in medium or hard water zones. The highest heart disease rates are in central Scotland, Merseyside, West Yorkshire, Teesside, Northern Ireland and parts of Wales. These closely match areas served by soft moorland waters.

The reasons for this are unknown – is it something in soft water, or something missing from it? The correlation between soft water and heart disease appears convincing, however.

The Royal Free study identified variations in hardness ranging from 528 milligrams per litre of calcium carbonate equivalent in

Hartlepool, to 10 milligrams in Colwyn Bay. Half of the towns sampled had water softer than 170 milligrams – the level below which increased heart disease was found.

The World Health Organization and the EC believe that it is preferable for hardness to be kept above 100 milligrams per litre. In some areas, however, water authorities still soften their supplies – despite a warning from the Royal College of Physicians (1976) that 'it would seem prudent in the present state of knowledge not to soften drinking waters unless there is some overwhelming need to do so'.

Water which is corrosive appears to exacerbate the situation. Ayr, Dumfries, Kilmarnock, Halifax and Dewsbury had the most corrosive water supplied in the survey, and also had higher than predicted heart disease levels. The scientists suggested that zinc corroded from brass tap fittings may be an additional hazard here.

The Department of Health and Social Security warns against the use of water for infants which has been artificially softened using a salt-regenerated ion exchange water softener: the high sodium content can lead to illness.

Lead in water Des Wilson's book *The Lead Scandal* (1983) gives an excellent description of the way in which lead affects the body. It is toxic (i.e. it acts as a poison), particularly affecting the nervous system and its relationship with the brain. At high levels of absorption into the body, it causes 'classical' or 'clinical' lead poisoning, leading to, among other things, epilepsy, convulsion, paralysis or even death.

Lower levels of exposure, such as occur through breathing lead-polluted air or drinking contaminated water, do not have such dramatic and obvious effects. Consequences of this exposure are, however, extremely serious. Lead is a poison that accumulates in soft tissue (i.e. muscle, brain, liver, spleen, kidneys, etcetera) and bone; it has the ability to inhibit the activity of many enzymes that are involved in normal brain functioning; and it affects a number of neurotransmitters and biological systems within the human body. This means that its effects are liable to be panoramic, that is, it won't affect just one aspect of neurological function, but all of them – IQ, behaviour, reaction times, memory, etcetera.

In addition to this, children are particularly at risk from lead exposure. Compared to adults, they have no barrier to lead entry into their nervous systems, which are still in the developmental stage, and therefore particularly vulnerable. Children have higher metabolic rates than adults, and on a dose-per-bodyweight basis, they absorb more of the poison. Young children have a higher rate of lead absorption from the gut (almost five times that for adults), and rapidly growing tissue is often more easily affected by toxic substances than is slower growing tissue. In addition to all this, infants are likely to have their lead load increased by contamination while in the womb (lead crosses the placental barrier with ease), and from their habit during early childhood of mouthing non-food items which may be contaminated.

Even at low blood levels there is a negative correlation between blood lead levels and IQ, of which the simplest explanation is that the lead produces these effects . . . There is a strong likelihood that lead in petrol is permanently reducing the IQ of many of our children. Although the reduction amounts to only a few percentage points, some hundreds of thousands of children are affected.

Source: a leaked letter from Sir Henry Yellowlees, Chief Medical Officer, DHSS, March 1981. Taken from Des Wilson, *The Lead Scandal*, p. 30.

The environmental pressure group CLEAR made lead in petrol an issue of public concern, and unleaded petrol is now becoming available in many of the UK's petrol stations (see AUTOMOBILE POLLUTION). However, as Fred Pearce points out in *Watershed*, lead in tapwater is a greater threat to many children than lead in petrol.

About half the homes in Britain have lead water pipes. In Scotland, many have lead tanks as well. These pipes are less harmful in places where the supplied water is not 'plumbo-solvent' – it does not dissolve lead. In parts of Scotland, Northern Ireland and northern England, however, the water is soft and acidic; and it dissolves lead very efficiently.

The Water Research Centre is quoted by Pearce as estimating that up to 2.5 million homes in the UK are at risk from lead in tapwater. Until 1968, it was common practice in Glasgow and in many other parts of Scotland to plumb houses with lead piping and lead tanks. In 1979, a survey revealed that 11 per cent of new-born babies in

Glasgow had blood lead levels higher than the EC limits for adults. Glasgow had the worst lead-poisoning problem in Europe.

Both the EC and the World Health Organization (WHO) propose a limit for lead in water of 100 microgrammes per litre. The EC also have a 50 microgrammes per litre 'warning level'. In 1975, 4.3 per cent of British daytime tapwater samples were over the WHO 100 microgramme limit, and 10.3 per cent were over the 'warning' value. Glasgow was a particularly polluted area, with other hotspots in the lead-mining areas of north Wales, and some unexpected areas such as Folkestone. Samples taken from the first water drawn each morning were always the highest, as the water had been standing in the pipes. For that reason, people in suspect areas are recommended to run their tapwater for a while before drinking it.

An ideal, but expensive, solution to the problem would be to replace all lead pipes. At about £600 per house, this would cost some £1.5 billion for the Water Research Centre's 2.5 million 'at risk' homes. The government has been experimenting with dosing water with lime to reduce the acidity of the supply water. This has been successful in Glasgow: doctors there, according to Pearce, expect the average intelligence of Glaswegian children to rise. Liming has not always been successful, however, in areas with long distribution systems – water is less alkaline at the tap than it is at the treatment works – or in places where liming is less practical, such as private water supplies.

Under pressure from the EC, the government has started to take action on lead in water, albeit slowly. Initially, Britain asked for exemptions from the EC lead water quality directive for more than 7 million people, including the whole of Scotland, Liverpool, Manchester, Birmingham, parts of Wales and the North-west of England. It now has a self-imposed target of eliminating high levels of lead from all public drinking water supplies by the end of 1989, although it admitted in December 1987 that it would not achieve its aim. Of 103 public supplies in Scotland which breached the 1985 EC directive, only 18 had since been improved; 47 more were expected to be cleaned in time. The remaining supplies serve 15 per cent of the Scottish population. Friends of the Earth (Scotland) published a list of affected areas in February 1989.

Meanwhile, new research indicates that lead affects human health at levels lower than the EC or WHO guidelines. According to the journal *Environmental Data Services* (November 1987), the drinking water limit of 50 to 100 microgrammes per litre would have to be revised downwards to 15 to 20 microgrammes per litre, to accommodate the new medical evidence. This would involve capital expenditure of £1.5–2 billion on water treatment and lead pipe replacement.

Nitrates   Nitrogen-based fertilizers are increasingly popular in modern agriculture, and according to the Royal Society report *The Nitrogen Cycle of the United Kingdom*, 1983, there is substantial potential for increased usage in the future.

If excessive quantities of nitrogen-based fertilizer, or even animal manure, are spread on fields, however, the crops are unable to absorb all the nitrate that is released. This unabsorbed surplus then runs off the fields into rivers and streams, or percolates through the soil to the nearest aquifer (i.e. natural underground reservoir). Aquifers, usually known as 'ground waters', supply most of the tap water in southern England, 35 per cent of all tapwater in England and Wales. Rivers and streams are also used as sources for drinking water.

The level of nitrate in both ground and surface waters is largely due to inputs from agriculture. Most arable areas typically leach about 70 kg of nitrogen per hectare per year, whereas for those receiving heavy applications of nitrogen fertilizer, annual losses can exceed 150 kg of nitrogen per hectare.

Consumption of nitrogen fertilizer in the UK increased from some 60,000 tonnes a year in the late 1930s, to just below 200,000 tonnes in the mid-1940s, to a 1985 figure of around 1.58 million tonnes.

Nitrates in water cause adverse environmental effects, and may also damage human health. Nitrates themselves are relatively non-toxic, although it is feared that they convert in the body to nitrites, which can in turn produce nitrosamines. Two risks have been identified: methaemoglobinaemia, or blue-baby syndrome, a potentially fatal threat to infants, caused by nitrites; and cancer, caused by nitrosamines in 39 species of animals. Evidence as to the human carcinogenicity of nitrosamines is currently inconclusive: blue-baby syndrome, although occurring extremely rarely in the UK, seems to be a threat that is taken seriously.

In the UK, the Chief Medical Officer advises that monitoring for infantile methaemoglobinaemia should occur in areas where levels of nitrate exceed 50 milligrams of nitrate per litre. The French have decided that water polluted to this level should not be given to pregnant women and babies.

The World Health Organization recommends a guideline value of 44.5 mg of nitrate per litre of water in order to protect public health. The EC Drinking Water Directive specifies a Maximum Admissible Concentration (MAC) of 50 milligrams of nitrate per litre of water.

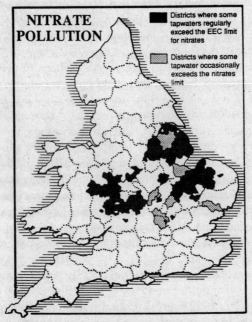

Source: *New Scientist*, 10 December 1987

The EC Directive came into force in July 1985, and appeared to be swiftly circumvented by the UK. 'Derogations', or exemptions from the need to obey the directive, were issued to 350 water sources, which supplied nearly a million people. At the same time, the interpretation of Maximum Admissible Concentration was massaged to allow average results over three months – a significant relaxation of the standard. Polluted drinking water, according to EC standards, was widespread. Friends of the Earth (FoE) point out that about one million people in the UK regularly receive drinking water which exceeds the EC's safety level. These people are mainly in East Anglia,

Lincolnshire, Nottinghamshire and Staffordshire. A further 3.8 million on one or more days between January 1984 and July 1985 received water approaching 50 mg per litre.

FoE issued a formal complaint to the European Commission, which decided to start formal procedure under Article 169 (of the Treaty of Rome) against the United Kingdom. The government was faced with a dilemma, as the uncertainty over legal action was prejudicing the forthcoming privatization of the water industry. In late 1987 it told the water authorities that MACs would have to be counted on an individual basis, rather than as an average. The authorities have calculated that this requirement would cost about £5 billion.

In the meantime, the problem of nitrate run-off into drinking water supplies remains unchecked. The water authorities want greater restrictions placed on nitrogen fertilizer use by farmers, but this move has up to now been resisted by the agricultural lobby.

Pesticides　Because of lack of funding, analytical techniques have not been developed which are capable of measuring the concentration in water of most pesticides now in use. The EC Drinking Water Directive (1985) specifies a Maximum Admissible Concentration (MAC) of 0.1 microgrammes per litre for individual pesticides, with an MAC for combined pesticides of 0.5 microgrammes per litre.

The government has used the lack of available analytical techniques to advise water authorities to 'ignore' EC limits for pesticides in water.

In addition, the authorities have granted provisional commercial clearance to a number of pesticides, even though the threats to human health and the environment have not been fully appraised – for example, by testing the 'cocktail effect' of mixing a number of pesticides together. Long-term effects of pesticide exposure do not appear to have been adequately tested.

The public are unable to assess the adequacy of current testing procedures for pesticides, because the government has refused to grant access to test data submitted by pesticide manufacturers which were cleared for use before October 1986 (see PESTICIDES).

As the pesticides have been inadequately tested, and small trace amounts cannot be identified in water bodies, it would seem reasonable for farmers to keep records of their pesticide use. The UK

Ministry of Agriculture stated on 19 December 1986 that this was a good idea in principle, but on balance it was not such a good idea as farmers weren't doing it at the moment . . .

Aluminium   Aluminium pollution of water supplies re-entered the news on 12 June 1988, when the *Observer* broke the story that water authorities were becoming concerned about a possible link between the level of aluminium in tap water and Alzheimer's disease – an increasingly common form of senile dementia.

In 1987, Norwegian researchers had indicated a statistical link between areas with high aluminium in drinking water and the Alzheimer syndrome – believing that the metal got into water after being freed from the soil by ACID RAIN. UK observers were not convinced, however, that the connection was firmly enough established.

The *Observer* story centred round leaked confidential minutes of a Water Authorities' Association meeting, which had been passed on to Friends of the Earth. The minutes contained unpublished results of Southampton University research, which appeared to indicate a correlation between the incidence of Alzheimer's disease and aluminium pollution. The water authority heads were said to have expressed 'growing concern' about the results.

The researchers were said to have examined levels of aluminium in drinking water over the previous ten years in 95 districts in England and Wales. The highest examined were at the European community's limit of 200 micrograms per litre.

The *Guardian* pointed out the following day that about 50 water supplies in the UK are believed to have derogations setting aside the EC limit. About 2 million people in Birmingham and Tyneside receive these supplies and other affected areas include Lancaster, Bolton, Oldham, Tameside and Stockport, in the north-west, and areas of Yorkshire, Wales and the south-west.

Aluminium is added to water supplies in some places, as a means of removing discoloration from the water. It will also be released into certain water bodies by the influence of acid rain on surrounding soil.

Other substances   The DHSS publication *Present-day Pratice in Infant Feeding: Third Report*, 1988, says: 'In the United Kingdom, the vast majority of households can depend on a public water supply that is safe, in microbiological and all other respects, for the purpose of infant feeding.' The report then discusses the problems of nitrates and lead in water (see above), and adds a proviso: 'The quality of small private supplies is often less reliable than the public supply, and water from private supplies is not always suitable for the purpose of infant feeding.'

ENDS Report 134 points out that the UK has 80,000 known private water supplies, serving 450,000 people. Up to 500,000 sources may, however, be in regular use, while sources used intermittently may bring the total up to one million. Official estimates in 1984 suggested that only 20 per cent of these sources comply with EC standards, and hazards to consumers are increasing due to falling bacteriological quality. (The UK's response to these statistics was to ask the EC for a delay of ten years in applying the standards to supplies serving fewer than 500 people, or 99 per cent of the known sources.)

Brian Price identifies other possible contaminants in *Pollution on Tap* (*Green Britain or Industrial Wasteland?*, 1986): micropollutants, produced as a result of killing bacteria with chlorine, may be present in water in literally hundreds of compounds which cannot all be identified – thus making the health risk difficult to quantify. Chlorinating some water supplies makes them more mutagenic, increasing the risk of getting cancer after drinking the water.

Other potential risks include leaching from PVC pipes of vinyl chloride monomer (a carcinogen), and asbestos fibres released into water from asbestos cement pipes (see ASBESTOS). Fluoride is added to some water supplies – this was made possible in the UK by a Bill passed in 1985 – although many books are non-committal about whether or not this addition is beneficial. The US Public Health Service has been advocating fluoridation of water supplies since the 1940s, and many American towns have fluoridated water. Germany and The Netherlands, however, have banned the practice. *The Green Alternative* (edited by P. Grunyard and F. Morgan-Grenville, 1987) lists the arguments against fluoride: in favour, it must be said that the balance of British medical opinion appears to believe that fluoride protects children's teeth.

In conclusion, it should be stated that the UK's drinking water supplies are usually good: but that this state of affairs persists as a result of investment, expenditure and diligence to ensure that standards are maintained. The government's actions concerning nitrates, lead, pesticides and EC Directives do not reassure that this standard of quality will always be maintained.

UK RIVERS, ESTUARIES AND GROUNDWATERS

The House of Commons Environment Committee reported in 1987 that 'river and estuary quality in this country is generally very high'. Of the 18,750 miles of river in England and Wales, 90 per cent are classified by the Department of the Environment as 'good' or 'fair'. A similar picture applies to the country's 1,875 miles of estuary length.

Within those figures, however, marked regional variations can be detected; and of extreme concern is the fact that, after 25 years of continuous improvement in river quality, the 1985 River Quality Survey showed for the first time an overall deterioration. This deterioration has been associated with lack of funding for sewage works and inadequate prevention of 'pollution incidents' from agriculture and industry.

At the same time, growing concern has been expressed about the state of Britain's groundwaters – natural underground reservoirs or aquifers, that supply 35 per cent of English and Welsh tapwater. Agricultural and industrial chemicals are beginning to pollute the country's groundwaters. Some 10 per cent of the total may already be polluted.

Rivers

The Department of the Environment's system of river quality classification has been criticized as ignoring wildlife, and is currently under review. It assesses rivers by their potential use for drinking water, fisheries and amenity value through a scale from class 1A (good) to class 4 (bad). Class 3 and 4 rivers cannot be used for any of these purposes. River and estuary quality are listed opposite.

A 'fair' river, however, is not necessarily a good place for wildlife: class 1A rivers are the most acceptable for wildlife protection, with class 1B or 2 rivers often unacceptable. The Nature Conservancy Council wants to see the maintenance of class 1A rivers to ensure the survival of wildlife habitats: only 34 per cent of rivers in England and Wales fall in this category. From an environmental point of view, there is much room for improvement.

Water quality: percentage of river and estuary length in each class

	Rivers		Estuaries	
	Good/Fair 1A, 1B, 2	Poor/Bad 3, 4	Good/Fair A, B	Poor/Bad C, D
Anglian	91	9	98	2
Northumbrian	97	3	70	30
North-west	78	22	72	28
Severn–Trent	87	14	100	0
Southern	97	3	97	3
South-west	94	6	100	0
Thames	93	7	100	0
Welsh	94	6	98	2
Wessex	93	7	97	3
Yorkshire	88	12	55	45
England and Wales	90	10	92	8

Source: House of Commons Environment Committee,
Pollution of Rivers and Estuaries, 1987

Water quality: percentage of Class 1A river and Good estuary length

	Rivers Class 1A	Estuaries Good
Anglian	10	87
Northumbrian	62	37
North-west	49	49
Severn–Trent	18	44
Southern	31	82
South-west	25	93
Thames	24	36
Welsh	53	76
Wessex	26	39
Yorkshire	40	13
England and Wales	34	68

Source: House of Commons Environment Committee,
Pollution of Rivers and Estuaries, 1987

Britain's rivers are getting dirtier. In the first half of the 1980s, 3,028 miles of water became cleaner, thanks to anti-pollution efforts. At the same time, however, 3,506 miles became filthier. This negative balance last occurred in 1958. The number of reported pollution incidents on rivers in England and Wales almost doubled from 12,500 in 1980–81 to 23,253 in 1987–8.

The House of Commons Environment Committee noted that one of the causes of this deterioration was that, in 1986, 22 per cent of all sewage works failed to meet the required standard of purity for their discharges. Friends of the Earth have pointed out that this situation – 'not an acceptable state of affairs', in the words of the House of Commons report – was actually worse than it appeared to be. The government had already relaxed the discharge consents for at least 1,800 of the 6,600 sewage treatment works, so the breaches were of standards that were less stringent than they had been in the past.

FoE also commented that the small net loss in overall river purity masks an overall deterioration in the ecology of most of the rivers in England and Wales in recent years. The scale of this is not apparent because of cutbacks in water authority monitoring.

Lack of investment and insufficient maintenance were the reasons given by HM Inspectorate of Pollution for the failure of sewage works to meet their discharge consents. Government financial restrictions appear to be the principal cause of the problem.

The government has been criticized by environmentalists for underfunding water quality schemes, and also for failing to take advantage of legislation that is already available.

- It has not implemented subsections 46(1) to (3) of the Control of Pollution Act (COPA), which would give water authorities the power to revoke discharge consents that have damaged plants or animals.
- It has not made regulations under subsection 31(4) of COPA which would allow a water authority to specify, for the purpose of pollution prevention, the precautions to be taken by people controlling poisonous or polluting matter.
- It has not made regulations under subsection 31(5) of COPA which would allow a water authority to prohibit or restrict polluting activities in specified areas.

The avoidance of regulations under subsection 31(5) of COPA was made despite a serious pollution incident on the River Dee in 1984, which resulted in chlorophenols entering the water supply of thousands of people, with possible long-term carcinogenic effects.

Environmentalists argue that the privatization of the water industry has left environmental protection at the margin: there are other, more pressing issues at stake. As an example, they point out that the government will benefit financially from the lowest possible water pollution standards being applied. It is proposed that the Secretary of State should set statutory river quality objectives for the new private organizations: if these are set as low as possible, the new water boards would have stretches of water course with spare pollution load capacity. Dischargers would have to pay for the right to pollute, so the pollution load capacity in any water course has a capital and revenue value. This increases the initial sale price of the water industry.

Eutrophication   Eutrophication is over-enrichment of water, caused by nitrates running off agricultural fields into local surface waters. A good description of the way this happens can be found in Nigel Dudley's *Nitrates in Food and Water*, 1986: in a natural lake or river, the amount of nitrogen and phosphorus in the water can be a limiting factor on the growth of water plants (and thus water animals). A small amount of fertilizer can increase the amount of water life, but if 'overdosing' occurs, the result is a runaway growth of algae.

The blanket of algae cuts off the supply of light to submerged plants, reducing their ability to photosynthesize, so that they die from lack of oxygen. Their remains, and those of dead algae, are decomposed by bacteria – using up the remaining oxygen in the water. The result is that most of the animal life disappears, leaving only surface-breathing insects.

Eutrophication needs both nitrogen and phosphorus to occur. In areas such as the Norfolk Broads, attempts are made to limit phosphorus, this being thought to be easier to control than nitrogen. Eutrophication is, according to Dudley, commonest in the arable lands of south and south-east England, and in Northern Ireland. The loss of fish from rivers and canals has been noted by anglers' groups, but the loss of numerous ponds and dykes, previously havens for plant and animal life, has gone largely unnoticed.

Estuaries

An estuary is the wide mouth of a river when it reaches the sea, a complicated system with fresh water in the upper reaches and salt water at the seaward end. Because there is a rich load of nutrient input, the lower reaches of estuaries support valuable shellfish fisheries, act as nursery grounds for fish, and are feeding grounds for vast flocks of birds. Britain's estuaries are important habitats, especially for birds – they attract about 40 per cent of all waders wintering in Europe.

The tenth Royal Commission on Environmental Pollution pointed out that chemical pollutants in these water bodies act in different ways, depending on currents, tides, and winds: 'estuaries are ecologically diverse and their responses to discharges of waste and other alien matter is particularly complex, and not wholly predictable'.

In a 1985 report for the Water Research Centre, Nigel Haigh describes the anomalous position of estuaries in relation to other water bodies. In 1978, the water authorities laid down short-term and long-term quality objectives for their water supplies, depending on the uses to which the supplies were put. (The objectives are supplemented by quality standards set in EC directives for surface water used for drinking, water for freshwater fish, shellfish waters, etcetera, and also by standards set for concentrations of six substances which are dangerous in water – chromium, lead, zinc, copper, nickel and arsenic.)

Two points should be noted: first, that the quality of water is determined, not as an aim in itself, but by the uses to which it is going to be put; and second, that the quality objectives do not apply to estuaries and coastal waters. The first point means that different industries, at different points on a water course, can be allowed various discharges of pollution, provided that the overall quality objective is not breached. The intention is not to clean up pollution as efficiently as possible, but rather to permit pollution up to a given level. This has profound implications for wildlife near the pollution source.

The second point follows from the first. As the river gets nearer the sea and the water volume gets larger, greater pollution can be negotiated for by industrialists, provided that the quality objective remains unbreached. As the estuary itself is free of quality objective restraint, the most polluting industries may find it logical to locate there. Many industries in Britain are located on estuaries, rather than inland where water pollution presents greater problems.

Until recently, there were no controls over discharges to coastal waters, and over some discharges to estuaries. Even today, a substantial proportion of estuarine discharges are covered by 'deemed consents', which are in Greenpeace's words, 'in effect, a "rubber stamp" to pollute the environment'. The first estuary to receive an environmental quality objective was the Humber in December 1984.

The resulting pollution loads have been high. The House of Commons Environment Committee noted in 1987: 'We were left in no doubt that the Mersey still counts as the most polluted river and estuary system in Europe.' Greenpeace have identified lead and mercury pollution in the Mersey, as well as contamination by chlorinated hydrocarbons, phosphorus, hydrocarbon oils and solvents based on iso-dodecane, acids, phthalates, phenols and derivatives, xylenes, toluene, cyanides, biocides and many more.

The Royal Commission on Environmental Pollution (1984) identified the Mersey, Tyne and Tees as blackspots. The Royal Commission also comments that 'the shortage of funds for investment by water and local authorities in new and improved sewage treatment works was the main reason for increases in and the continued presence of estuarine waters of low quality'.

Groundwaters

Much of the drinking water in the UK is supplied from natural underground reservoirs – also known as aquifers, or groundwaters. These provide most of the supplies in southern England, and 35 per cent of all drinking water in England and Wales. Groundwater is cheap and in the past has been very pure, as rainwater filtering through hillsides into aquifers is cleaned of bacteria on its way down.

Groundwater problems started to occur with the development of new agricultural and industrial chemicals. Agricultural pollution is caused by nitrates; industrial pollution is capable of penetrating the water supply and, even in relatively small quantities, making it unsuitable for human consumption. The UK Department of the Environment has become so concerned about the threat to aquifers that in September 1987 it announced an urgent review of the problem.

The industrial contaminants are called chlorinated organic

solvents, and were variously introduced between 1920 and 1950. The four most widely used in British industry are:

tetrachloroethylene (also called perchloroethylene)
trichloroethylene
methylene chloride
methyl chloroform (also called 1,1,1-trichloroethane)

They are used for degreasing, paint-stripping, drycleaning and to power aerosols.

World Health Organization guidelines for permissible concentrations of these compounds in drinking water are very low (in the range of 10 to 30 microgrammes of substance per litre of water), because of their carcinogenic effects on animals. As a report from the British Geological Survey (BGS) comments, they are thus very serious groundwater pollutants, 'and even a small spill of a few litres in volume could, in theory, contaminate many millions of litres of groundwater'.

The BGS report notes that all of the chlorinated solvents are volatile and evaporate rapidly to the air: polluted surface waters will lose large amounts of the contaminants through evaporation. Evaporation processes, however, are not so significant under the ground.

The solvents are discharged directly to groundwaters, or are dumped into or onto the ground as a result of spillage or casual disposal, and eventually make their way to the natural reservoir. The solvents are denser than water and do not readily mix with it. This tends to result in rapid and very deep contamination of aquifers.

If significant concentrations reach the groundwater table, there is a considerable risk of pollution of neighbouring water-supply boreholes. This depends on soil types and the local water flow system. The rate of pollution transport and level of pollutant retention cannot be predicted with much confidence, given the current state of knowledge of the behaviour of these compounds in groundwater systems.

What is known, however, is that significant pollution has already occurred. *New Scientist* has listed three discoveries by one water authority, Anglian Water.

• Anglian closed down a large borehole close to the US Air Base at Mildenhall, Suffolk, in 1983 after discovering a huge leak of trichloroethylene (used to clean engines). The solvent turned up in water drawn from the local chalk aquifer used to supply 40,000 people, at levels almost three times the World Health Organization's tentative 'action level'. The pollution came from a sump, which drained into a ditch. The same base had poured 45,000 litres of aviation fuel into the aquifer in 1978.

- A leather tannery in Cambridge polluted the city's groundwaters with tetrachloroethylene. The Cambridge Water Company demanded compensation of £1 million, the cost of providing an alternative source.
- A spill of trichloroethylene from an engineering factory near Norwich contaminated the Thorpe borehole, which supplies water to part of the city. The authority shut the borehole.

New Scientist quotes Mike Price, a hydrogeologist at the British Geological Survey, who believes that the chalk downlands of England are particularly vulnerable to pollution. They supply 15 per cent of all the water drunk in England and Wales, and are recharged by 4.4 billion cubic metres of rainwater per year. Yet, according to Price, 'less than five tonnes of some pollutants would be sufficient to contaminate one year's recharge for the entire chalk outcrops'.

Scientists at Imperial College, London, have carried out a study of solvents in British groundwaters. They concluded that concentrations of chlorinated solvents above international guidelines may occur in up to 10 per cent of British groundwaters used for public supply. Of those groundwaters tested, trichloroethylene was found in 61 of the 168 groundwaters used for drinking, in concentrations ranging up to 204 microgrammes per litre – seven times the WHO's guideline limit.

The British Geological Survey quoted above also noted a significant threat of groundwater pollution from PESTICIDES, especially herbicides used in cereal areas.

WORLD WATER SUPPLY

The United Nations Environment Programme's report, *The State of the World Environment 1987*, gives a concise but thorough overview of the world's water supplies.

Approximately 97 per cent of the world's water is in the oceans and 3 per cent is on land. Of the land supplies, some 77 per cent is stored in ice caps and glaciers, 22 per cent in groundwater (i.e. underground natural reservoirs), with the remaining tiny fraction available as lakes, rivers and streams. A large proportion of the groundwater stock is more than 800 metres below the ground, so is thus very difficult to extract.

Global water use can be divided into three categories: irrigation (73 per cent), industrial uses (21 per cent), and public use (6 per cent). Water use patterns differ significantly from one country to another, with 40 per cent of water use in developed countries going to industry, while the bulk of consumption in developing countries is for irrigation. Total annual water use was estimated at 2,600 to 3,000 cubic kilometres in 1980, and 3,500 to 4,000 cubic kilometres in 1985: an average rate of increase of about 6 per cent per year.

Water availability

A large number of people have no access to safe, clean water. According to the UNEP report, a recent World Health Organization survey revealed that in 1983, 61 per cent of the rural population of developing countries, and 26 per cent of the urban population, did not have access to clean water supplies. At the same time, 86 per cent of rural people and 47 per cent of urban dwellers were not covered by sanitation services. The UNEP report comments:

The lack of clean drinking water and appropriate sanitation is the main reason for the prevalence of communicable diseases in developing countries. Diarrhoeal diseases are endemic throughout the developing countries and are the world's major cause of infant mortality. Cholera, typhoid fever, and different intestinal parasites also affect hundreds of millions of people. Studies estimate that the provision of clean water and basic sanitation would reduce the incidence of diarrhoea by 50%, cholera by 90%, sleeping sickness by 80% and Guinea worm infestation by 100%.

Lack of clean water and sanitation has direct consequences. The United Nations Children's Fund (UNICEF) notes in its report *The State of the World's Children 1988* that one death in every three in the world is the death of a child under the age of five. Each week, more than 250,000 young children die in the developing world, from frequent infection and prolonged undernutrition. Diarrhoea is the most common disease of childhood, with resultant dehydration killing 3 million children a year. For the 90 per cent of children for whom the disease does not become life-threatening, the danger is malnutrition, as frequent attacks can take away the appetite and limit the absorption of food. Diarrhoeal disease is probably responsible for up to half of all child undernutrition.

The UNICEF report lists 131 countries' access to drinking water, 1983–6, in groupings according to Under-Fives' Mortality Rate (U5MR). In the 33 countries with very high U5MR, the median population percentage with access to clean water was 29 per cent.

The International Drinking Water Supply and Sanitation Decade (1981–90), launched by the United Nations, has heightened awareness among policy-makers of the importance of providing safe water. The objective of the decade, of providing all people with clean water and appropriate sanitation by 1990, will, however, not be achieved. By the end of the decade, only about 79 per cent of people in urban areas, and 41 per cent of those in rural areas, will have access to safe water supplies. Sanitation facilities will reach only 62 per cent of urban dwellers, and 18 per cent of rural inhabitants.

Water pollution

While the priority of concerned world organizations is to guarantee the provision of adequate water supplies, there is also scope for cleaning polluted water courses. UNEP notes that, in the 24 developed countries that belong to the Organization for Economic Co-operation and Development (OECD), general water quality has improved. This is attributed to the effects of clean water legislation. The amount of biological oxygen demand (BOD) from introduced waste has dropped, as has contamination by pollutants such as lead, chromium and copper.

On the other hand, concentrations of nitrates increased in most rivers. This is a consequence of overuse of nitrogen-based fertilizers. A number of water bodies have also been seriously damaged by acid rain (see ACID RAIN; AUTOMOBILE POLLUTION).

In the developing countries the situation varies, although water pollution appears to be a growing problem. In India, for example, about 70 per cent of surface water is polluted. Fifty-four of the 78 rivers monitored in China are seriously polluted with untreated sewage and industrial waste. More than 40 major rivers in Malaysia are so polluted that they are nearly devoid of fish and aquatic mammals. The main pollutants are oil palm and rubber processing residues, sewage and industrial waste.

Groundwater pollution is also causing concern. More than 50 per cent of the drinking water supply, and 80 per cent of rural domestic and livestock needs of the United States are supplied from groundwaters (i.e. natural underground reservoirs). Pollution from nitrates, pesticides and industrial wastes is becoming particularly serious. In Denmark, the overall level of nitrate concentration has trebled within the last 30 years. In the US, groundwater contamination from applications of pesticides to fields has been reported in California, New York, Wisconsin and Florida, with the most widespread problems involving debromochloropropane and aldicarb (see PESTICIDES). In the UK, up to 10 per cent of groundwaters are estimated to have been polluted by industrial solvents.

The risk of contamination to groundwaters is compounded by the number of land disposal sites containing wastes which would be unacceptable in the water supply. UNEP lists figures from three countries: in the US, there are estimated to be 76,000 active industrial landfills, mostly unlined, from which contaminants may leach into groundwater; in Denmark, 3,200 abandoned landfill sites have been found, 500 containing chemical wastes. In The Netherlands, there are 4,000 abandoned sites, 350 of which require immediate remedial action. In the UK, industrial disposal of wastes at landfill sites is only now beginning to attract public attention (see CHEMICAL WASTES).

See also ACID RAIN; ASBESTOS; MARINE POLLUTION; NORTH–SOUTH RELATIONSHIP; PESTICIDES

REFERENCES

Birch, Tim, *Poison in the System*, Greenpeace UK, 1989.

Dudley, Nigel, *Nitrates in Food and Water*, London Food Commission, 1986.

Friends of the Earth, *Background Document, UK Government's Environmental Record* (unpublished), 1987.

Friends of the Earth (Scotland), *Don't Drink Lead – Complain Instead*, 1989.

Grunyard, P. and F. Morgan-Grenville, *The Green Alternative*, Methuen, 1987.

Haigh, Nigel, *Pollution Control Philosophy in the United Kingdom*, Institute for European Environmental Policy, 1985.

House of Commons Environment Committee, *Pollution of Rivers and Estuaries*, 1987.

Pearce, Fred, *Watershed*, Junction Books 1982.

Pearce, Fred, 'Dirty Water under the Bridge', in Goldsmith and Hildyard (eds), *Green Britain or Industrial Wasteland?*, Polity Press, 1986.

Price, Brian, 'Pollution on Tap', in Goldsmith and Hildyard (eds), *Green Britain or Industrial Wasteland?*, Polity Press, 1986.

Royal Commission on Environmental Pollution, *Tenth Report*, 1984.

Royal Society, *The Nitrogen Cycle of the United Kingdom*, 1983.

United Nations Environment Programme, *The State of the World Environment 1987*, UNEP, Nairobi, April 1987.

UNICEF, *The State of the World's Children 1988*, OUP, 1988.

Wilson, Des, *The Lead Scandal*, Heinemann, 1983.

DHSS, 'Present-day Practice in Infant Feeding: Third Report', 1988.

Environmental Data Services (ENDS) Report no. 154, 'Drinking Water Quality'.

ENDS Report no. 155.

Guardian, 13 June 1988.

Friends of the Earth, 'Nitrate: Boon to Bane', 1986.

Lawrence, A. R. and S. S. D. Foster, 'The Pollution Threat from Agricultural Pesticides and Industrial Solvents', *Hydrogeological Report 87/2*, 1987 (British Geological Survey, Wallingford, Oxfordshire).

Observer, 12 June 1988.

Pearce, Fred, 'The Hills are Alive with Nitrates', *New Scientist*, 10 December 1987.

CONTACTS

Anti-Fluoridation League
Coastal Anti-Pollution League
Friends of the Earth
Greenpeace
Institute for European Environmental Policy
London Food Commission
Marine Conservation Society
Oxfam
Save the Children Fund
Socialist Environment and Resources Association (SERA)
United Nations Children's Fund (UNICEF)
United Nations Environment Programme (UNEP)
War on Want

Wetlands

'Wetlands' is the collective name for all areas outside the oceans which are permanently or periodically covered in water. Historically, places such as bogs, fens and marshes have been regarded as little more than useless, to be drained wherever possible: nowadays, however, their ecological importance is recognized, and many wetland areas are protected by international treaty.

The Ramsar Convention (the 'Convention on Wetlands of International Importance, especially as Waterfowl Habitat'), is the only international treaty to deal with a specific habitat type. Ramsar's 45 signatory nations agree to formulate their national planning so as to promote the wise use of wetlands on their territory; to list those wetlands in their country which are of international significance because of their wildlife, botanical interest, etc.; and to promote the conservation of wetlands, whether listed or not, by the establishment of nature reserves.

Although progress has been made in the understanding of wetlands and their importance to the environment, they are still perceived by many, especially people seeking to develop the land they occupy, as a nuisance. Internationally, the decline in the number of wetland areas is continuing: in the UK, the issue has surfaced in controversies as to the development of places such as Duich Moss, the Flow Country in Scotland (see FORESTRY IN THE UK), the Norfolk Broads and Halvergate Marsh.

Importance of wetlands

The Ramsar Convention defines wetlands as 'areas of marsh, fen, peatland or water, whether natural or artificial, permanent or temporary, with water that is static or flowing, fresh, brackish, or salt'. The definition includes marine waters less than six metres deep, and all rivers and coastal areas, as well as most coral reefs.

Wetlands are among the world's most productive environments. The World Wide Fund for Nature has included their protection among its top three conservation priorities because of:

- their biological productivity;
- the habitat they provide for many species;
- the fuel, food and livelihood they provide for millions of people;
- their role in flood control;
- the recreational opportunities they give.

WWF point out that wetlands can produce up to eight times as much plant matter as wheat fields. About half the world's population live in Asia: rice, a wetland crop, is the diet of most of them. The high productivity of the wetlands supported many early civilizations, and continues to provide food and income for rural populations. Two-thirds of the world's fish harvest are species which grow up in tidal areas and then swim out to the open sea. The watery environment found in marsh, estuary and coast provides some of the planet's most fertile areas, supporting flora and fauna which could not survive anywhere else.

Wetland birds are particularly vulnerable: although they are often present in large numbers, the habitat they depend on is available at relatively few sites, so removal of these sites hits them particularly hard. It was with the intention of conserving these species that the Ramsar Convention was negotiated, although it is now acknowledged that there are other pressing reasons for wetland conservation.

Not the least of these is the role that many wetlands play in flood control. They can absorb sudden influxes of water and release them slowly: this sponge-like reaction can save human lives, as well as being an unobtrusive and economical control system. The US Army Corps of Engineers has calculated that a loss of 40 per cent of the wetlands in the Charles River Basin, USA, would increase flood damage by more than $3 million annually. Loss of the entire wetlands would result in flood damage costs of $17 million per year. On the basis of the study, the Corps estimated that the most economical way to minimize flood losses in the basin was not to build a control reservoir, but to protect the existing wetlands.

Wetland areas, which vary from the Camargue to the Wadden Sea to the tropical mangrove forests, fulfil a number of different roles which are not always appreciated. Vienna, with a population of

1.7 million people and an inadequate sewage treatment system, relies on the Hainburg riverine forest to purify its drinking water by its natural filtering process. Calcutta has no chemical waste treatment plants, but has extensive 'salt lake' wetlands nearby which have 'treated' the sewage of the city for the last 50 years. Tropical mangrove forests, with their network of interlinking roots, stabilize the soil and also protect heavily-populated areas from the brunt of tropical storms.

On a much smaller scale, local ponds provide food and water for wildlife, but are also a useful leisure amenity for people. It is not possible to allocate a cost benefit for walking, birdwatching or just sitting near a water body; but that does not mean that a benefit does not exist. Wetlands, on a small as well as an international scale, have a place in the environment, as much as forest land, agricultural land or urban areas.

Wetland losses

It is difficult to establish accurate figures as to loss of this valuable ecological resource, but the WWF reckon that half or more of all the world's wetlands have disappeared, with most of the destruction taking place this century. The causes are various, but can be generally linked to agricultural and industrial development.

Agricultural drainage is one of the biggest single culprits. On the coasts of Europe, important breeding habitats for wading birds and wintering grounds for ducks, geese and other species have been reduced in some areas by 50 per cent in the last 40 years, to be put to farm use. Field drainage and river canalization have had similar effects. In the 1970s, over 100,000 hectares (a quarter of a million acres) were being drained every year in Great Britain. In the UK, as in other countries, this destruction has been made possible only by drainage subsidies paid by the tax-payer. Government grants of up to 80 per cent are given for agricultural drainage.

Peat bogs and peat flows, which were once widespread in the higher latitudes of the northern hemisphere, are now dramatically reduced. This has implications for the UK: blanket peat is common in Scotland, but highly restricted elsewhere in the world. Britain contains about one-seventh of the world's blanket peatland, mostly in Scotland. Controversies such as the tax-driven afforestation of the Flow Country should not be seen merely as a domestic issue: the disappearance of wetlands such as these represents the loss of a dwindling global resource (see FORESTRY IN THE UK). As it is, the UK Nature Conservancy Council has found that 87 per cent of the raised mire which was present in lowland Britain in 1850 had gone by 1978.

In the United States, over 50 per cent of the wetlands which existed in colonial times have now disappeared. From the mid-1950s to the mid-1970s, 200,000 hectares a year (half a million acres) were being lost, nine-tenths of this being due to agricultural development.

In the Third World, large drainage schemes and major dams are either removing the wetlands or degrading them because of knock-on effects. In 1985, Lake Chad, one of Africa's largest freshwater lakes, virtually dried out: the effects of the Sahel drought had been aggravated by the construction of numerous dams on the lake's tributary rivers. After the Aswan dam was built on the Nile, the silt load carried by the river, previously deposited on the floodplain, is now deposited in the lake itself. The floodplain suffered a loss in productivity as its annual fertilization had disappeared. Much of the area – 60 per cent of Egypt's cultivated land – now requires increased use of fertilizers.

In West Bengal, between 1,300 and 1,500 square kilometres of mangrove forests have been destroyed and drained in the last 100 years, leading to difficulties in water management and lost protection against cyclonic floods. In many areas the land has subsided as it dried out and now lies below tide level. Catastrophic flooding with heavy loss of life now occurs in these regions (see DEFORESTATION).

Pollution has been another factor leading to the loss of wetlands and the wildlife communities they support. The most widespread example of this is ACID RAIN, which has devastated lakes in southern Sweden, Norway and parts of Europe and North America.

The Ramsar Convention

The Ramsar Convention, the oldest international conservation treaty of its type, was signed at Ramsar, Iran, in 1971. Its intention was to mobilize action, both nationally and internationally, against the rapid loss of wetlands around the world. Of the original 35 signatories, 21 were from Europe and only 13 from developing countries: since then the number of signatories has increased to 45, although a number of developing countries with important wetland sites have not joined. The reason given for this is lack of financial resources to support Ramsar commitments.

Ramsar Sites in the UK

The UK has listed 32 sites under Ramsar, covering nearly 100,000 ha:

Bridgwater Bay, Somerset
Bure Marshes, Norfolk
Cors Fochno and Dyfid Dyfed, Gwynnedd, Powys
Hickling Broad and Horsey Mere, Norfolk
Lindisfarne, Northumberland
Loch Duidibeg, Loch a'Machair and Loch Stilligary, Western Isles
Loch Leven, Tayside
Loch Lomond, Strathclyde, Central
Loch Neagh and Loch Beg, Antrim, Londonderry, Tyrone, Armagh Down
Minsmere – Walberswick, Suffolk
North Norfolk Coast, Norfolk
Ouse Washes, Cambridgeshire and Norfolk
Rannoch Moor, Tayside
Abberton Reservoir, Essex
Cairngorm Lochs, Grampian, Highland
Claish Moss, Highland
Loch Lintrathen, Tayside
Rostherne Mere, Cheshire
Silver Flowe, Dumfries and Galloway
Chesil Beach and the Fleet, Dorset
The Dee Estuary, Cheshire, Clwyd
Derwent Ings, North Yorkshire, Humberside
Holburn Moss, Northumberland
Irthinghead Mires, Cumbria, Northumberland
The Swale, Kent
Alt Estuary, Merseyside
Leighton Moss, Lancashire
Martin Mere, Lancashire
Loch Eye, Highland
Loch Skene, Grampian
Rockliffe Marshes, Cumbria
Chichester and Langstone Harbours, West Sussex, Hampshire

Source: *Hansard*, 24 November 1987

Three hundred and fifty-seven sites have now been listed as wetlands of international importance, totalling over 22 million hectares (about 50 million acres). So far, the Convention has been successful in achieving governmental commitment to wetland conservation: no site listed under Ramsar has yet had to be deleted due to damage, although a number are under threat. The Convention has also been successful in heightening government and public awareness as to the importance of wetlands, although there is still a long way to go. Agricultural drainage, pollution and the almost inexorable pressure to develop 'wasteland' areas are continuing the loss of wetlands in the developed world; and if the developing world is to be further persuaded towards preservation of its wetland areas, some pressing economic arguments or incentives will need to be found.

See also ACID RAIN; DEFORESTATION; FORESTRY IN THE UK; NORTH–SOUTH RELATIONSHIP; WATER

REFERENCES

Conservation Foundation, 'A better system to protect wetlands is needed?', *Conservation Foundation*, Letter No. 5, 1988.
Hansard, 24 November 1987
RSPB, *Forestry in the Flows of Caithness and Sutherland*, 1987.

WWF, *Wetlands Conservation and the Ramsar Convention*, WWF Position Paper, Spring 1987.
WWF, *Wetlands Fact Sheets*, 1985.
WWF, *Wetlands Pack 5*, 1985.

CONTACTS

Conservation Foundation (USA)
International Union for the Conservation of Nature and Natural Resources (IUCN)
Royal Society for the Protection of Birds (RSPB)

World Wide Fund for Nature (WWF – formerly World Wildlife Fund)

Whales and Whaling

Whales are classified according to the presence of teeth or baleen (a horny plate growing in the palate of certain whales). The largest group – odontocetes, or toothed whales – includes porpoises, dolphins, killer whales and sperm whales. In *The Book of Whales*, Richard Ellis points out that there is no accepted sequence for the classification of cetaceans, nor is there total agreement on the names and status of all species. He lists some ten baleen and more than sixty toothed whales. The box is a simplified version of his list:

WHALES

Mysticeti (baleen)	*Odontoceti* (toothed)
Minke	Sperm whales
Bryde's	Pilot whales
Sei	Bottlenose whales
Fin	Beaked whales
Blue	Beluga whales
Humpback	Killer whales
Gray	Narwhal
Right	All species of dolphin
Greenland right	
Pygmy right	All species of porpoise

Source: adapted from *The Book of Whales*, 1981

Human beings have traditionally been less interested in the various species of whales, and more concerned with the byproducts from the animals.

As Erik Eckholm points out in *Down to Earth* (1982), whaling has been going on for centuries. Whales provide meat, fats and valuable oils in large quantities with each kill, although nowadays they are mainly killed for their meat. The normal pattern has traditionally been for whalers to destroy one whale stock, then move on to another. In the 1700s, high-seas fleets covered the North Atlantic and then the seas of the world: by 1890 some northern hemisphere stocks had been seriously depleted. Over the last century, technological improvements permitted larger-scale, long-distance operations: these, of necessity, began to concentrate their operations in the southern hemisphere.

The International Whaling Commission

Efforts to control whaling began in 1946, with the signing of the convention that established the International Whaling Commission (IWC). For the next 25 years, however, the IWC was dominated by the interests of the whaling nations: although quotas and seasonal limits were set, they tended to follow stock depletion rather than try to prevent it. The IWC included most, but not all, whaling nations – whaling by non-member countries increased, sometimes with the covert support of IWC members. Eckholm describes how, during the first two-and-a-half decades of so-called regulation, the catches of several whales – including the blue, fin, sei and humpback whales – followed the classic pattern of overshoot and collapse.

By the late 1960s, outrage about the ineffectiveness of these controls was mounting among scientists and a growing proportion of the public. The disappearance of the planet's whales was a powerful emotional issue, and a strong network of non-governmental organizations began campaigning on the subject. In 1970, the United States banned commercial whaling and the importation of whale products. Year on year, the whale catch has dropped, as whale populations fall and environmental concern increases. The Table below shows the reduced whale catch in the period 1964–5 to 1982–3.

Fin and sei catches have dropped because the populations have been seriously depleted. Two species not on this Table – the blue whale and the humpback – have suffered even greater damage.

Number of whales caught – four selected species

	1964/5	1967/8	1970/1	1973/4	1976/7	1979/8	1982/3
Sperm	25,548	24,080	22,642	21,421	12,239	2,211	414
Sei	25,453	16,960	10,460	6,239	2,021	102	100
Fin	12,317	5,268	4,547	2,142	310	472	277
Minke	3,234	3,270	4,538	10,446	10,199	9,948	11,660

Source: UNEP, *Environmental Data Report*, 1987

Another species, the bowhead whale, is believed to be in danger of total extinction, and has not been hunted commercially since the 1920s.

Increased minke hunting during the 1960s and 1970s was the result of the protection afforded to the larger species. The minke became the only viable remaining option.

Sperm whales are known to exist in hundreds of thousands in some areas, but the impact of hunting has been much disputed: whales of the necessary social and sexual maturity are scarce because of over-fishing. For this reason, some ecologists have argued that sperm whales will decline for many years even in the absence of hunting. In 1981, the IWC reduced sperm whale quotas in all but one region to zero. In 1982, a moratorium on commercial whaling was announced – a temporary ban, to begin in 1985 and be reviewed not later than 1990.

Estimated whale populations at the end of the 1970s show that, of the species, only the minke and the gray survived the decade with more than 80 per cent of their original stocks remaining: and the gray had an extremely small population to start with. Sperm whales finished the 1970s with less than 80 per cent original stocks, sei around 40 per cent, fin about 30 per cent, humpback and blue less than 20 per cent. These figures do not encourage the belief that the world's whale populations will survive.

In 1985, seven of the 24 OECD countries were catching whales (see table on opposite page). These nations caught 7,995 tonnes, out of a world total catch of 13,865 (the balance being caught by East European countries, notably the USSR).

When the commercial ban was announced, four countries – Japan, Iceland, Norway and the USSR – objected to it, and announced their

1985 whale catch (tonnes)

Canada	1,159
USA	12
Japan	3,025
Denmark (inc. Faroe Islands)	2,596
Iceland	344
Norway	771
Spain	48

Source: OECD, *Environmental Data Compendium, 1987*

intention of continuing commercial whaling. In addition, the Faroe Islands maintained that they would continue their annual kill of some 2,400 pilot whales. The IWC has no formal powers to restrain its members, and was unable to take any enforcing action.

The USA, however, has domestic legislation that provides for the penalization of countries for 'diminishing the effectiveness' of the IWC. This economic weapon was threatened against Japan, which made a series of deals with the US to enable Japanese commercial whaling to continue until 1988. Norway also announced that its commercial whaling would continue.

'Scientific' whaling

In 1986, Iceland and South Korea started a programme of 'scientific' whaling, in which whales were caught allegedly for scientific purposes. The whale meat and products were disposed of commercially, in order to offset the costs of the operation.

In 1987, the year before the enforced end of their commercial whaling programme, the Japanese announced that they, too, would be running a 'scientific' programme – in which they would catch 825 minke and 50 sperm whales every year until the year 2000: approximately 40 per cent of the country's previous commercial requirements. This was negotiated down to 350 minke in 1988, though only 241 were caught.

Scientific whaling is allowed under Article VIII of the Convention, with nations granting scientific permits to themselves. The stated purpose of this type of whaling is to try to determine whale populations by killing specimens at random and attempting to extrapolate the data into herd sizes and ages. As a system of measurement it has become much discredited: partly because, instead of killing specimens at random, whalers habitually kill the largest animal they can find, thus frustrating the whole point of the exercise – but also because there are other measurement systems available that do not involve killing.

Conservationists believe that 'scientific' whaling is little more than a cover for a continuance of commercial whaling: and this appeared to be borne out when the scientific programmes were examined at the 1987 IWC meeting in Bournemouth. The Korean research was described by the scientific committee of the IWC as lacking any scientific value; the Icelandic programme was described by a long-standing scientific committee member as having 'little relevance to what we're trying to do'; and the Japanese proposals were regarded as biased and impractical.

Ways of bypassing IWC

The ban on commercial whaling was imposed in an attempt to stop whale populations from becoming extinct. A few nations appear to be placing short-term profit above the protection of a global natural resource. Japan, the last market for whale meat, is the prime mover behind the drive to continue whaling.

It seems that Japanese attempts to continue the trade have not been restricted merely to finessing the IWC with its scientific programme. In a hard-hitting 1987 report, Greenpeace documented a number of illegal attempts by the Japanese to bypass the IWC. The allegations include:

1. Repeated, deliberate efforts by Japan openly to subvert IWC regulations through its sponsorship of illegal whale hunts.
2. In the latter half of the 1970s, Japan established a whaling operation in Brazil, then set up illegal whaling operations – outside IWC control – in Chile, Peru and Taiwan. It made deals with the non-IWC whalers of Spain and Korea to import the bulk of their whale produce.
3. Japan helped to establish the pirate whaling vessel *Sierra* and its sister ships, *Tonna* and *Cape Fisher*. These vessels, like the other Japanese-sponsored pirate whalers, killed thousands of whales, usually of the most endangered species – blue, humpback, fin

and even right whales – and shipped the whale meat back to Japan.

4. Japanese businessmen set up an illegal whaling operation in the Philippines which operated between 1983 and 1986. The ships caught Bryde's whales, in violation of an IWC zero quota, and shipped the meat back to Japan, in contravention of a 1983 CITES agreement. The illegal 'cold' harpoon was used, with pregnant and lactating females being taken indiscriminately – again in violation of IWC regulations. The operation was closed down in 1986.

In its report, Greenpeace concludes that there will always be a market for whale meat in Japan. As long as this market continues it will always be possible for Japan to set up pirate whaling operations anywhere in the world and to launder the meat, undetected, onto their domestic market. The only way to guarantee the survival of whales is to end all whale hunting in order that any illegal catches can be more easily monitored through the appearance of whale products being traded in Japan.

The 1987 IWC meeting passed a USA proposal instructing the IWC to notify member nations when their research proposals did not come up to scratch; it also recommends governments not to allow any scientific whaling if the IWC has decided its scientific criteria are not being met. The new resolution might now allow the domestic legislation of the USA to be brought to bear against 'scientific' whalers. Commercial pressure may eventually stop Japan's whaling activities.

The same pressure may also halt Iceland's whaling activities. In 1988, Greenpeace co-ordinated a boycott of Icelandic fish, in an attempt to exert economic leverage. At the beginning of 1989, a number of British supermarkets expressed interest in buying fish from other markets; cancelled fish orders from Germany and the USA amounted to $50 million. Iceland's income from fishing dwarfs its revenues from whaling, and there have been heated debates in the Icelandic Cabinet as a result of the boycott campaign. In the middle of 1989, Iceland announced a two-year moratorium on whaling.

See also ANIMALS; MARINE POLLUTION; SPECIES EXTINCTION

REFERENCES

Eckholm, Erik P., *Down to Earth*, Pluto Press, 1982.

Ellis, Richard, *The Book of Whales*, Robert Hale, 1981.

Greenpeace Environmental Trust (UK), *Japanese Whaling in the Philippines*, 1987.

OECD, *OECD Environmental Data Compendium, 1987*.

United Nations Environment Programme, *Environmental Data Report*, Basil Blackwell, 1987.

World Resources Institute, IIED, *World Resources 1986*, Basic Books, 1986.

Cherfas, Jeremy, 'With Harpoon and Pocket Calculator', *New Scientist*, 2 July 1987.

'Japan to Slaughter Whales "in the Name of Research"', *New Scientist*, 11 June 1987.

Mulvaney, Kieran, 'The Killing Goes On', *Guardian*, 12 June 1987.

Pain, Stephanie, 'Age Miscalculations Threaten Bowhead Whales', *New Scientist*, 25 March 1987.

CONTACTS

Convention on International Trade in Endangered Species of Wild Fauna and Flora (CITES)

Environmental Investigation Agency

Greenpeace

International League for the Protection of Cetaceans

International Union for the Conservation of Nature and Natural Resources (IUCN)

International Whaling Commission (IWC)

People's Trust for Endangered Species

United Nations Environment Programme (UNEP)

Whale Conservation Society

World Wide Fund for Nature (WWF – formerly World Wildlife Fund)

List of Contacts

A

Advisory Committee of Pollution of Sea, 3 Endsleigh St, London WC1H 0DD

Anglers' Cooperative Association, 23 Castlegate, Grantham, Lincs NG31 6SW

Arboricultural Association, Ampfield House, Ampfield, Romsey, Hants SO5 9PA

Armament and Disarmament Information Unit, Science Policy Research Unit, Mantell Building, University of Sussex, Brighton

Association for the Conservation of Energy (ACE), 9 Sherlock Mews, London W1M 3RH

Association for the Protection of Rural Scotland, 14a Napier Rd, Edinburgh EH10 5AY

Association of Professional Foresters, Brokerswood Park, Brokerswood, Westbury, Wilts BA13 4EH

B

BBC Wildlife, Broadcasting House, Whiteladies Rd, Bristol BS8 2LR

Beauty without Cruelty International Ltd, 11 Lime Hill Rd, Tunbridge Wells, Kent TN1 1LJ

Bhopal Victims Support Committee, 50/52 King St, Southall, Middx

British Antarctic Survey, High Cross, Madingley Rd, Cambridge CB3 0ET

British Association of Nature Conservationists (BANC), Rectory Farm, Stanton St John, Oxford OX9 1HF

The British Butterfly Conservation Society, Tudor House, Quorn, Loughborough, Leicestershire LE12 8AD

The British Deer Society, Church Farm, Lower Basildon, Reading RG8 9NH

British Ecological Society, Burlington House, Piccadilly, London W1V 0LQ

British Entomological and Natural History Society, c/o the Alpine Club, 74 South Audley St, London W1Y 5FF

British Herpetological Society, c/o Zoological Society of London, Regent's Park, London NW1 4RY

British Organic Farmers, Leggatts Park, Potters Bar, Hertfordshire

British Ornithologists' Union, c/o British Museum of Natural History, Akeman St, Tring, Herts HP23 6AB

British Trust for Conservation Volunteers, 36 St Mary's St, Wallingford, Oxon OX10 0EU

British Society for Responsibility in Science, 9 Poland St, London W1V 3DG

British Trust for Ornithology, Beech Grove, Station Rd, Tring HP23 5NR

British Union for the Abolition of Vivisection (BUAV), 16a Crane Grove, Islington, London N7 8LB

British Waste Paper Association, Highgate House, 214 High St, Guildford, Surrey GU1 3JB

British Waterways Board, Melbury House, Melbury Terrace, London NW1 6JX

British Wind Energy Association,
4 Hamilton Place, London W1V 0BQ

C

Campaign Against Arms Trade
(CAAT), 11 Goodwin St, London N4
3HQ

Campaign Against the Namibian
Uranium Contract, PO Box 16,
London NW5 2LW

Campaign Against Sea Dumping, 8 Bay
Rd, Clevedon, Avon BS21 7BT

Campaign For Freedom of Information,
3 Endsleigh St, London WC1H 0DD

Campaign for Lead-free Air (CLEAR),
3 Endsleigh St, London WC1H 0DD

Campaign for Nuclear Disarmament
(CND), 22/24 Underwood St, London
N1 7JQ

Can Makers Recycling Information
Service, 25 North Row, London
W1R 2BY

Captive Animals' Protection Society,
36 Braemore Court, Kingsway, Hove,
E. Sussex BN3 4FG

Catholic Institute for International
Relations, 22 Coleman Fields,
London N1

Centre for Alternative Technology,
Machynlleth, Powys, Wales
SY20 9AZ

Centre for Human Ecology,
c/o University of Edinburgh,
15 Buccleuch Place, Edinburgh
EH8 9LN

Christian Aid, 35–41 Lower Marsh,
Waterloo, London SE1 7RL

Christian Ecology Group, 58 Quest Hills
Rd, Malvern, Worcester
WR14 1RW

CITES, c/o IUCN, Rue de Maupas 6,
CP78, CH-1000, Lausanne-9,
Switzerland

Civic Trust for Wales, St Michael's
College, Llandaff, Cardiff CF5 2YJ

Clean Air Council, Becket House,
Lambeth Palace Rd, London SE1

Climate Action Network, c/o Media
Natura, London Ecology Centre, 45
Shelton St, London WC2H 9HJ

Coastal Anti-Pollution League,
94 Greenway Lane, Bath, Avon
BA2 4LN

Common Ground, 45 Shelton St,
London WC2H 9HJ

Commonwealth Human Ecology
Council, 57–58 Stanhope Gdns,
London SW7 5RF

Commonwealth Secretariat,
Marlborough House, Pall Mall,
London SW1Y 5HX

Community Service Volunteers,
237 Pentonville Rd, London N1 9NJ

Compassion in World Farming (CIWF),
20 Lavant St, Petersfield, Hampshire
GU32 3EW

The Conservation Foundation, Fairholt
House, 2 Pont St, London SW1X 9EL

The Conservation Foundation of
America, 1250 Twenty-Fourth St
NW, Washington DC 20037, USA

The Conservation Trust, National
Environment Education Centre,
George Palmer School,
Northumberland Avenue, Reading,
Berks RG2 0EN

Council for Environmental Conservation
(CoEnCo) – see Environment Council

Council for Environmental Education,
School of Education, University of
Reading, London Rd, Reading, Berks
RG1 5AQ

Council for National Parks, London
Ecology Centre, 45 Shelton St,
London WC2H 9HJ

Council for the Protection of Rural
England (CPRE), Warwick House, 25
Buckingham Palace Rd, London
SW1W 0PP

Council for the Protection of Rural
Wales, 31 High St, Welshpool, Powys
SY21 7JP

Country Landowners' Association,
16 Belgrave Sq, London SW1

Countryside Commission, John Dower House, Crescent Place, Cheltenham, Glos. GL50 3RA

Countryside Commission for Scotland, Battleby, Redgorton, Perth PH1 3EW

The Cycling Campaign Network, Cotterell House, 69 Meadrow, Godalming, Surrey GU7 3HS

Cyclists' Touring Club, Cotterell House, 69 Meadrow, Godalming, Surrey GU7 3HS

D

Department of Energy, Thames House South, Millbank, London SW1P 4QJ

Department of the Environment, 2 Marsham St, London SW1P 2EB

Department of Transport, 43 Marsham St, London SW1P 3PY

E

Earth Resources Research (ERR), 258 Pentonville Rd, London N1 9JY

Earthwatch, Harbour View, Bantry, County Cork, Ireland

Ecological Parks Trust, 45 Shelton St, WC2H 9HJ

Ecological Physics Research Group, Cranfield Institute of Technology, Cranfield, Bedford MK43 0AL

Ecological Building Society, 8 Main St, Cross Hills, Keighley, W. Yorks BD20 8TT

The Ecologist, Worthyvale Manor, Camelford, Cornwall PL32 9TT

Ecology Centre, 45 Shelton St, London WC2H 9HJ

Ecology Party of Ireland, Washington Lodge, Grange Rd, Rathfarnham, Dublin 14, Eire

Elms Across Europe, c/o Pitney Bowes plc, The Pinnacles, Elizabeth Way, Harlow, Essex

Energy Conservation Group, Building 156, AERE Harwell, Didcot, Oxon OX11 0RA

Energy Technology Support Unit (ETSU), Energy Efficiency Research, Building 156, AERE, Harwell, Didcot, OX11 0RA

Environment Council, London Ecology Centre, 80 York Way, London N1 9AG

Environmental Consortium, 62–66 Whitfield St, London WC1P 5RN

Environmental Data Services (ENDS), Finsbury Business Centre, Unit 24, 40 Bowling Green Lane, London EC1R 0NE

Environmental Education Advisers' Association, Pendower Teachers' Centre, West Rd, Newcastle-on-Tyne NE15 6PP

Environmental Investigation Agency, 208–9 Upper St, London N1 1RL

Ethical Investment Research Investigation Service, 401 Bunderay Business Centre, 71 Bunderay, London SW8 1SW

European Environmental Bureau (EEB), 29 rue Vautier, 1040 Brussels, Belgium

European Nuclear Disarmament (END), 11 Goodwin St, London N4 3HQ

European Proliferation Information Centre (EPIC), 258 Pentonville Rd, London N1 9JY

F

Farm and Food Society, 4 Willifield Way, London NW11 7XT

Farming and Wildlife Trust, National Agricultural Centre, Stoneleigh, Kenilworth, Warwicks CV8 2RX

Fauna and Flora Preservation Society, c/o Zoological Gardens, Regent's Park, London NW1 4RY

Federation of Environmental Trade Associations, Unit 3 Phoenix House, Phoenix Way, Heston, Greater London TW5 9ND

Field Studies Council, Preston Montford, Montford Bridge, Shrewsbury, Shropshire SY4 1HW

Findhorn Foundation, The Park, Forres, Grampian, Scotland IV36 0TZ

Food Additives Campaign Team (FACT), Room W, 25 Horsell Rd, London N5 1XL

Forestry Commission, 231 Costorphine Rd, Edinburgh EH12 7AT

Free Range Egg Association (FREGG), 39 Maresfield Gardens, London NW3

FREEZE, 82 Colston St, Bristol BS1 5BB

Freshwater Biological Association, The Ferry House, Far Sawrey, Ambleside, Cumbria LA22 0LP

Friends of the Earth (FoE), 26–28 Underwood St, London N1 7JQ

Friends of the Earth Scotland, 15 Windsor St, Edinburgh EH7 5LA

G

The Green Alliance, 60 Chandos Place, London WC2N 4HG

Green Deserts Ltd, Rougham, Suffolk IP30 GLY

Green Drum, 18 Cofton Lake Rd, Birmingham B45 8PL

The Green Party, 10 Station Parade, Balham High St, London SW12

GreenNet, 26 Underwood St, London N1 7JQ

Greenpeace International, Greenpeace UK, 30–31 Islington Green, London N1 8XE

H

Habitat Scotland, Hazelmount, Viewfield Rd, Portree, Isle of Skye

The Hawk Trust, c/o Birds of Prey Section, Zoological Society of London, Regent's Park, London NW1 4RY

Henry Doubleday Research Association, National Centre for Organic Gardening, Ryton-on-Dunsmore, Coventry CV8

The Herb Society, 77 Great Peter St, London SW1P 2EZ

The Humane Research Trust, Brook House, 29 Bramhall Lane South, Bramhall, Cheshire SK7 2DN

The Hyperactive Children's Support Group, 59 Meadowside, Littlehampton, West Sussex, BN16 4BW

I

Inland Waterways Amenity Advisory Council, 1 Queen Anne's Gate, SW1H 9BT

Inland Waterways Association, 114 Regent's Park Rd, London NW1 8UQ

Inland Waterways Protection Society, Browside Farm, Mudhurst Lane, Lyme Handley, Whaley Bridge, Cheshire SK12 7BT

Institute for European Environmental Policy (London Office), 3 Endsleigh St, London WC1H 0DD

Institute for Marine Environmental Research, Prospect Place, The Hoe, Plymouth, Devon PL1 3DH

Institute of Estuarine and Coastal Studies, University of Hull, Cottingham Rd, Hull, Humberside HU6 7RX

Institute of Chartered Foresters, 22 Walker St, Edinburgh EH3 7HR

Institute of Terrestrial Ecology, 68 Hills Rd, Cambridge CB2 1LA

Institute of Waste Management, 3 Albion, Northampton, Northants NN1 1UD

Intermediate Technology, 9 King St, London WC2E 8HN

International Centre for Conservation Education, Greenfield House, Guiting Power, Cheltenham, Glos GL54 5TZ

International Council for Bird Preservation, 32 Cambridge Rd, Girton, Cambridge CB3 0PJ

International Dolphin Watch, Parklands, North Ferriby, Humberside HU14 3ET

International Fund for Animal Welfare (IFAW), Tubwell House, New Road, Crowborough, E. Sussex TN6 2QH

International Institute for Environment and Development (IIED), 3 Endsleigh St, London WC1H 0DD

International Institute for Strategic Studies, 23 Tavistock St, London WC2E 7NO

International League for the Protection of Cetaceans, 2 Meryon Court, Rye, East Sussex TN31 7LY

International League for the Protection of Horses, PO Box No 166, 67a Camden High St, London NW1 7JL

International Planned Parenthood Federation, Regent's College, Inner Circle, Regent's Park NW1 4NS

International Primate Protection League, 19–25 Argyll St, London W1V 2DU

International Society for the Prevention of Water Pollution, Little Orchard, Bentworth, Alton, Hants GU34 5RB

International Solar Energy Society UK Section, Royal Institution, 21 Albemarle St, London W1

International Union for the Conservation of Nature and Natural Resources (IUCN), Avenue du Mont Blanc, 1196 Gland, Switzerland

IUCN Conservation Monitoring Centre, 219c Huntingdon Rd, Cambridge CB3 0DL

Irish Wildlife Federation, 8 Westland Row, Dublin 2, Eire

J

Joint Committee for the Preservation of British Insects, c/o Royal Entomological Society of London, 41 Queen's Gate London SW7 5HU

K

Keep Scotland Beautiful, Old County Chambers, Cathedral Sq, Dunblane, Central Scotland FK15 0AQ

L

League Against Cruel Sports, 83–87 Union St, London SE1 1SG

London Food Commission, 88 Old St, London EC1V 9AR

The London Green Belt Council, 1–4 Crawford Mews, London W1H 1PT

London Hazards Centre, 3rd Floor, Headland House, 308 Gray's Inn Rd, London WC1X 8DS

London Wildlife Trust, 80 York Way, London N1 9AG

Long Distance Walkers Association, 8 Upton Grey Close, Winchester, Hants SO22 6NE

M

The Mammal Society, c/o The Linnean Society, Burlington House, Piccadilly, London W1V 0LQ

Marine Conservation Society, 9 Gloucester Rd, Ross-on-Wye, Herefordshire HR9 5BU

Maritime Trust, 16 Ebury St, London SW1W 0LH

Media Natura, London Ecology Centre, 45 Shelton St, London WC2H 9HJ

Men of the Stones, The Rutland Studio, Tinwell, Stamford, Lincs PE9 3UD

Men of the Trees, Turners Hill Rd, Crawley Down, Crawley, W. Sussex RH10 4HL

N

National Animal Rescue Association, 8 Waterpump Court, Thorpelands, Northampton NN3 1XU

National Anti-Fluoridation Campaign, 36 Station Rd, Thames Ditton, Surrey

National Anti-Vivisection Society, 51 Harley St, London W1N 1DD

National Association for Environmental Education, West Midlands College of the Gorway, Walsall WS1 3BD

National Council for Voluntary Organisations, 26 Bedford Square, London WC1B 3HU

National Pure Water Association, Bank Farm, Pigott, Westbury, Shropshire SY5 9HH

National Society for Clean Air (NSCA), 136 North St, Brighton BN1 1RG

National Trust, 36 Queen Anne's Gate, London SW1H 9AS

National Trust for Scotland, 5 Charlotte Sq, Edinburgh EH2 4DU

Natural Environment Research Council (NERC), Polaris House, North Star Avenue, Swindon, Wiltshire SN2 1EU

Nature Conservancy Council (NCC), Northminster House, Peterborough PE1 1UA

Nature, 4 Little Essex St, London WC2R 3LF

NATTA, c/o the Energy and Environment Research Unit, Faculty of Technology, Open University, Walton Hall, Milton Keynes, Bucks

New Scientist, Kings Reach Tower, Stamford St, London SE1 9EL

Noise Abatement Society, PO Box 8, Bromley, Kent BR2 0UH

O

Organisation for Economic Cooperation and Development (OECD), 2 rue Andre-Pascal, 75775 Paris Cedex 16, France

Open Spaces Society, 25a Bell St, Henley on Thames, Oxon RG9 2BA

The Otter Trust, Earsham, Bungay, Suffolk NR35 2AF

The Other Economic Summit (TOES), 27 Thames House, South Bank Business Centre, 140 Battersea Park Rd, London SW11 4NB

Oxfam, 274 Banbury Rd, Summertown, Oxford OX2 7DZ

P

Partizans, 218 Liverpool Rd, London N1 1LE

People's Trust for Endangered Species, Hamble House, Meadrow, Godalming, Surrey GU7 3JX

Pesticides Trust, c/o 20 Compton Terrace, London N1 2UN

Political Ecology Research Group, PO Box 14, 34 Cowley Rd, Oxford OX1 1HZ

Population Concern, 231 Tottenham Court Rd, London W1P 9AE

Pure Water Preservation Society, Lane End, Highlands Lane, Westfield, Woking, Surrey GU22 9PU

R

Ramblers Association, 1–5 Wandsworth Rd, London SW8 2XX

Rare Breeds Survival Trust, 4th St, National Agricultural Centre, Kenilworth, Warwickshire CV8 2LG

Red Deer Commission, Knowsley, 82 Fairfield Rd, Inverness, Highland IV3 5LH

Resurgence, Ford House, Hartland, Bideford, Devon

Royal Agricultural Society of England, National Agricultural Centre, Stoneleigh, Kenilworth, Warwicks CV8 2LZ

Royal Botanic Gardens, Kew, Richmond, Surrey TW9 3AB

Royal Commission on Environmental Pollution, Church House, Great Smith St, London SW1P 3BL

Royal Entomological Society, 41 Queens Gate, London SW7 5HU

Royal Geographical Society, 1 Kensington Gore, London SW7 2AR

Royal Horticultural Society, Horticultural Hall, Vincent Square, London SW1P 2PE

Royal Horticultural Society of Ireland, Thomas Prior House, Merrion Rd, Dublin 4, Eire

Royal Scottish Forestry Society,
26 Forrest Rd, Edinburgh
EH1 2QN

Royal Society for Nature Conservation
(RSNC), The Green, Nettleham,
Lincoln LN2 2NR

Royal Society for the Prevention of
Cruelty to Animals (RSPCA), The
Manor House, The Causeway,
Horsham, Sussex RH12 1HG

Royal Society for the Protection of Birds
(RSPB), The Lodge, Sandy,
Bedfordshire

S

Save the Children Fund, Mary
Datchelor House, 17 Grove Lane,
London SE5

Science Policy Research Unit (SPRU),
Mantell Building, University of
Sussex, Brighton

Scientists Against Nuclear Arms
(SANA), 9 Poland St, London
W1V 3DG

Scottish Campaign to Rid the Atomic
Menace (SCRAM), 11 Forth St,
Edinburgh

Scottish Civic Trust, 24 George Sq,
Glasgow G2 1EF

Scottish Conservation Projects, Balallan
House, 24 Allan Park, Stirling
FK8 2QG

Scottish Inland Waterways Association,
11 Arden St, Edinburgh EH9 6BJ

Scottish Landowners' Federation,
18 Abercromby Place, Edinburgh
EH3 6TY

Scottish Ornithologists' Club, 21 Regent
Terrace, Edinburgh
EH7 5BT

Scottish Pure Water Association,
3 Moray Drive, Clarkston, Glasgow
G76 8NW

Scottish Wildlife Trust, 25 Johnstone
Terrace, Edinburgh EH1

Sea Shepherd, PO Box 114, Plymouth
PL1 1DR

Socialist Environment and Resources
Association (SERA), 9 Poland St,
London W1V 3DG

Society for the Prevention of Asbestosis
& Industrial Diseases (SPAID),
38 Drapers Rd, Enfield, Middlesex
EN2 8LU

Soil Association, 86–88 Colston St,
Bristol BS1 5BB

Stockholm International Peace Research
Institute (SIPRI), Sveavagen 166,
S-113 46 Stockholm, Sweden

Strawberry Research, Strawberry
Cottage, York YO1 5NJ

T

Third World First, 232 Cowley Rd,
Oxford OX4 1UH

The Tidy Britain Group, The Pier,
Wallgate, Wigan WN3 4EX

Town and Country Planning
Association (TCPA), 17 Carlton
House Terrace, London
SW1Y 5AS

Town Trees Trust, 11 Gainsborough
Gardens, London NW3 1BJ

Transport 2000, Walkden House,
10 Melton St, London NW1 2EJ

Tree Council, 35 Belgrave Square,
London SW1X 8QN

Trees for People, 141 London Rd,
St Albans AL1 1TA

U

UK Centre for Economic and
Environmental Development
(UKCEED), 10 Belgrave Sq, London
SW1X 8PH

UK Reclamation Council, 16 High St,
Brampton, Huntingdon,
Cambridgeshire PE18 8TU

Ulster Countryside Committee, Hut 6,
Castle Grounds, Stormont, Belfast
BT4 3SS

Ulster Society for the Preservation of the
Countryside, 2 Madison Avenue,
Cavehill Rd, Belfast BT15 5BX

United Nations Children's Fund (UNICEF), Palais des Nations, CH-1211, Geneva 10, Switzerland

United Nations Economic Commission for Europe (UNECE), Palais des Nations, CH-1211 Geneva 10, Switzerland

United Nations Environment Programme (UNEP), Palais des Nations, CH-1211 Geneva 10, Switzerland

United Nations Educational, Scientific, and Cultural Organisation (UNESCO), 7 Place de Fontenay, 75700 Paris, France

United Nations Association, 3 Whitehall Court, London SW1A 2EL

United Nations Information Centre, Ship House, 20 Buckingham Gate, London SW1E 6LB

Urban Wildlife Group, 131–3 Sherlock St, Birmingham B5 6NB

V

The Vegan Society, 47 Highlands Rd, Leatherhead, Surrey

The Vegetarian Society, Parkdale, Dunham Rd, Altrincham, Cheshire WA14 4QG

Vincent Wildlife Trust, Baltic Exchange Buildings, 21 Bury St, London EC3A 5AU

W

War on Want, 37–9 Great Guildford St, London SE1 0ES

The Warmer Campaign, 83 Mount Ephraim, Tunbridge Wells, Kent, TN4 8BS

Watch, 22 The Green, Nettleham, Lincoln LN2 2NR

Water Authorities Association, 1 Queen Anne's Gate, London SW1H 9BT

Wateraid, 1 Queen Anne's Gate, London SW1H 9BT

Wild Flower Society, 69 Outwoods Rd, Loughborough, Leics, LE11 3LY

The Wildfowl Trust, Slimbridge, Gloucester GL2 7BT

Wildlife Link, Ecology Centre, 45 Shelton St, London WC2H 9HJ

Wind Energy Group, c/o Taylor Woodrow Construction Ltd, Taywood House, 345 Ruislip Rd, Middx UB1 2QX

Woodland Trust, Autumn Park, Dysart Rd, Grantham, Lincs NG31 6LL

World Bank, 1818 H Street NW, Washington DC 20433

World Conservation Monitoring Centre, 219c Huntingdon Rd, Cambridge CB3 0DL

World Food Assembly, 5 Harrowby Court, Harrowby St, London W1H 5AF

World Health Organisation, Avenue Appia, CH-1211 Geneva 27, Switzerland

World Information Service on Energy (WISE), PO Box 5627, 1007 AR Amsterdam, The Netherlands

World Resources Institute, 1735 New York Avenue NW, Washington DC 20006, USA

World Society for the Protection of Animals, 106 Jermyn St, London SW1Y 6EE

World Wide Fund for Nature UK (WWF), Weyside Park, Godalming, Surrey GU7 1XR

Y

Young People's Trust for Endangered Species, 19 Quarry St, Guildford, Surrey GU1 3EH

Z

Zoo Check, Cherry Tree Cottage, Coldharbour, Dorking, Surrey RH5 6HA

Zoological Society of London, London Zoo, Regent's Park, London NW1 4RY

Index